SKEWED

Psychiatric hegemony
and the manufacture of mental illness
in Multiple Chemical Sensitivity,
Gulf War Syndrome,
Myalgic Encephalomyelitis and
Chronic Fatigue Syndrome

Martin J. Walker

SLINGSHOT PUBLICATIONS

London

2003

Skewed

Psychiatric hegemony and the manufacture of mental illness in Multiple Chemical Sensitivity, Gulf War Syndrome, Myalgic Encephalomyelitis and Chronic Fatigue Syndrome.

First published August 2003.
© Slingshot Publications 2003
BM Box 8314 London WC1N 3XX England

Type set by Viviana D. Guinarte
In Times New Roman 11/12, B Times Bold,
Times, Book Antiqua, and Windings.
Printed by Queimada Gráficas.
Cover designed by Andy Dark.

British Library Cataloguing in Publication Data
Written by Martin J. Walker
Skewed: Psychiatric hegemony and the manufacture of mental illness in Multiple Chemical Sensitivity, Gulf War Syndrome, Myalgic Encephalomyelitis and Chronic Fatigue Syndrome.
1. Psychiatric and organic aetiology – unexplained illness. 2. Myalgic encephalomyelitis. 3. Gulf War Syndrome. 4. Multiple Chemical Sensitivity. 5. Chronic Fatigue Syndrome. 6. Mental illness – Diagnosis.
I. Title
616'.075

ISBN 0–9519646–4–X

Dedicated to

Margaret Williams, Professor Malcolm Hooper and Miah

Together with all those who suffer from fatigue illnesses of any kind in the hope that they will find the strength, the will, the friends and the knowledge to fight for and gain more comfortable, productive and pain free lives.

~

Acknowledgements

Whatever their authors think, most books are collective ventures. A large number of people were involved in the conception, execution and production of this book: activists, campaigners, academics, fifteen readers of various stages of the manuscript and three lawyers who nit-picked over words, phrasing and construction as if their lives depended on the outcome. Particular thanks go to Abbey, Albert, Andy, Anne, Anne, Carla, Frank, Geoff, John, Len, Margaret, Michael, Michael, Peter, Peter, and Tina. I have also to thank those who have indirectly helped Slingshot survive over the last decade, in particular, Alfred et al, Andy, Audrey, Cynthia, Elaine, Eric, Finlay, Frederica, George, Gordon, Jill, Joan, John, Judith, Liz, Loic, Mar, Stephen, and Stephen.

Contents

Waiting for help[1]

Life is now memories,
As is your work, your study, your interests,
Lost in the murk, of the pain,
With the sickness, nausea, faintness and vertigo,
Shattering symptoms you can't even show.
They ruin you and rack you and lay you at length
As helpless as Lazarus
Curled on his bench.

Like him, you would call for a miracle hand
To touch you and wipe quite away,
Like a mark in the sand
The destruction this illness has wrought,
continuance each day, so painfully bought.

~

ME is a serious illness, with no known cure. It has taken many years for
that to be properly recognised. The illness has a profound effect on
individuals and on entire families. In Britain, ME or CFS affects up to
25,000 children and, it is estimated, between 100,000 and 300,000 adults.
Fifty per cent of long-term sickness absence from schools is attributable
to ME. The cost of the illness is estimated at £4 billion.[2]

~

I was a solicitor but had to give up work six years ago when I could no
longer understand the documents on my desk. I have spent the last six
years lying down 22-23 hours a day. My life is hell. I think about suicide
every single day, because, for me, life has ended. I have no 'future' apart
from a life of pain, exhaustion and poverty. [3]

---

1 Two verses of a longer poem, *Anthem for doomed youth 2003*, by Dora Isabel,
the mother and carer of a once-young sufferer of severe Myalgic Encephalomyelitis.

2 Lord Clement-Jones. Hansard (Lords) 894-910, Chronic Fatigue Syndrome/ME:
16th April 2002.

3 From the Suicide Register, organised by Sheila Barry after her twenty seven year
old daughter, who suffered from ME, committed suicide. Mrs. Sheila Barry, 38
Shaw Crescent, Huby, York YO61 1JF, England. s.d.barry@btinternet.com

Foreword

Per Dalen

MEDICAL CULTURE IS obsessed with mechanisms of disease, but actual causes are not a favourite topic. We don't know enough about causes to inspire the lay public and ourselves with confidence in our science by discussing them. Our lack of success in preventing many important diseases is of course largely due to ignorance. It is not uncommon for a medical scientist to mention an unsolved problem in terms like 'the exact causes are not yet known, but . . .' The discussion is then usually moved to the safer ground of mechanisms.

One tacit assumption is that we should first of all learn as much as possible about the many biochemical and physiological mechanisms that may be involved in the production of symptoms, autoimmunity for instance, or changes in neurotransmitter levels. With a more complete biological 'Meccano', it should be possible to build more and more comprehensive models of how various diseases develop. Will this automatically lead to causal understanding at the level where prevention becomes possible? Not necessarily, I am afraid. New causal knowledge may more often be found serendipitously and in other more direct and less time-consuming ways than this inching along in the search for mechanisms. However, such a direct approach is usually not encouraged by the scientific community.

There is an additional reason why mechanisms are important in medicine. When we draw the line between science and non-science in the health field, we usually exclude procedures and theories that cannot be understood in terms of accepted mechanisms. Homoeopathy is a case in point. It doesn't really matter if it works in practice; its theory is utterly at odds with conventional medical thought. Any positive results in patients are simply explained as placebo effects. In this way knowledge of mechanisms becomes indispensable as a badge of scientific authority.

My training in psychiatry started in the late 1950s, when neuroleptics and antidepressants were already available and the specialty was showing more scientific promise than ever before. Hysteria was something that neurologists encountered. Experienced psychiatrists would tell stories of supposedly hysterical patients who had been referred back to their neurologists or internists without a psychiatric diagnosis, but with the suggestion that further investigation might be indicated – whereupon a brain tumour or some other serious illness was revealed.

The average psychiatrist was then (and still is) fully occupied with patients whose histories and symptoms were predominantly psychiatric. The idea that large numbers of patients in general practice might need our attention for 'medically unexplained symptoms,' freely labelled as somatized, was simply unheard of.

'Somatization' is not a novel word. The oldest entry in the Oxford English Dictionary is from 1925 and shows that the origin of the word is in psychoanalysis: 'conversion of emotional states into physical symptoms.' This is of course a sanitized version of the hysteria concept, a psychiatric diagnosis. Sigmund Freud put forward a number of psychological postulates styled as mechanisms that seeped into popular culture but were less successful in the medical field. Psychoanalysis is perhaps somewhat too speculative to mix well with ideas based on biology.

Medicine has a kind of vigilance or 'immune' system which resists intrusion of thoughts that fall short of a slightly pedantic standard of scientific credibility. The grapevine telegraph keeps us

Foreword

alert and updated. Inevitably though, there is no natural or man-made vigilance without blind spots.

Emotional states can give rise to bodily symptoms; this is a matter of everyday experience. It is, however, deceptively easy to exaggerate the importance of this mind-body connection. The necessary question therefore becomes *what*, and *how much* can be reliably attributed to *which* emotional causes and for *how long*. This can only be answered from experience and common sense, since the actual mechanisms are very poorly understood and systematic clinical evidence is scarce.

A generation ago physicians usually trusted their own clinical judgements, but in recent years the notion of 'evidence based' medicine has altered this. We are now supposed to look for evidence, preferably statistical evidence, in the current literature. In some areas, such as somatization, there is simply no solid evidence, and yet the grapevine is silent about this. A vacuum is created where other forms of persuasion can find their way to the medical profession.

It is interesting that another blind spot can be found in the area of *placebo*. Somatization and placebo are like the two sides of a coin. Both are believed to possess great power, the one of causing disease, the other of restoring health. Their mechanisms of operation are essentially unknown, and systematic studies have in fact yielded little or no evidence in clinical situations.

There is no denying it; medicine uses a double standard in relation to scientific evidence. The placebo has been an integral part of our medical culture since the 1950s. Somatization gained prominence relatively recently. Scientific ideas normally have an interesting history, including a genealogy and a record of arguments pro and con. Important ideas rarely enter the scene fully fledged and unruffled by controversies, but somatization was presented even without a reference to psychoanalysis.

SKEWED

Today we are sometimes told that somatization is *the* disease process to consider when physicians fail to explain the symptoms of the patient. The rather too flattering implication would be that medical science can now explain so many things that most of the remaining problems can be bundled together under a collective psychiatric label without further investigation. The truth, however, as we have seen, is that causal understanding is poorly developed. Explaining symptoms means something else here.

When an officially accepted diagnosis has been found in a given case, for example, multiple sclerosis, the principal symptoms of the patient are seen as constituent parts of a familiar *picture*, and predictions can be made about prognosis, possible treatments can be chosen, et cetera. The physician is satisfied by this result, even though the cause of multiple sclerosis remains unknown, prevention is impossible, and treatments do not offer much hope of permanent recovery.

An accepted diagnosis is not always enough, however. Recurrent or chronic low back pain is sometimes mentioned as a possible form of somatization. The reason for this is that most cases show no structural changes upon thorough investigation. Orthopaedic surgeons see innumerable patients with this very common affliction, and treatment results are poor. So why not call this a psychiatric problem?

To my knowledge, psychiatry has never been officially or openly asked whether it is acceptable to use, or abuse, the concepts and tools of this specialty in new and unexpected ways. Psychiatrists tend to be hungry for acceptance by their non-psychiatric colleagues, and have not so far protested very audibly against what is going on under the label of somatization. GPs aided by psychologists skilled in cognitive behaviour therapy can apparently do the actual work with the patients.

Foreword

A major problem with the somatization approach is that its proponents take for granted that the causes of all those illnesses relabelled as psychiatric are psychological. In modern psychiatry the trend has long been in the opposite direction, away from the dogmatism once inspired by psychoanalysis. Classical psychiatric illnesses have unknown causes just as often as do somatic illnesses, and wholesale psychological explanations are increasingly a thing of the past.

For some years now I have been convinced that the concept of somatization is being exploited for reasons that are only partly transparent. Scientifically there is no basis for the remarkable expansion of this field. The lives of large numbers of patients are touched and often made more difficult by what is going on. Psychiatry is apparently being abused, and it is of course very important to find out more about the background in order to do something about it. This is an area where concerned citizens have already begun to organise.

In *Skewed* Martin Walker investigates the vested interests involved in the problem of somatization and 'unexplained illness.' On reading the manuscript, I found that viewing this apparently medical question from a sociological perspective gave me a new insight into this growing area of ostensibly psychiatric disorders. Readers who are not yet familiar with the tragic erosion of the truth-seeking scientific spirit in medical research will, I hope, also find this book an excellent introduction to these problems.

Per Dalen, MD, PhD.,
Associate Professor of Psychiatry
University of Gothenburg, Sweden

Preface

SOME PEOPLE DISCOVER illnesses that are then named after them; these illnesses can belong to their finders in perpetuity. Others have illnesses inhabiting their bodies; they live with them, learning to love and to hate them; these people have custody of their illnesses until they are cured or they die. Pharmaceutical companies claim rights over illnesses for the period of drug patents; for this time these illnesses, their definition, diagnosis and treatment literally belong to the pharmaceutical company – are only addressed in the mainstream by that company's products and doctors loyal to that company. Still others lay claim to illnesses and areas of pathology in order to enrich themselves, to advance their careers or simply to become experts.

This book tells how a small group of clinicians and academic psychiatrists have attempted over the last two decades to gain control of a number of medically unexplained illnesses, some clearly linked to chemical exposure and including myalgic encephalomyelitis (ME) and Chronic Fatigue Syndrome (CFS), a name given in 1988 to a range of fatigue illnesses of different origins. Readers looking for detailed explanations of these illnesses will be disappointed with this book, which is, as its wordy subtitle attests, not about unexplained illnesses but the diagnostic approach of these psychiatrists who insist that the illnesses are psychogenic in origin and do not need biomedical explanations.

The book is written almost completely on behalf of sufferers and carers of those with unexplained illnesses. Its intention overall is to describe the social, professional and cultural factors affecting the construct of illnesses which are not recognised, at least by a

Preface

small and powerful group of doctors, as having physical origins. The book presents the case for those sufferers, who from the point of their first psychiatric diagnosis, despite protestations, are left without effective help by much of the medical profession, social welfare agencies and most private insurance companies.

On the whole this is not a positive book, it does not give sufferers erudite information that might lead to them understanding their illness or prescribe hope of better management. Rather it tries to give sufferers a map of the medical politics of their illness, and tries to alert them to minefields while colouring in the uniforms of different actors whom they might meet on the battlefield.

Finally, the book is written with the rare hope that defining the sides to the conflict might help those who suffer to draw their resources together, organise, fight for and win the development of genuine, well funded biomedical science research which will prove once and for all that their illnesses do not originate in the mind.

Like most social relationships, those between medical professionals and individuals suffering illnesses are based upon power. The source of the physician's power, and that of insurance and pharmaceutical companies, is the control of information about illnesses and an ability to diagnose and apparently successfully treat them. The physicians' power stems essentially, if not from ownership, at least from the creation of an often closed and apparently knowledgeable intimacy with any illness.

Ironically, the more difficult to diagnose the illness, the more steadfastly medical professionals create and cling to diagnoses which give them power over both patients and illnesses, as if by entering into a free and honest debate control over the illnesses might escape them. The more high-tech and scientific the search for a *cure* becomes, the more determined the medical profession seems to defend its monopoly control of identification, research, diagnosis and treatment of any particular unidentified illness.

SKEWED

The more technologically advanced society becomes, the more health and its therapies spin away, firstly from the public and then from therapists and clinicians into the hands of researchers and academic theoreticians. In a post-industrial society, the interpretation of an illness can become more important than its physical reality. While people today do still have consultations with their clinician and are able to exercise limited choice over treatment, the trend is increasingly towards social policy supporting a hidden administrative relationship between patients and medical research workers, academics and scientists. In this nexus, the clinician is little more than a cipher. The advent of 'evidence based medicine' and such tools as the Cochrane Reviews, together with increasing exclusive specialisation in many areas of medicine, has lessened even more the choices available to the general medical practitioner and therefore the patient. Modern allopathic practitioners no longer have the time or the money which it represents, nor often the intellectual curiosity, to embark upon empirical observations of individual patients.

It is in this undisclosed relationship between groups of patients and those beyond the physician who decide what illness is and which treatments are best, that the agencies of politics and industry lie in wait, forever eager to turn illness to profit. The determination or the refusal to determine an illness category and the sanctioning or deprivation of treatments is a highly profitable business.

The conflict generated by the new power relations which lie increasingly submerged between victims of illness and medical scientists and academics is at its most raw in a number of what might be called 'emerging illnesses,' sometimes related to industrial development or the State's actions, where clinicians and researchers have no immediate aetiological answers or ready cures. Such disorders include some forms of allergy, chemically induced illnesses, Multiple Chemical Sensitivity (MCS), Gulf War Syndrome (GWS),

Preface

Organophosphate (OP) poisoning and a small number of illnesses, the causes of which are presently medically unexplained, like Myalgic Encephalomyelitis (ME) and a variety of chronic fatigue conditions, collectively referred to as Chronic Fatigue Syndrome (CFS).

This book traces the history, ideas and actions of those academics, physicians, mainly psychiatrists who have spent part of their careers denying the physical nature of a number of illnesses, and offering instead the diagnosis of mental illness. The book is not a scientific treatise and it does not attempt to scientifically or even academically explain the cause of any illness. The book does not even pose a definite physical cause of any illnesses, nor does it try to apportion polarity to either the body or the mind. It is a most *un*medical book, mainly interested in examining the lives, work, motivation and organisations of those who proffer only a psychiatric diagnosis, denying any physical or organic reality to certain illnesses.

The noise generated by the conflict between psychiatric professionals, some orthodox physicians and a relatively large numbers of sufferers from ME and CFS has become deafening. The disparagement of ME and CFS sufferers by journalists, medical scientists and physicians has sunk into the fabric of our health culture to such an extent that it is now commonly accepted by many that those who suffer from such illnesses are simply seeking excuses for mental inadequacy.

In the baffling world of ME and CFS, doctors are at war with their patients, and despite the absence of supporting scientific evidence, chronically ill patients are told that they are not physically ill but suffering from 'aberrant illness beliefs.' For these individuals it is as if they have arrived at a hospital with an acute pain in their groin, only to be told by the attending physician that if they think positively about their lives the pain will disappear; if it doesn't they can always get antidepressants from their GP.

SKEWED

In the UK, against all the best international advice, certain patients with physical illnesses are treated with diagnostic guess-work, mind-changing psycho-therapies and brain-deadening drugs. Patients who try hard to raise their voices and exert control over their existence are berated, dismissed, ridiculed, abused and their families taken before the courts, by those charged with healing them.

In November 1998, the Department of Health and the Chief Medical Officer (CMO), Professor Liam Donaldson, announced the membership of a CMO's Working Group on ME/CFS. Although this Working Group was set up only to look at treatment, it followed many other reports, produced in Britain and other countries, which had endorsed the idea that there was no physical cause for ME or CFS and that primary source of these illnesses grew from the mental health of the sufferers. When the CMO's Report was published in January 2002, it sustained the fears of its most knowledgeable critics. While stating again what had been stated a thousand times, that ME and CFS were in fact 'real illnesses,' it advanced no other causes or treatment for these illnesses than psychiatric ones and failed to realistically increase physical research possibilities in the area.

* * *

A note on style: this book is written mainly for lay people who might become involved in the world of undiagnosed illness because they know, or are related to, someone who has these conditions.

It is popular in post-modern times to write about one thing in order to explain another thing. While twenty years ago, writing about the psychiatric view of a particular illness, an author might have done just that, today this approach might be criticised because it appears to take for granted any number of assumptions which underlie the approach of psychiatrists. Today it is more popular to question the underlying assumptions as well as the ideas which they shape. This book, from the beginning takes a critical view of the

Preface

psychiatric diagnosis of a number of unexplained illnesses. It does this by putting these views in a historical context, particularly of chemical company propaganda and later in the book, of insurance company practice. This is not to say that ultimately, either chemicals will be found to be the cause of all the undiagnosed illnesses mentioned, or that insurance companies will be found to be the agencies most responsible for proselytising a psychiatric aetiology for these illnesses.

The book does not follow any one particular idea about the cause of the unexplained illnesses at which it looks; as might be expected, many explanations are proffered for presently 'unexplained illnesses'; some convincingly fit some illnesses while by-passing others completely, some explanations have been scientifically explored while others constitute speculation.♦

Although it might ultimately transpire that the specific causes of each of the illnesses referred to in the text, are different, they all have similar symptomatic pictures and they have all been the subject of attention by psychiatrists. Clearly it is impossible, when writing about psychiatric aetiology, to mention *all* of the illnesses, on every occasion they are referred to. It is my hope that the reader will include 'and other unexplained illnesses of this kind' each time they read ME, CFS, MCS, GWS, etc.

♦ There are a number of different physical explanations for ME, CFS, and GWS. They range from viral explanations, to bacterial [See Donald W. Scott: *There is no such thing as Chronic Fatigue Syndrome/CFS/Fibromyalgia/Myalgic Encephalomyelitis . . . Journal of Degenerative Diseases* Vol. 2 (3)] and wholly chemical explanations [See Professor Malcolm Hooper, *Engaging with Myalgic Encephalomyelitis.*] Professor Malcolm Hooper and his team have found that a test they were using in the Autism Unit at Sunderland, the IAG test, was highly positive in Gulf War veterans. This led to the testing of other chemically poisoned people; in nearly every case, high levels of IAG appeared in their urine. For this to be happening means a dysfunctional gut and sufferers from these overlapping conditions show evidence of an increased permeability of the gut wall due to damaged membranes (cont).

SKEWED

As with my previous books, I have been as scrupulous as possible with reporting quotes and referring to the writing of others. However, although I would generally argue in favour of academic method, my experience with *Dirty Medicine*, which contained around 2,500 references, was that those who were against me ignored the accuracy of the research and manufactured criticisms to suit their case and those who were with me often made my arguments more extreme than the references sanctioned. It is also increasingly the case that researchers and writers glean some of their information from the Internet. Giving references for web sites presents a major problem for any writer as the sites change, disappear and re-appear frequently, and not all readers are familiar with computers.

For the reasons above, and because I believe that too many *numerical* references placed in the text obstruct the narrative for most lay readers, I have decided not to use *numerical* references to support every statement in the text but instead I have tried to explicitly mention the source of quotes in the text, as well as including a general bibliography. I have used footnotes where there is interesting information beyond the text which, in my opinion, does not fit into the narrative.

♦ (cont.) (leaky gut). Hooper explains very clearly how this happens in people who are described by certain psychiatrists as exhibiting 'MUPS' (multiple unexplained physical symptoms.) He shows that their multitude of symptoms are not 'unexplained' at all and that they are entirely organic in origin. Still other commentators [See Albert Donnay of MCS Referral and Resources] suggest that the whole range of fatigue illnesses and many more unexplained illnesses are caused by carbon monoxide poisoning. In their paper of August 1999, *Chronic Fatigue Syndrome – Is prolonged exposure to environmental level power line frequency electromagnetic fields a co-factor to consider in treatment?* D. Maisch et al. discuss the possibility that the impaired immune function associated with CFS might be due to chronic low level exposure to extremely low frequency electromagnetic fields.

Introduction

In September 1986, Ean Proctor, an 11 year-old boy living on the Isle of Man, became ill with a flu-like illness from which he did not make the anticipated recovery. Ean began to complain of an overwhelming debility affecting his arms and legs, he felt permanently nauseous, had a vacillating temperature, severe headaches, sweating, mouth ulcers and swollen glands. He began to have difficulty in controlling his speech and developed a mental fatigue which left him struggling to finish a sentence and unable to remember things. By January 1987, with the illness persisting, he had begun to drag one leg and lose his sense of balance. Over the next ten months Ean Proctor attended the Royal Liverpool Children's Hospital, where he was diagnosed with Post Viral Fatigue Syndrome, and the local Noble's Hospital, where it was suggested that he might be suffering from 'school phobia.'

Ean's parents, Barbara and Rob Proctor, considered themselves an ordinary couple. When Ean's illness began, Barbara, aged 46, was a full time housewife and 47-year-old Rob was an accountant. The Proctors had one other son, Gary, who was seven years older than Ean.

When the Proctors asked if Ean could be referred to a research Professor on the mainland, they were informed that they would be wasting NHS money. The Proctors offered to pay themselves but were still refused. Eventually, however, it was suggested that the Proctors seek help in London at the National Hospital for Nervous Diseases (NHND). Here Ean was seen by Dr. Morgan-Hughes, a consultant neurologist, who after an hour-long examination diagnosed severe myalgic encephalomyelitis, the illness known by its initials ME.

SKEWED

The Proctors knew nothing about ME but were glad to have a diagnosis. Morgan-Hughes told them that their son should be cared for at home and that school would be out of the question for the foreseeable future. By the end of 1987, Ean was partially paralysed and had lost his voice; he would be unable to speak again for almost three years. During the first year of coping with Ean's illness, the Proctors learned more about ME from campaigners, independent research and from their consultant.

Myalgic encephalomyelitis has been a disorder recognised by the medical profession internationally for over sixty years. It has been observed in both epidemic and sporadic forms with acknowledged similarities to other fatigue illnesses and the post-polio syndrome (PPS). There had been over sixty-three recorded outbreaks of ME since 1934, including pre-war epidemics in Wisconsin, America, in 1936, in Switzerland in 1937 and one in a Middlesex sanatorium, England, in 1939. In the immediate post-war years there was an epidemic in a Pennsylvania hospital in 1945 and two epidemics in Iceland. In the period from 1984 until 1992 there were eight recorded epidemic incidents in North America.

In 1956, the disorder then known as 'atypical poliomyelitis' was given the term benign myalgic encephalomyelitis (ME). Dr. Melvin Ramsay and colleagues defined three cardinal features of this illness: muscle fatigue lasting several days after even minor physical effort, a remarkable variability of symptoms and physical signs even within separate episodes, and in many cases a relapsing and remitting course over months and years.

In 1959, the illness was considered of such consequence to the fledgling NHS that Donald Acheson carried out a major review. In 1962, the distinguished neurologist Lord Brain included ME in his standard textbook of neurology. In 1978, the Royal Society of Medicine concluded the foreword to a report of its symposium on the illness with the words, 'it is hoped that as a result of the meeting,

Introduction

sufferers from this miserable illness will, in future, be more sym-
pathetically managed.' In 1981, what became known as the 'Ramsay case' description was published.

Dr. Melvin Ramsay was one of the first British physicians to
take a committed interest in ME and to come into head-on collision
with psychiatrists over its aetiology. Born in Lancashire in 1901,
Ramsay epitomised the kind of courteous and caring physician who
always treated his patients with respect. In 1947 he became Consultant in Infectious Diseases at the Royal Free Hospital. In July 1955
members of staff at the hospital went down with a new apparently
infectious illness. By November of that year, the epidemic number-
ed around 300 cases, nearly all of whom were Royal Free medical
and nursing staff; the illness became temporarily known as the
Royal Free disease. Following the outbreak at the Royal Free, Melvin Ramsay spent the remainder of his life until his death in 1990
fighting for the recognition of ME.

Almost twenty years after the outbreak at the Royal Free Hospital, two psychiatrists, McEvedy and Beard, wrote a paper claiming that there had been no illness at the hospital but an outbreak of
mass hysteria.[4] Neither McEvedy nor Beard ever saw, examined or
interviewed any patients from the outbreak and used only carefully
selected case-notes to support their claim that there were no
physical signs of the illness.

At the time the Proctors began looking into ME, more clinical
work was beginning on it. Over the next decade, ME would be
proved to be a potentially severe, chronic and disabling disorder
from which complete recovery was unlikely. Often starting with
diarrhoea, that might continue chronically throughout the illness,
sufferers experience persistent headaches, vertigo and dizziness.

---

4 *Royal Free Epidemic of 1955: A Reconsideration.* Colin P. McEvedy, A.W.
Beard. *BMJ* 1970:1:7-11.

SKEWED

The most striking feature of the illness was an incapacitating post-exercise muscle fatigue, recovery from which is delayed for at least 24 hours, together with extreme malaise, which is quite distinct from everyday 'fatigue.' All muscles are affected, including the heart.

People with ME may suffer permanent damage to skeletal or cardiac muscles, as well as to the liver, pancreas, endocrine glands and lymphoid tissues. Injury to the brain stem results in a disturbance of the production of cortisol required for stress control.[5] Because of damage to the hypothalamus, pituitary and adrenal glands there is not only muscle but joint pain. Pain is often extreme and intractable and many patients can walk only very short distances and require a wheelchair.[6]

Sufferers sometimes have sudden attacks of breathlessness, problems with swallowing and voice production. Cognitive impairment includes difficulties with memory sequencing, processing speed, word searching and spatial organisation. Cycles of severe relapse, together with the evolution of further symptoms over time, are common in ME. Death occurs almost entirely from end-organ damage, mainly cardiac or pancreatic failure.[7] Because of many doctors' determined lack of understanding, suicide in ME patients is not uncommon.

---

5 Former President of the UK ME Association Dr. E. Dowsett in her Presentation to the All Party Parliamentary Group on ME, January 2001, entitled 'The Late Effects of ME: can they be distinguished from the Post-polio syndrome?' Also in Dr. John Richardson *Enteroviral and Toxin Mediated Myalgic Encephalomyelitis / Chronic Fatigue Syndrome and Other Organ Pathologies*, 2001, The Haworth Press Inc, New York.

6 Prof. Paul Cheney in his Testimony before the US FDA Scientific Advisory Committee, 18th February 1993. Also a major Report by the charity Action for ME found that 77% of sufferers experienced severe pain. *Severely Neglected: ME in the UK*. Report from Action for ME. March 2001.

7 Dowsett, ibid.

Introduction

All the symptoms which Ean Proctor suffered had previously been recorded as assailing patients who had been diagnosed with ME. In April 1988 Ean and his parents flew again to London for another appointment at the NHND. On this visit the Senior Registrar in Psychiatry, Dr. Simon Wessely, took an interest in Ean's case.

By 1988, when he first saw Ean Proctor, Dr. Wessely had met up with a number of medical sceptics based in Britain and America. In Britain this informal group officially launched themselves in 1988 as the Campaign Against Health Fraud, later changing their name to HealthWatch. The group was generally in favour of orthodox medicine and pharmaceutical intervention, while opposed to what they considered fashionable but unevidenced illnesses or concepts of environmental illness and their 'alternative' treatments. Dr. Wessely's main contribution to this group, over the next six or seven years, was to be his argument that ME was not an organic illness but one which originated in the mind.

On the day of the Proctor's second visit to the NHND, Dr. Wessely dropped into the consulting room and asked the Proctors if they would help with his research into ME. Even at this early stage, Dr. Wessely, who later suggested that Ean's inability to speak was *elective mutism* and that he had a 'primary psychological illness', seemed convinced that children did not suffer from ME.

Looking back, after their talk with Dr. Wessely, the Proctors reviewed previous comments about 'school phobia' and other psychological descriptions of his illness and for the first time became concerned that they had entered an area of medical conflict.

Later that day, it was suggested by a number of doctors at the NHND that Ean should be referred to the neighbouring Great Ormond Street Hospital for Sick Children. At this point, two other psychiatrists, Dr. Lask and Dr. Turk became involved in Ean's case. Dr. Lask was uncommitted to the ME diagnosis and wanted to initiate a psychiatric management programme of graded exercise together with family therapy. The doctors at the NHND wanted Ean admitted to a closed psychiatric ward.

It became clear to the Proctors that some doctors did not accept ME as a physical illness. Shocked by this conflict among experts, the Proctors told the doctors they could neither afford the time off work nor the money to fly backward and forward to the hospital in London each week. The doctors seemed adamant that unless the Proctors allowed psychiatrists to assess their relationship with Ean he was unlikely to get better.

On their return to the Isle of Man, the Proctors dropped a letter in at their GP's telling him what had happened and asking him to contact them. Two weeks went by before the GP informed them that he could not accept the original diagnosis of ME. Before anything else was done, he suggested, they should all await a report from Great Ormond Street. Mr. and Mrs. Proctor then sought help from a medical practitioner who was also a homoeopath.

Unbeknown to the Proctors as they sought their own support and treatments, their local Social Services team was acting upon an assessment prepared by doctors at the NHND and Great Ormond Street for the Proctor's GP. This report included a statement from Dr. Wessely stating his professional opinion that Ean's apparent illness, appeared to be 'out of all proportion to the original cause' and that his parents were 'over-involved in his care.' In a later letter of June 1988, to the principal social worker in Ean's case, Dr. Wessely stated: 'I feel that Ean needs a long period of rehabilitation, part of which will involve very skilled management of separation from his parents.'

Although the Proctors did not know it at the time, Dr. Wessely's view was shared by a number of other psychiatric professionals and formed, to their mind, a consistent, useful and professional approach to an illness, the treatment of which had eluded doctors for many years.

Introduction

Early in June 1988, social workers on the Isle of Man met with doctors and Child Care Department workers from the Island. Of the two doctors present at this and subsequent meetings, only one had seen Ean. The report from Great Ormond Street Hospital informed the participants that Ean was in a life or death situation and had already suffered serious deterioration. The inference of both the report from Great Ormond Street and the doctors' evidence at the meeting was that Ean's parents were to be blamed for Ean's condition, having imposed 'false illness beliefs' upon him. A decision was taken to obtain a Care Order, which would enable Social Services to take Ean from his parents and place him in the care of the State.

The following day social workers, with an order from the court and evidence provided by London doctors, accompanied by police officers, called without prior arran gement at the Proctors' home. Under threat of force they took Ean to Noble's Hospital. Watching from their front door as social workers took their sick child, Mr. and Mrs. Proctor had no way of knowing when or under what circumstances they would see him again.

The Proctors were advised by social workers that they should obtain the services of a lawyer. It was their lawyer who then negotiated their right to see their son; he advised them that the hospital psychiatrist was the only person able to grant them visits. After a week, the Proctors were allowed to visit Ean for half an hour a day. His parents did not even know if Ean had been told *why* they had not been to see him over that traumatic week of separation.

At Noble's Hospital the doctors began to conduct a series of experiments upon Ean without his parents' knowledge or consent. Doctors ordered Ean to be put into a swimming pool without any swimming aids in order to shock him into behaving 'normally'; unable to move his arms, he sank to the bottom of the pool. On another occasion, Ean was taken out of the hospital to a local fun fair where, he was put onto the Ghost Train; his doctors believed he would be forced to cry out and so prove that he *was* able to speak. Despite Ean's chronic condition, the doctors at Noble's Hospital continued with a regime of forced exercise.

The doctors on the Isle of Man appeared determined to re-orientate Ean's acceptance of his belief that he was ill. Everything possible was done to censor the communication between Ean and his parents, so that the Proctors did not again reinforce this belief. In desperation, the Proctors managed to locate a paediatrician on the mainland willing to travel to the Isle of Man. The paediatrician was insistent that Ean did have ME; however, it was October 1988 before Ean was allowed out of hospital to be treated by this physician. Even then doctors and social workers, fearful that their methods, diagnosis and 'treatment' would be made public, insisted on going through the Court and pretended that *they* had located the independent doctor, to whose involvement the parents had raised objections.

A year after Ean's release from hospital in the autumn of 1989, the Parliament of the Isle of Man, the Tynwald, appointed a Select Committee to address a *Petition for Redress of Grievance*, which had been entered by Mr. and Mrs. Proctor. In its final report to the Parliament, the Committee recorded that it was 'beyond doubt that the Proctor family have suffered a painful, costly experience over a long period.' They recognised that there were two views amongst doctors about ME and that one view had overwhelmed social workers who had proceeded with the care order.

The Committee recorded that they had obtained a great deal of written evidence about ME, particularly from the ME Association. One of the most disturbing things they had learned was that some experts suggested that if ME sufferers over-exerted themselves, their condition could be exacerbated, a view that flew directly in the face of the rehabilitation programme advised by doctors at Noble's

Hospital, the NHND and Great Ormond Street Hospital for Sick Children.

Of Mrs. Proctor and her parenting skills, which had, throughout the case, been brought into question, the Select Committee reported that 'Mrs. Proctor became distressed because the doctors and consultants on the Isle of Man and many in England did not seem to accept that Ean was suffering from an illness in the ordinary sense but said that he had psychological problems.' In the opinion of the Committee, Mrs. Proctor was, however, an extremely caring mother whom they found to be intelligent, articulate and equipped with a good memory. The Committee commented that, though his mother might have been protective towards Ean, this was surely her entitlement.

The Tynwald report agreed unanimously that the case conference held to discuss Ean Proctor's case, in the absence of the Proctors and without hearing a balancing medical view of ME, had been inappropriate and not in the best interests of Ean: 'there should not have been an application for a Care Order without a visit by the social worker to the Proctors,' they concluded.

Unfortunately for the Proctors and for other sufferers of ME, the Tynwald Select Committee decided that any compensation award should be decided by another inquiry. To this end, the McManus Inquiry, headed by a lawyer and composed of a paediatrician and a retired Director of Social Services, sat in 1992. The McManus Inquiry found that the Proctors were not entitled to any compensation because Mr. and Mrs. Proctor had brought everything upon themselves and were themselves responsible for their son's illness.

The findings of the McManus Inquiry were a substantial victory for the psychiatric lobby. The Inquiry's decision not to recognise ME and grant compensation for the traumatic manner in which the Proctors were treated was the first of concentric ripples which would lap through the courts whenever this illness was discussed over the next decade. The McManus finding, in opposition to the

Tynwald Select Committee Report, inevitably affected any claims against the authorities for those who found their children taken from them for psychiatric treatment.

Over the next decade, Dr. Simon Wessely became a world expert on ME, its psychiatric origins, and its sibling illnesses that were to be relabelled in their entirety as Chronic Fatigue Syndrome (CFS). Publicly he distanced himself from the interventionist approach, which had been advocated in the Proctor case. By the end of the century, however, the suggestion that parents were abusing their children by enforcing false illness beliefs on them, was to be used increasingly as a legal argument by those seeking care of children.

Ean's case was to cost the Proctors dear. They were forced to move home because of cruel behaviour from neighbours who made their life hell. Believing that Ean's illness was psychiatric, they gathered from the lack of facts rumoured around the village and the 'evidence' that Ean was forcibly taken into care, that the Proctors were abusing him. Neighbours chanted outside the Proctors' home, they pushed stones through the Proctors' letterbox and smeared dog dirt onto the Proctors' car door handles.

When Ean's illness began Barbara's hair was brown streaked with grey; two years later, by the time the worst of the nightmare was over, her hair was completely white. Rob Proctor, who had been working in the aerospace industry, was made redundant and was unemployed for three and a half years, as a consequence of the time he took off to accompany his son on his search for treatment. Their son's illness just about bankrupted the Proctors.

CHAPTER ONE

Stifling Science

Major chemical companies tried to suppress Silent Spring, and when excerpts appeared in the New Yorker, a chorus of voices immediately accused Carson of being hysterical and extremist.[8]

Analysis of disease trends shows that the environment is the primary determinant of the state of general health of any population.[9]

Proponents of both the psychiatric and organic causes of unexplained illness have devolved into their arguments elements of the other, that is, psychiatric aetiologists admit to real physical symptoms and organic aetiologists admit to precipitated psychological factors such as depression, stress and anxiety. The two arguments are, however, diametrically opposed.

Those who propose the view that these illnesses have a psychological origin, really mean just that – these illnesses and all their manifestations are produced by a disturbance of mental processes, an aspect of mental ill health. On the other hand, those who propose the view that these illnesses have presently unknown organic or physical origins, also mean just that – these illnesses and all their manifestations originate with organic physical processes. Whether these processes are consequent upon exposure to chemicals, the activity of viruses or precipitated by years of physical degeneration, they will ultimately be explained by physical science.

---

8 Al Gore.

9 Ivan Illich, *Medical Nemesis; The Expropriation of Health*. Calder & Boyars, Ideas in Progress, London 1975.

Inevitably, the reverberations in the material world of these two opposed ideas, have different effects upon the sufferer. Not least of these effects is that while those diagnosed with mental illness are encouraged to believe that they have no one but themselves to blame, final proof of organic illness caused, for instance, by chemicals would leave some industries and professional groups open to actions for liability.

To understand the position of contemporary proponents of the psychiatric aetiology of ME and CFS and a number of other 'new illnesses,' such as Gulf War Syndrome, it is helpful to look at the developing understanding of chemically induced illness. This is not only because some researchers have postulated chemicals as a co-factorial cause of some of these illnesses but principally because the argument that those who claim to suffer from ME and CFS have psychiatric problems can be clearly seen, and has consistently been used, against those who claim to suffer the adverse effects of chemicals. By following the course of the psychiatric idea and the debate which surrounds it in respect of chemicals, we can more easily understand why there has been such a hard-fought battle over the definition, research and treatment of these illnesses.

Following the 1939-1945 war, principally because of research carried out on pesticides and nerve agents by Bayer in Nazi Germany, farmers, particularly in the USA and the British Commonwealth, began using large quantities of pesticides. The use of these pesticides and other forms of chemical production grew considerably following the war; synthetic pesticide production, for example, grew from 124,259,000 pounds in 1947 to 637,666,000 pounds in 1960.

In the fifty years between the end of the war and the end of the century, it is estimated that more than 100,000 man-made chemicals were introduced to the environment and more than 1,000 new chemicals developed each year. John Robbins, author of *Diet for a New*

America, suggested in 1987 that the US was producing pesticides at a rate more than 13,000 times faster than in 1950. The US Natural Resource Defense Council (NRDC) reports that US pesticide use reached an all-time high in 1995, when more than 1.2 billion pounds of pesticides were used. Regardless of location, many North Americans might now have any of 250 synthetic industrial chemicals present in their bodies that were not present in the bodies of their grandparents. In one of the most recent comments on chemicals in Britain, the 2003 Royal Commission on Environmental Pollution Report, *Chemicals in Products: Safeguarding the Environment and Human Health*, suggests that there are now 30,000 chemicals in constant daily use in Britain, only 4,000 of which have been tested.

In 1962, Rachael Carson published *Silent Spring*, which examined the damage pesticides did to both wild life and humans. Within months of its publication Carson had become a household name in America. US chemical companies who had tried to stop the book prior to publication, used established organisations like the American Medical Association and the American Nutritional Foundation to mount an all-out attack upon her and her supporters. The organisation of the chemical industry's rebuttal of *Silent Spring* ushered into place strategies which would be used consistently in the future against their critics.

By the 1970s, the chemical companies had begun organising across the board to defeat ideas which suggested that chemicals caused damage to human health. In the late 1970s, reports about new illnesses caused by chemicals increased, forming the foundations of clinical ecology, a branch of medicine pioneered in the 1940s by Dr. Theron Randolph, a physician and allergist.

In the 1950s, Theron Randolph was working clinically with patients who he was sure had become ill from exposures to chemicals at doses far below the levels normally considered safe. These patients, both adults and children, were prone to allergies, fatigue, irritability, behaviour problems, depression and confusion. Unlike conventional allergic triggers, chemical sensitivities appeared to create a condition of weakness in the host, which made them vulnerable to other debilitating conditions. In 1965, Randolph founded the Society for Clinical Ecology, which was later to become the American Academy of Environmental Medicine.

Conventional treatments for allergy had always been relatively basic. In a crisis during a serious life-threatening allergic response, called anaphylactic shock, patients who got quickly to medical help could be given injections of adrenalin and hydrocortisone, and then left to rest. Orthodox medical opinion generally was that when the attack subsided, if the allergen responsible was obvious, then it should be avoided. If, however, the allergen was not obvious, although the patient might try an elimination diet, it wasn't really worth searching through hundreds of substances to find the culprit. This lack of energy on the part of physicians to look for or find allergens was often linked to their funding or relationship with producers of industrial food, pharmaceuticals or other chemicals. As reports of 'allergy' began to grow, physicians fought shy of being involved in the production of lists of commercial products which might cause them.

As clinical ecologists and others began to publish their findings that chemicals were producing adverse 'allergic' responses, classical allergists threw up their hands in horror. As they had done with homoeopaths in the nineteenth century, orthodox physicians began to ostracise those who worked on the edges of allergy and chemical induced conditions. Some orthodox doctors and medical epidemiologists, if they had not been married to industry already, joined forces with the chemical, pharmaceutical and food lobbies, denying any possibility that chemicals could cause damage; they became entrenched in a mutually supporting cycle of medicine and commercial interests. On the other hand, apparently shunned by industry and lacking commercial support for their new ideas, clinical ecologists joined together to develop an alternative and independent specialisation.

Inevitably, orthodox physicians and medical scientists formed organisations too, to fight clinical ecologists. These organisations and confederations opposed anything which they claimed 'de-professionalises' the practice of medicine. In particular, they attacked a variety of diagnostic techniques and treatments used by clinical ecologists, which, they claimed, were unscientific.

Serious disputes over competition and professional boundaries in medicine began to occur increasingly in the nineteen seventies. They tended to centre upon alternative forms of diagnosis and treatment, practices like chelation therapy and chiropractic.♦

There was, however, always the smallest window through which these practices might eventually enter the portals of respectable medicine. The most enduring disputes engendering bitter acrimony occurred in the fields of cancer diagnosis, alternative treatment and environmental illness. Sometimes for the same reason – that both issues might be linked to environmental carcinogens – the medical establishment was utterly unprepared to allow either of these areas of medicine into their established canon.

Just like alternative cancer therapists, clinical ecologists felt the full effect of being exiled by orthodoxy. In the eyes of most doctors and their professional organisations, clinical ecologists were at best quacks and at worst criminals. Except in exceptional circumstances,

---

♦ Chelation Therapy is the practice of using vitamins, minerals and an inexpensive chemical pharmaceutical to 'clean' heavy metals particularly from arteries. The practice is only minimally invasive and low-cost, while its supporters say that it is as efficient, in certain circumstances, as for example heart by-pass surgery. Chiropractic is a practice of bone and muscle manipulation similar in some respects to osteopathy; it has a long tradition in North America.

their papers went unpublished, insurance cover was withdrawn from their practices and professional representation was withdrawn at board inquiries.♦

By the 1980s, it was becoming clear that some orthodox physicians had gained the support of much bigger and more organised forces in their fight against clinical ecology. Just as the tobacco industry had organised support for their multi-disciplinary attack upon anyone and anything which adversely linked smoking and health, so chemical companies of all kinds were coming together to create a front which would repel clinical ecology. The chemical, processed food and pharmaceutical companies began using positive information campaigns, called by *Rachel's Environment & Health Weekly* ■ 'good news campaigns,' in an attempt to sell chemicals to the public. And, in an attempt to divert attention from adverse clinical effects of chemicals, they began to suggest a link between chemical sensitivity and pre-sickness psychological problems or physical idiosyncracies in sufferers.

At this time, particularly in Britain, the psychiatric argument came of age; it began to be used by chemical companies against exposed claimants; by orthodox doctors and medical experts against the claiming patients of clinical ecologists; it was even used against clinical ecologists themselves and ultimately it has been used against the parents of children who fall ill after chemical or viral exposure.

Those who argue psychiatric aetiology are an oddly combined group, who also tend to argue that chemicals do no harm, that there is no such thing as environmentally created illness, that pharmaceutical chemicals rarely create iatrogenic illness.

♦ See the author's *Dirty Medicine: Science, big business and the assault on natural health care*. Slingshot Publications, London 1993.

■ *Rachel's* can be obtained free by e-mail from the web site of the Environmental Research Foundation at: www.rachel.org

The real thing

The first edition of Nicholas Ashford and Claudia Miller's book, *Chemical exposures; Low levels and high stakes*, published in 1991, reviewed several hundred studies describing common themes. Individual chemical sensitivity, they concluded, appears to occur in two stages: firstly initiated by a high exposure or by recurrent moderate exposure to strong chemicals, symptoms were then 'triggered' by extremely low exposure to many different chemicals, including those found in fragrances, tobacco smoke, pharmaceuticals or foods.♦

In contemporary developed society, individuals are exposed to thousands of chemicals in a multitude of circumstances. Chemicals are in food, they out-gas from cheap furniture, carpets, polishes, air fresheners, washing liquids, fabric treatments; they are ambient in many workplaces in industrial processes, coming off photocopiers and even photocopy paper, hair dyes, dry-cleaning chemicals and exhaust emissions.

Throughout the 1970s, 1980s and 1990s, there were constant reminders that people were affected adversely by chemicals (the term Multiple Chemical Sensitivity was not defined until 1987.) Ashford and Miller cite a survey of epidemiological data which suggests that between 15% and 30% of Americans (37 to 75 million people) were unusually sensitive or 'allergic' to certain common chemicals such as detergents, perfumes, solvents, pesticides, pharmaceuticals, foods, and even the smell of dry-cleaned clothes. Physicians in North America had diagnosed an estimated 5% (13 million people) as being especially sensitive.

♦ This was not an entirely new idea, scientists working with certain chemicals from the turn of the nineteenth century had recorded just such reactions. In the 1920s, Alfred Stock, the famous German chemist, reported on his own greatly increased sensitivity to mercury vapour, which was accompanied by increased sensitivity also to tobacco smoke, and certain volatile chemicals.

Many people especially sensitive to chemicals were found to react so strongly that they could become disabled from very low exposures to common substances. Typically recorded symptoms included prolonged fatigue, difficulty with memory, dizziness, light-headedness, difficulty concentrating, depression, feeling spaced-out or groggy, loss of motivation, feeling tense or nervous, shortness of breath, irritability, muscle aches, joint pain, headaches, chest pains, difficulty in focusing the eyes, and nausea.

By the nineteen nineties, Multiple Chemical Sensitivity was being recognised in a growing number of academic and clinical circumstances. In 84 articles and letters in peer-reviewed literature between 1993 and 1996, reviewed by Albert Donnay of MCS Referral and Resources, the majority supported the view that MCS was a distinct clinical entity. Of the original articles, 51 identified non-psychiatric causes as being of major importance while only 14 attributed the condition to psychiatric causes.

Despite clinical recognition, the exact mechanism of MCS remained elusive. However, the traditional course of science, namely testing hypotheses against material reality and clinical cases together with epidemiological work, continued to supply pieces of the jigsaw.

A 1988 report from the US National Academy of Sciences Institute of Medicine, concluded that 'Many primary-care physicians lack the training and support needed to diagnose and treat illnesses caused by toxic chemicals in the workplace or the general environment.'

The Report noted that environmental medicine was 'in its infancy' and that there were only about 1,000 American board-certified physicians in occupational medicine, most of whom were employed in industry or academia and not in clinical practice. Throughout the 1990s there were a number of events that brought forward the medical recognition of Multiple Chemical Sensitivity.

Stifling Science

In 1999, a group of 34 experienced clinicians and scientists issued a Consensus Statement on MCS. The statement was introduced with a reference to the fact that some doctors were still suggesting that Gulf War Syndrome had psychiatric origins. That Consensus Statement published in the Archives of Environmental Health, built upon a previous consensus of 1994 in which the American Lung Association, the American Medical Association, the US Environmental Protection Agency and the US Consumer Product Safety Committee had all agreed 'that MCS should not be dismissed as psychogenic, and a thorough workup is essential.'

The Consensus Statement cited surveys conducted by the Health Departments of California and New Mexico, which found that 2% and 6% respectively of adults had already been diagnosed with MCS and around 16% claimed to be unusually sensitive to everyday chemicals. The Consensus Statement also cited, and was partly motivated by, a controlled sample of Gulf War veterans which reported 15% chemical sensitivity amongst previously deployed soldiers, a three-fold increase over the control group. The Consensus Statement considered that Chronic Fatigue Syndrome and MCS showed such an overlap that any applications for research into either Multiple Chemical Sensitivity or Chronic Fatigue Syndrome should consider both conditions. The statement detailed six consensual criteria, which in the absence of any other single illness signified MCS.

In its November 2000 update of the 10th Revision of the International Classification of Diseases (ICD 10), Germany became the first country in the world to list Multiple Chemical Sensitivity in its edition of the WHO International Classification of Disease manual; this was significant because diseases don't officially exist in countries until they have a code in this nationally specific manual.

SKEWED

One of the most important scientific breakthroughs for ME/CFS sufferers in recent years, found that there could be a link between the adverse effects of chemicals and the symptomatic picture in ME and CFS. Professor Robert Suhadolnick et al, gave a paper in 1998 at the American Association of Chronic Fatigue Syndrome's Research and Clinical Conference held in Massachusetts, demonstrating anomalies in the '2-5A RNase L antiviral pathway,' now considered by some world researchers to underlie the pathology of ME/CFS; crucially it was demonstrated by Professors Vojdani and Lapp that this same antiviral pathway was also affected by chemicals. This work made clear one link between the effect of chemicals on the human system and the increase in illnesses such as ME and Chronic Fatigue Syndrome.

The need for recognition and acceptance of MCS by mainstream medicine has escalated in recent years. In Britain, not only the plight of the Gulf War veterans but incidents like Camelford♦ and the problems caused by organophosphate sheep dip have brought MCS to the fore. In Europe, America, Australia and New Zealand, recognition has been forced as a consequence of Gulf War Syndrome and different local chemical incidents. These pressing circumstances have lifted the question of MCS out of the area of occupational illnesses and placed it firmly in the area of environmental health. At the same time, the stakes for those opposed to the recognition of MCS have also been raised, because any credible public admission relating to any chemical illness in any country could open the floodgates to liability claims and consequential provision of hitherto unrecognised and costly health care services.

♦ In Camelford, a community in Cornwall, hundreds of people were made ill after a large quantity of aluminium sulphate and other chemicals was accidentally tipped into the water supply.

An outbreak of mental disorder

The stark contrast between the scientific view that MCS is an organic illness and the view put forward by industry, that it is a product of hysteria, was thrown up by the *Report of the Advisory Committee on Environmental Hypersensitivity to the Department of the Ministry of Health in the Province of Nova Scotia, Canada*. The Report, which became known as the Langley Report, was published in June 1987 alongside a minority report written by a dissenting Committee member, Dr. Patricia Beresford, the only clinical eco-logist on the Committee.

In 1982 Dr. Gerald Ross, who worked at Camp Hill Hospital in Halifax, Nova Scotia, became seriously ill with no obvious clinical cause. After lengthy tests and many clinical examinations, it was decided that his illness was linked to an exposure to dry-cleaning fluid that had seeped into the town's drinking water. After treatment by Dr. William Rea, a leading clinical ecologist based in Texas, Ross's condition improved.

Things did not improve at Camp Hill Hospital, however, where throughout the early eighties more than 600 nurses, doctors and technicians became ill for no apparent clinical reason. In 1986 the Nova Scotia government set up a Committee of eight physicians to study these illnesses. The Committee reported in 1987 that there was no scientific evidence that environmental hypersensitivity existed and all the illnesses were stress-related and psychological in origin.

Dr. Beresford noted in her dissenting report that in her opinion the Committee had 'wilfully' ignored research findings from Nova Scotia's Environmental Health Center and the Dallas Environ-mental Health Center where Dr. Ross had been sent and where 25,000 patients had previously been treated over 23 years. The Committee had, she said, relied on interviews with just four patients. Dr. Beresford also pointed out that the Committee omitted any evidence about low levels of chemical exposure:

> The summary of various testings done at the Camp Hill site identified measurements of over 20 volatile organic compounds . . . Throughout these investigations, there appeared to be little correlation made between clinical problems experienced with specific staff and their particular exposures, and there was no follow-up . . . there were, in fact, in the order of thirty potential incitants in the form of vaporized chemicals, as well as all of the other substances reviewed, present at low levels, that could have triggered typical pictures of multiple chemical sensitivity.

Dr. Beresford points to the haphazard manner in which the report was investigated, and the fact that clinical information on patients was gathered slowly and cases were not followed up.

Dr. Beresford suggests that the Committee should have looked at all chemical pollutants not from a toxicological perspective but in terms of sensitivity. Despite various haematological abnormalities such as decreased platelets, high blood chemical levels, a seemingly high incidence of thyroid disease, skin lesions, reactive airway disease, mineral deficiencies, interstitial cystitis, and neuro-cognitive abnormalities, the Committee still identified 'the stress on the staff . . . as possibly mitigating and promulgating events' and concluded a psychological aetiology to the illnesses. Dr. Beresford made the point that:

> 684 persons were reported as having symptoms, and 66% of these people went off work, 119 workers remain off work, and some others work part-time. There is a striking resemblance with respect to symptoms and odour intolerance experienced by the Camp Hill workers to those described in the literature on multiple and diverse groups around the world. Can all these persons be suffering from stress? Why would doctors, nurses, physiotherapists, dieticians, office workers, and kitchen workers all risk loss of their careers, and all say that they were

experiencing multiple symptomatology including progressive sensitivities to multiple chemicals, foods and inhalants, and severe fatigue if this were not the case?

Dr. Beresford suggested that scientifically, it was critical to search exhaustively for any biological causes of the illnesses. In this conclusion, Dr. Beresford put her finger on the most important thing which separates the science of the organic aetiologists from the non-science of the sceptics; it crops up again and again in relation to MCS, ME and CFS. The scientists consistently ask for more research and more analytical investigations.

Chemical agents

The movement to discredit doctors, patients and impartial scientific observers and their arguments about chemical damage is like a tree. Its roots and trunk consist of the arguments against chemical sensitivity; as the branches develop they try to cover any area of clinical medicine that might have to do with chemicals, or might lead to discussion about chemical sensitivity or finally any illness which might be caused by industrial production, whether it is to do with chemicals or not.

Confirmation that the chemical companies, who had been organising since the attack on Rachael Carson in the 1960s, have specifically used the argument of prior psychiatric condition can be found in the North American Chemical Manufacturers Association's *Environmental Illness Briefing Paper* published in 1990.♦

♦ It is possible to find a number of early case histories where chemical companies have used the arguments that chemicals only created problems for vulnerable individuals and because of this, it was the individual who was responsible not the company. Donald W. Scott places the beginning of the use of psychological arguments to cover up the true cause of ME and CFS type illnesses in 1959. Scott's argument is that ME and CFS are actually New Variant Brucellosis, which leeched into society from germ warfare experiments. Scott says that a crystalline form (cont.)

SKEWED

At the time of publication, the Chemical Manufacturers Association (CMA) lobbied on behalf of approximately 175 member companies supporting twenty full-time lobbyists in Washington. Members paid dues based on a sliding scale, beginning at $7,000 annually for small manufacturers. The CMA was at that time in the process of establishing a Political Action Committee (PAC) to accommodate contributions to the campaigns of political candidates.

The CMA *Briefing Paper* tries to deny clinical ecologists their area of expertise by referring to the field as '*medically* unrecognised.' At the same time, the document fails to explain that clinical ecologists were almost all qualified doctors, who by 1990 had their own legally and academically constituted professional organisations.

♦ (cont.) of brucellas bacteria was isolated in 1946 by Pentagon consultants. During the nineteen forties, there were a number of accidents in military laboratories. At Camp Detrick, in Frederick, Maryland, 17 workers were affected by the bacteria. Two papers reported on the progress of these affected workers and their illnesses. In one of the papers (Trever et al. Brucellosis. *Archives of Internal Medicine*, 1959) it is suggested that the victims of Brucellosis with a propensity for psychological illness might be more vulnerable. [Cited in *Myalgic Encephalomyelitis as New Variant Brucellosis*, Donald W. Scott, *Journal of Degenerative Diseases,* Vol. 2]. As with most secret endeavours in both the US and Britain after the 1939-1945 War, propaganda and military stratagems and experiments of the Pentagon, the CIA and the British Secret Services were also worked on by large corporations. The stratagems of the Pharmaceutical and Chemical, PR and Newspaper industries and the intelligence agencies overlapped at many points.

Individual vulnerability described by a company, might be either psychological or physical. This following example occurred in the Vinyl Chloride Industry and is cited by the author in his paper *Company Men, Part II: Sir Richard Doll, Death, Dioxin and PVC*. 'Around 1964, a hand disability (acro-osteolysis) was recognised among VCM workers who cleaned huge, blender-like reactors, and the Goodrich company sought research help from Cincinnati University's Kettering Laboratory. By 1966, it was clear that acro-osteolysis was endemic to the industry. A 1967 article authored by four Goodrich medical officials in *JAMA* suggested, however, that the disease was not serious or common, and was probably due to 'personal idiosyncrasy.'

Stifling Science

One of the initial strategies used in attacking chemical sensitivity involved stressing the wide ranging list of names for the condition and the number of illness symptoms, so that the condition appeared bizarre to the layperson. The CMA pronounced that a wide range of names for a condition suggested a wide range of symptoms, claiming that the more physical symptoms of which a patient complains, the greater the likelihood of psychiatric disorder being the cause. In fact the wide range of names for the complaint meant simply that a specific illness which fitted the symptoms had not been isolated.

> Known variously by more than 20 names, among them chemical hypersensitivity syndrome, total allergy syndrome and 20th century disease, 'environmental illness' is a subject of intense controversy within the field of medicine . . . *environmental illness* has become the label for a constellation of complaints *for which orthodox medical science has so far found no acceptable explanation* and includes headaches, fatigue, depression, anxiety and digestive problems which occur principally after exposure to barely measurable amounts of virtually all synthetic chemicals found in food, water, air, clothing and everyday surroundings.

According to the chemical companies, these symptoms were unsupported by physical findings or laboratory tests.♦

From the briefing paper we see that the chemical companies purposely used the classic description of allergy to attack chemical sensitivity, accusing environmental medicine specialists of believing their patients severely 'allergic' to the world in which they lived.

♦ The example of allergy to clothing – an issue substantially invented by the chemical companies – was taken up by Caroline Richmond (the founder of the Campaign Against Health Fraud). In 1987, she was allowed space in the *BMJ* to advertise the setting up of a fake organisation called DRAB – Dye Related Allergies Bureau.

SKEWED

The mainstay of the strategic arguments used by the chemical industry, however, involves the attempt to identify those who claim to have any kind of chemical sensitivity as mentally disturbed. The type of psychiatric condition diagnosed in these patients is never identified but hangs somewhere between neurosis and obsessive compulsive disorder. A kind of 'cult' mentality is suggested to exist amongst patients who become isolated and cut off from the broader, 'welcoming' family of society.

> They [these patients] are determined to consume only organic foods grown without insecticides, sprays and fertilizers. They may use only items made of glass, porcelain, stainless steel and untreated animal or plant fabrics (cotton, linen, silk, wood and leather.) Often, this results in social isolation, difficulty within the community and unemployability.

In England and America this kind of psychological and social analysis led in the early 1990s to 'health fraud' groups teaming up with cult-deprogrammers to attack clinical ecologists.

The references given for MCS in the CMA briefing rely on three papers produced by two authors, Dr. A. Terr and Dr. D. Stewart. From the mid-1980s, both these researchers had been suggesting consistently that those who claimed to be suffering from multiple chemical sensitivity actually had serious psychological difficulties.

One of the principal fears of the chemical industry is clearly spelt out in the *Briefing Paper*. Even in 1990, the matter of civil liability claimed in damages via the courts hovered over chemical sensitivity in exactly the same way that the claims for asbestos damage hung over the world insurance markets.

> Despite unsubstantiated evidence, environmental medicine specialists and their patients persistently advocate that environmental illness exists. What they have failed to prove in the scientific arena, they are attempting to legitimise in the media, in the legislature, and in the courts. Legislative initiatives

have so far failed to legitimise environmental illness, but it would not be difficult for legislators to misperceive the goals of environmental medicine as medically legitimate. And lawsuits, of which several are currently pending, could multiply.

Court cases and legal precedents are an evident source of concern to the chemical industry, as is the worry that the government might end up paying via the social benefits system for the damage they do. The *Briefing Paper* attempts to alarm industrialists and ultimately the public, suggesting that those with chemical sensitivity will become parasitic on the welfare system. To an industry that had fought workers' occupational claims of all kinds for more than a century, the consequence of MCS raised fearful spectres.

Environmental illness advocates believe they are entitled to a number of sources of financial support; monetary damage for increased illness resulting from exposure; monetary damages for existing fear of contracting future illness; disability benefits from private insurance policies and Social Security; reimbursement for medical costs; Workers' Compensation payments; a variety of workplace protections (from termination, demotion, pay cuts, etc.); rehabilitation services; and financial assistance for alteration of living space.

The impact, however, would not be restricted to the chemical industry. Commonly used chemicals are found everywhere, in the home, the workplace, outdoors, shopping malls, and even hospitals. Potentially affected industries include the textiles, clothing, lawn care products, household cleaners, dry cleaners, paints and solvents, perfumes, hair treatment products, plastics, paper and many other consumer goods industries.

In dealing with the media, the chemical industry realised from the early days that they needed men in white coats who would give credence to the health-affirming qualities of chemicals.

Because environmental illness is a health issue, its debate is best left primarily to physicians; the chemical industry, for example, should not get overly involved in such debates. Nonetheless, a

ready response for media queries is a prudent precaution. Should
reporters, editors, news directors or other media question
industry about environmental illness, it would be appropriate to
respond in a limited way. Steps best taken are: *Identify medical
personnel familiar with environmental illness who can speak as
experts.* Informally offer guidance and background materials to
reporters, based on their degree of knowledge.

It was as a consequence of these last instructions and others like
them that the chemical companies, along with the pharmaceutical
and insurance companies, either through small agencies, industry-
backed institutes or PR companies, came to have a number of physicians and medical researchers on permanent stand-by. The idea of
having medical personnel on call is a ploy clearly spelt out by
specific chemical companies in the late eighties and early nineties.

Another vital function of the industry-available 'expert' is the
giving of expert evidence on behalf of the defence in claims hearings. It is the task of the chemical-company-funded physician to
snipe continually at clinical ecologists and to get as much critical
paperwork published as possible, in order to provide an accumul-
ation of seemingly authoritative evidence which could then be used
in court proceedings.

However, in each case the plaintiff bears the burden of proof on
the issue. Often the plaintiff needs a person accepted by the court
as an expert who will testify that there is a cause and effect
relationship to a reasonable degree of medical certainty. The
qualifications for being an expert vary from jurisdiction to
jurisdiction and even from judge to judge, as does the meaning of
'reasonable degree of medical certainty.' While there have been a
few exceptions, in most cases environmental illness proponents
have not been excluded from giving Expert testimony.

The veiled suggestion is that industry experts might try to get
'environmental illness' proponents excluded from giving evidence.
The struggles of Dr. Jean Monro in England, as well as Dr. William

18

Rea and Dr. Grace Ziem♦ in North America are examples of how this idea has been turned into practice.

Since the publication of the CMA briefing document, new organisations have been set up, publishing new versions of their strategies, holding meetings, organising conferences and, most importantly, providing experts to write books and papers. This kind of organisation is best illustrated by looking at American examples. All these organisations are identifiable as having a common link by virtue of their use of a psychiatric ascription for Multiple Chemical Sensitivity (MCS) and other related illnesses.

The Environmental Sensitivities Research Institute

The Environmental Sensitivities Research Institute (ESRI) is a chemical-industry-linked association set up in 1994 by Dr. Ronald Gots. An unusual 'research institute' it has only a PO Box address, no office and, in 2001, only one member of staff.

The ESRI offers grants for research into MCS, individually limited to $10,000, the same amount as the cost of ESRI's annual 'Enterprise Membership' fee. Some commentators have suggested that as the tobacco companies did, this provides companies with an

---

♦ These cases are dealt with in other parts of this book. Dr. Jean Monro is a clinical ecologist who runs the Breakspear Hospital in England, which was severely criticised in a World in Action television programme called *The Allergy Business*, initiated by the Campaign Against Health Fraud. [In this programme during a piece of film showing the Breakspear hospital, the voice over suggested that many of the patients were psychologically ill.] Dr. William Rea is an American thoracic surgeon who is an expert in chemical sensitivity and runs a clinic in Dallas, Texas. The case of both these doctors and their disparagement is recorded in *Dirty Medicine: Science, big business and the assault on natural health care* by the author. Dr. Grace Ziem is an occupational health physician who was heavily attacked by John Stossel in an ABC television programme called *Junk Science*.

obvious way to launder research funding through an apparently objective organisation. However, in the six years since its founding, by the year 2000, ESRI acknowledged funding only one research project.

Enterprise members of ESRI include Dow Chemicals, Proctor and Gamble, Amway, Colgate-Palmolive, Responsible Industry for a Sound Environment (RISE), and the Cosmetic, Toiletry and Fragrance Association (CTFA).

One of ESRI's objectives is to 'proactively respond to the rising number of MCS cases.' A typical 'advertorial' from the ESRI trade journal *The Merchandiser* in 1990 promotes the organisation's view on MCS. Headed *Multiple Chemical Sensitivities: Fear of Risk or Fact of Life?* it reads:

> Scientists are increasingly concerned that a doubtful new diagnosis – supposedly caused by everything 'man-made' in the environment – is unnecessarily making thousands of Americans miserable each year. One of these so-called 'modern diseases' is called MCS, for Multiple Chemical Sensitivities. Many established scientists and physicians doubt MCS actually does exist; *it exists only because a patient believes it does* and because a doctor validates that belief. For information on MCS, write the Environmental Sensitivities Research Institute. [Italics added.]

This advertorial explicitly makes the case which is the foundation of the psychological argument and which crops up again and again in relation to contemporary arguments about GWS, pesticide exposure, ME and CFS: that these illnesses exist *only in the minds of sufferers* and have no objective clinical or biological reality.

Dr. Gots, the founder of ESRI, is also involved with Responsible Industry for a Safe Environment (RISE) and was the founder of National Medical Advisory Service, Inc. (NMAS). These organisations were specifically formed to promote and defend the use of chemicals. Both ESRI and NMAS, which have shared offices and in the past have used the same fax number, promote the notion that MCS is an imaginary or psychoneurotic phenomenon and not an organic or physical illness.

Although ESRI has set up a 5-member Scientific Advisory Panel to review applications for grants, its Board of Directors still has the final say. Three of the five advisors to the ESRI in the year 2000, including the chairman of the panel, Dr. Frank Mitchell, had previously expressed the view that MCS is psychogenic. ESRI's review procedures make clear that the scientific advisory panel will only consider a proposal if it has received prior approval from the Chairman of the Board. In 2001, the Chairman was John DeFazio, senior regulatory lobbyist for the Chemical Specialties Manufacturers Association.

Responsible Industry for a Sound Environment

Created in 1991, RISE is affiliated to the American Crop Protection Association (ACPA) and is a lobbying and public relations trade organisation set up to defend 'urban usage' of specialist pesticides. These products include pesticide products used in and around homes, businesses and public buildings; in commercial greenhouses and nurseries; on golf courses, sports turf and other recreational areas; in forestry; for vegetation management along roadways, railroads and aquatic management. RISE shares ACPA's Washington DC offices, which probably means that they have a desk in the organisation's offices.

Inverting the environmental message, RISE claims pesticide use in schools is necessary to protect children's health. The 150 coalition members of RISE include Monsanto, DuPont and Dow Agro-Science. RISE works with other coalitions like American Crop Protection Association, Chemical Manufacturers Association, Chlor-

21

ine Chemistry Council, Fertilizer Institute, Global Climate Coalition, Grocery Manufacturers Association, National Association of Manufacturers, National Endangered Species Act Reform Coalition, National Mining Association and the Vinyl Institute. They donate huge amounts of money during elections in the hope of weakening or eliminating existing environmental laws.

RISE works hard supporting the use of pesticides. In 1992, the organisation won an honourable mention from the American Society of Association Executives after they put together a 'grassroots' coalition in Missoula to defeat a ballot that would have required pesticide applicators to notify residents about the kinds of pesticide which were being sprayed in and near their homes. Before RISE intervened, the proposed law had majority support, after two weeks of 'education', voters defeated the proposal 57 percent to 43 percent.

'Grassroots' campaigns play on the basic fears of the community, including the fear of unemployment for local workers and the fear of illness amongst children. The message is essentially right- wing and the campaigns are often specifically opposed to 'do-gooding' or 'liberal' environmentalists. RISE prides itself, in its propaganda, on its lobbying capability to defend pesticides behind the scenes: 'Sometimes it's what you don't see that benefits you most as a member of RISE. For instance, legislation that never made it into law, a congressional vote that wasn't cast, a negative article that wasn't published. There are countless times when proactive measures by RISE keep onerous actions from occurring.'

RISE opposed the School Environmental Protection Act (SEPA),♦ introduced in October 1999, which tried to control the use of pesticides in and around schools. RISE suggested that the passage

---

♦ The US General Accounting Office released a report in January 2000, which found that among the 2,300 documented cases between 1993 and 1996 where (cont.)

of SEPA would 'needlessly prolong children's exposure to dangerous pests,' claiming that children 'are especially vulnerable to insect bites and stings from wasps, ticks, scorpions, and fire ants.'

Apart from straightforward lobbying, RISE and other chemical organisations run campaigns inside schools. In co-operation with the US Environmental Protection Agency, National School Boards Association, National Pest Control Association and Professional Lawn Care Association of America, RISE has developed an information kit that responds to concerns about pesticide use in schools. It was mailed initially to over 16,000 school districts. RISE representatives respond to negative news stories by visiting media decision-makers as soon as possible. They have established relationships with journalists and medical personnel that they believe will influence public opinion. The executive director of RISE meets regularly with newspaper and magazine editors and television and film producers.

A good example of how RISE organises its campaigns occurred when a producer of alternative 'botanical' pesticides, Eco-Smart Technologies, launched a campaign alerting parents to the potential risks that conventional products may pose to their children. Actress Jane Seymour initiated the campaign at a news conference in New York City. The campaign, called *Care for Kids*, urged parents to 'look for and eliminate harmful pesticides from their homes and children's schools and day-care centers . . . and replace them with safer alternatives.'

When the *Care for Kids* campaign was launched, RISE immediately became involved by using consultants to try to denigrate

---

♦ (cont.) people were exposed to pesticides in schools, 329 needed medical attention. The report found schools do not keep records of pesticide use or possible exposure rates. The report concluded that pesticides 'are harmful to all human beings, but children are at greater risk.' Cited by Environmental Working Group, reported in the *Austin American-Statesmen*, January 5, 2000.

the campaign. Allen James, the then executive director was quoted in one paper as saying that pesticides used to rid schools of cockroaches and other pests, 'are safe and do not result in excess exposure to children.' Predictably, RISE furnished the paper with a scientific witness: Dr. Miles M. Weinberger, a paediatrician and asthma expert at the University of Iowa, said no conclusive scientific evidence exists that proves asthma is triggered by exposure to pesticides. Exposure to second-hand smoke and open burning of leaves and garbage is a much more important risk factor, he said. 'More kids are hurt by walking across the street than by insecticides.' And just for good measure RISE's parent organisation got in on the act: Ray McAllister, an official of the American Crop Protection Association, accused Eco-Smart of using the *Care for Kids* campaign to run down the competition so it could 'gain market share.'

On MCS, RISE says that the expression Multiple Chemical Sensitivity has gone out of fashion and been replaced by the term 'Idiopathic Environmental Intolerances' (IEI). According to this definition, no general rules can apply to such reported illnesses, no one knows their cause, and only certain people who have a vulnerable personality (usually, they suggest, people with pre-exposure psychological problems) develop sensitivities.

RISE's 1995-96 Strategic Plan described as one of its objectives, 'to promote the use of industry products as valuable pest management tools to enhance the quality of life and the environment.' To achieve this objective, the RISE strategic plan identified two 'tactics' to be used by its Communications Committee: first, 'Host forums for industry user groups that are taking positive pesticide messages to schools' and, second, 'Conduct two MCS phenomena seminars.'

On September 9 1995, RISE sponsored one of these seminars on MCS. Despite the obvious anti-MCS bias of Dr. Gots and RISE,

Stifling Science

Johns Hopkins Medical Institution at the University in Baltimore, one of the top research institutions in the US, in conjunction with the National Institute of Occupational Safety and Health (a federal agency) co-sponsored the symposium. The symposium was called 'Multiple Chemical Sensitivities: State-of-the-Science Symposium' and it was heavily weighted in favour of pro-industry, anti-consumer and anti-MCS-patient viewpoints.

Albert Donnay of MCS Referral & Resources Inc., an energetic campaigner for MCS sufferers, filed a complaint against the conference following ESRI's lack of disclosed involvement in the planning and funding of the event and the failure of six speakers, including the co-chair, to disclose their ESRI affiliation. As a result of the complaint, the Johns Hopkins Office of Continuing Medical Education (CME) got a letter of reprimand from the National Accreditation Council for CME and was put on probation for a year.

In 1999, another RISE sponsored symposium, 'Low Level Environmental Exposures: State-of-the-Science,' was held in Arlington, Virginia. Advertised topics for the day-long symposium included: Asthma, Allergy and Immunology; Odors and Irritation; Neurological Function and Overlapping Syndromes. The overlapping syndromes session included two papers, one given by Dr. Daniel Clauw, of Georgetown University, on Overlap of Environmental Intolerances with Chronic Pain & Fatigue Syndromes and another by Clement Furlong, PhD, of the University of Washington, on PON1 Status and Differential Sensitivity to Organophosphate Compounds.

Psychiatrist Dr. Donald Black, of the University of Iowa, gave a talk on psychiatric aetiology: 'Psychiatric Risk Factors for IEI: Clinical Study of Gulf War Veterans.' Black was at that time on ESRI's scientific advisory board, which was chaired by Dr. Frank Mitchell; he also received the only research grant awarded by ESRI, which he used to update the findings of an earlier study he had published. Presenting the update in August 1998 at the MCS Symposium of the American Chemical Society, Black failed to disclose either his funding from ESRI or his membership of the ESRI's board of directors and its science advisory panel (the very group which reviews grant requests.)

For some years, Dr. Black was funded to investigate MCS among active duty and reserve Gulf War veterans in the CDC's Iowa study; this study was published in the *Journal of the American Medical Association* in 1997, without Black's contribution. When he was scheduled to discuss his research and present his unpublished findings at the CDC's Gulf War Research Planning Conference in Atlanta, even the CDC failed to disclose Black's ESRI affiliation in the conference materials or in its already published paper, which still listed Black as a co-author despite his failure to present his findings.

Dr. Black's position on Multiple Chemical Sensitivity has always been unequivocal, and is well summarised in this quote from an interview with a journalist:

> 'It's clear just from talking with some [MCS patients] that they had ordinary depression,' said Dr. Black, whose study on the subject appeared in the Journal of the American Medical Association . . . 'If they were offered standard antidepressant treatments, their symptoms would probably go away very promptly.'

International Society of Regulatory Toxicology and Pharmacology

Both the above symposia organised by ESRI and supported by RISE were also organised with the International Society of Regulatory Toxicology and Pharmacology (ISRTP). ISRTP published the proceedings of the first seminar, paid for by the ESRI, in a special supplement of its journal.

Stifling Science

Set up in 1975, the ISRTP is sponsored by the American Chemistry Council, Bristol-Myers Squibb, Dow Agro Sciences, Eastman Kodak, Merck, Proctor and Gamble, RJ Reynolds Tobacco Company, Schering-Plough Research Institute and SmithKline Beecham Pharmaceuticals.

According to the Society's mission statement, ISRTP 'strives to ensure that the best scientific evidence, applied in an unbiased and transparent manner, underpins the formulation and implementation of policy and regulations of health, safety, and the environment.' On paper at least, the ISRTP attracts high fliers to its society such as Albert C. Kolbye, a former assistant US surgeon general and a past Society president.

ISRTP's Council meetings are held not in its own offices but in those of a law firm. Dr. Gots often attends and meetings may include visiting members of groups like the Chemical Manufacturers Association. At the ISRTP Council Meeting on Friday June 4 1999, when the second conference was organised, Dr. Ronald Gots was representing the International Center for Toxicology and Medicine and the ISRTP. Other groups which entered the Council meeting discussion were the Chlorine Chemistry Council, ILSI and the Cosmetic, Toiletry and Fragrance Association (CTFA).

The Cosmetic, Toiletry and Fragrance Association

In its own words, CTFA campaigns 'to ensure that the personal care products industry has the freedom to pursue creative product development and compete in a fair and responsible marketplace.' CTFA has approximately 600 member companies, including active members like manufacturers and distributors of finished products and associate members, including suppliers of ingredients, raw materials and packaging, as well as consumer and trade publications.

CTFA has its own Science Department, which helps provide evidence on regulatory standards and health matters for product liability cases. More than one-third of CTFA's budget is devoted to science and 40 percent of the Association's staff works in science-related areas. The Department consists of seven scientists and three staff members. In the year 2000, Dr. Gerald McEwen, the Vice President-Science, was also an FDA Advisory Panel member and Chair-man of the Board of ESRI.

Like RISE, CTFA campaigns to defend the unregulated use of chemicals. The Association fought efforts to amend Massachusetts Committee Against Discrimination regulations by adding multiple chemical sensitivity (MCS) to the list of conditions covered by the state's public accommodations law. It also helped defeat New Mexico legislation that would have funded research programmes relating to MCS.

The Association worked with allies to prevent enactment of Proposition 65 clones in Connecticut, Delaware, and Massachusetts. These would have required warnings in connection with some cosmetic and personal care products. The Association successfully opposed New York proposals to require sunscreens to be labelled with expiration dates and storage instructions, and to require warning labels on cosmetic talc products.

The Chlorine Chemistry Council

The CCC is a business council of the American Chemistry Council, a national trade association based in Arlington, Virginia, representing the manufacturers and users of chlorine and chlorine-related products. Chlorine is widely used as a disinfecting agent and a basic component in pharmaceuticals. Members of the CCC include Dow Chemicals, Du Pont Chemicals, Occidental Chemical Corporation and Olin Chlor Alkali Products.

Stifling Science

The chlorine industry is also a heavy user and producer of dioxins. In the International Society of Regulatory Toxicology and Pharmacology comments on the EPA's 1994 reassessment of dioxin, Albert C. Kolbye, ventures to explain why dioxins are still *considered* dangerous:

> . . . many bureaucrats, consumer and environmental organisations, plaintiff trial lawyers, politicians and researchers . . . have financial, political or power interests in claiming that dioxin-like compounds are causing much more severe problems to human health than objective scientific scrutiny of the evidence would support. Their claims are generally not accurate and distort perceptions of risks to public health. For the most part, dioxins et al. are non-problems for the American people and elsewhere for the simple reason that human exposures are very low and non-effective in creating damage to human health.

Flying in the face of research which links even low levels of dioxins to ill health, this critical review claims that extensive studies of people exposed to *large amounts of dioxins* show that the chemicals do not pose a risk to human health.

CASE HISTORY ONE

HRT poisoning diagnosed as mental illness

Pharmaceuticals have chemical components which can affect individuals in ways that are not intended; they can also create allergies and sensitivities which radically affect the body and consciousness of the individual.

Joan[10] was thirty-nine when she consulted her GP regarding fatigue. At the time, she thought that she might have a calcium deficiency. Her GP suggested that she might start taking HRT (Hormone Replacement Therapy.) He told her very little about it, except that it increased oestrogen levels. Because Joan had complete trust in her GP and had also worked as a nurse all her adult life, she decided to try HRT.

HRT turned out to be more than a 'quick fix' for Joan; she remained on the drug for almost twelve years. During most of that time, she kept fairly well, and, looking back, it appeared that the drug had carried her through her daily life. There was, however, no monitoring of the drug at any time and she had no physical check ups.[11]

Nine years after she began taking the drug, at the age of forty-eight, Joan began to experience a number of physical and mental changes. Physically, she developed a blood-stained vaginal discharge, abdominal pain and increasing fatigue. Her family began to tell her that her personality was changing.

---

10 The real name of this person and other details have been changed to protect the person's identity.

11 Most HRT manufacturers recommend that there should be an annual complete physical check-up.

Stifling Science

She saw a consultant at her hospital and she was diagnosed with an ovarian cyst for which hysterectomy was suggested as the only cure. This procedure was carried out within a month of her first consultation.

Following the operation, still taking her dose of the HRT treatment, her life changed; she felt, as she says, 'unable to get into gear.' Her GP diagnosed depression and prescribed Prozac; his comment as he wrote out the prescription was: 'I know that you don't believe in these things, but indulge me.' Her doctor also increased her HRT prescription and referred her to a psychiatrist. Joan didn't take the prescribed Prozac or go to visit the psychiatrist: she did, however, increase her consumption of HRT.

Now classified as 'long-term sick,' Joan was sent to see a Department of Health and Social Security doctor. After listening to her, he diagnosed a psychotic condition.

Joan's life became more and more difficult; she sank into despair, finding it increasingly difficult to concentrate. She lost all interest in clothes and shopping. She began to experience the world at a distance; she strained to hear what people said to her. She could not retain or concentrate on anything she read.

She continued taking the almost double doses of HRT, until she could hardly lift her head from the pillow in the morning. She suffered constant dizziness, started vomiting and having hallucinations. When, suddenly, small lumps erupted all over her body, she made a decision to throw all her medication in the bin. A couple of days after that, black hairs appeared from the middle of the lumps and she knew from her nursing experience that she had oestrogen poisoning. Her GP referred her yet again to a psychiatrist.

SKEWED

Since coming off all medication and taking an interest in nutrition and natural medicine, Joan has been healthy and happier. She now works for a counselling organisation for women with problems caused by HRT.

CHAPTER TWO

The Politics
of Medical Cynicism

Language is taken over by doctors: the sick person is deprived of meaningful words for his anguish, which is further increased by linguistic mystification. [12]

'Funny business this Flu. You see, it's a disease for which we really haven't discovered the micro-organism responsible, so we can't arrive at an efficient prophylaxis.' Paul saw that the doctor loved using the learned terms that were probably unintelligible to a layman. [13]

Tracing the history of the arguments used by psychiatrists that ME does not exist and that Chronic Fatigue Syndrome is the end-result of an aberrant belief system might be difficult, were it not for the fact that 'health fraud activists' and 'greenwashers'♦ have used the same arguments consistently in relation to other illnesses.

---

12 Ivan Illich, *Medical Nemesis; The Expropriation of Health*. Calder & Boyars, Ideas in Progress. London 1975.

13 Ernest Raymond, *We, the accused*. Pan Books, 1960. London.

♦ The 'health fraud' movement began in the 1980s with groups established in North America and Britain. These groups are discussed later in this chapter. Members of 'health fraud' groups are diverse individuals, with a more or less common position on specific issues to do with orthodox pharmaceutical-based medicine and its alternatives. Throughout this text, I have called people in these groups or those who espouse their position 'health fraud' activists. The expression *greenwash* came into existence in the 1990s in North America; it denotes anyone or anything, like a book or a report, which whitewashes adverse industry involvement in green issues. People active in this milieu I have termed greenwashers.

SKEWED

Since the 1980s, leading 'health fraud' activists, pro-industry doctors and academics in both Britain and North America have promoted the idea of a psychiatric aetiology in relation to food allergy, multiple chemical sensitivity, ME and Chronic Fatigue Syndrome, Repetitive Strain Injury, organophosphate exposure, Gulf War Syndrome, the American Love Canal dispute and the Camelford water poisoning case, as well as in a number of other situations. In all these circumstances conflicts between sufferers and physicians have become common.

The development of publicly organised disputes between patients and doctors is a relatively recent phenomenon, only occurring after the advent of the National Health Service. Sporadic disputes between government health agencies, advised by doctors, and citizens have, however, occurred over the last two centuries, in relation to issues as diverse as vaccination and the pasteurisation of milk.

The first signs of the recent generation of conflicts came in the radical period of the nineteen sixties when the women's movement campaigned generally against male doctors, especially on issues to do with sexuality and reproduction. In this period as well, British patients faced their first major conflict with a pharmaceutical company over the damage done by thalidomide.

Serious public and collective conflicts around and within medicine were clearly recognisable in the nineteen eighties. The emergence of group conflicts reflected a number of different factors, most of them consequent upon a monolithic centralised state health care system: an increasingly educated and conscious population of patients; a deeper recognition of either large scale 'new' illnesses, like Multiple Chemical Sensitivity, or older illnesses like asthma, which have been virtually ignored; the adverse effects of pharmaceuticals; increasing desire on the part of drug companies to recoup high cost research and development funding, using intensive market penetration and saturation advertising, especially to doctors and through patient groups; growing insecurity amongst many about damage caused by orthodox pharmaceutical medicine; the increased use of alternative and complementary therapies; and, finally, structural threats to the orthodox medical profession precipitated by an increasing exposure of mistakes, failures and inefficiencies.

With doctors, a long-established powerful group of professionals, entering a period of structural instability it was inevitable that those under threat would come together in their collective defence. This is a period when one expects to see not only the chemical and pharmaceutical companies battling to consolidate, stabilise and maintain markets, while fending off liability claims over illnesses, but also physicians defending their professional status and career structure by attacking alternative and complementary medicine. Then there is science, at the heart of contemporary health care delivery, needing to continually validate and confirm its status.♦ This is a period of hidden-interest conflicts in medicine, of undeclared vested interests, covert agencies and propaganda. All these factors led to the growth of 'health fraud' movements in Britain and North America, which piggy-backed onto the already established industry-organised anti-ecology campaigns which had come into existence in the post-*Silent Spring* era.

The 'health fraud' movement had two principal functions: to protect and defend the professional status of orthodox physicians and pharmaceutical medicine, and to protect and defend industry, especially the chemical industry, particularly in relation to claims that chemicals cause ill health.

Only a few 'health fraud' activists and environmental health greenwashers can lay claims to serious scientific or academic work.

♦ So called 'scientific' medicine is totally dependent upon vivisection and drug testing on animals. The fraudulent-science, irrationality and cruelty of these procedures have done much to turn people against orthodox medicine. See Hans Ruesch, *Slaughter of the Innocent*, Slingshot Publications, 2003.

Some of the main activists, however, can boast hundreds of publications, books or papers which appear to make them the world's
greatest experts on a subject. Some 'health fraud' activists have
previously worked in a branch of industrial science with the processed food industry or the pharmaceutical industry and some of them
have done promotional work for industry. Many of them have been
called as 'expert witnesses' in court cases or professional-body
tribunal cases; some work as consultants for insurance companies.
A minority have worked in the media or are now media personalities; in the main they exude an aura of cynicism and world-wear-
iness. They speak with the confidence of professional ideologues
but rarely enter into public discussions. The main characters are
litigious beyond reason against anyone who criticises them and
against those whom they target as enemies of orthodoxy.

Both the National Council Against Health Fraud in North
America and HealthWatch in Britain (initially called the Campaign
Against Health Fraud [CAHF]) have close links with statutory
authorities. In North America, the 'health fraud' movement grew
out of meetings between quasi-statutory organisations while in
Britain the Campaign Against Health Fraud approached the
Department of Health suggesting a role for themselves within its
regulatory framework. Both groups also have close links with non-
statutory commercial interests such as the health insurance industry
and industry-supported information groups such as British or North
American nutrition groups.

* * *

The American 'health fraud' movement is slightly older than its
British counterpart and its attacks on clinical ecology and defence
of the chemical and pharmaceutical industry more brazen. The
principal US 'health fraud' organisation, the National Council
Against Health Fraud (NCAHF), is interlinked with two other
organisations: the Committee for the Scientific Investigation of

Claims of the Paranormal (CSICOP) and the American Council on Science and Health (ACSH).♦ These three organisations mount constant attacks upon alternative medicine and clinical ecology while defending multi-national industry, especially the pharmaceutical and chemical industries; between them they are linked to some of the most important pro-industry health academics and scientists in Britain and America.

The American Council on Science and Health

Set up in 1978, the American Council on Science and Health (ACSH) made it an early objective to publish position papers on a wide range of products and substances and their effect upon health. Elizabeth Whelan, the organisation's founder, claimed that the Council would 'bring reason, balance and common sense to public debates about food, nutrition, chemicals, pharmaceuticals, lifestyles, the environment and health.'

Whelan, still the head of ASCH, is an able propagandist credited with having coined such expressions as 'toxic terrorist,' 'self-appointed environmentalists' and 'carcinophobia.' She refers to the research work of the Greens and clinical ecologists as 'voodoo statistics.'

ACSH was in existence for two years before it declared the money it received from industry. The organisation was pump-primed, with a grant of $125,000, by the Sarah Scaife Foundation, the stock of which was heavily based upon Gulf Oil. Two years after ACSH was set up, Ronald Reagan became US President and the causes of the Right were taken into the administration.

On its present board ACSH has representatives of the most powerful PR companies in America, especially Ketchum Com-

---

♦ The relationship between these three organisations is explored at greater length in the author's book *Dirty Medicine: Science, big business and the assault on natural health care*, Slingshot Publications 1993.

munications, whose 'environmental' clients include Dow Chemicals and groups like the National Pharmaceutical Council. ACSH and Elizabeth Whelan side with the chemical companies against the tobacco companies, suggesting that while tobacco represents a substantial health threat, any threat from chemicals is small. While speaking out against the health risks of tobacco, ACSH has defended asbestos and DDT.

ACSH is funded by many of the largest chemical companies, such as: American Cyanamid, Amoco Foundation, Dow Chemicals of Canada, Hooker Chemical and Plastics Corporation, Mobil Foundation, Monsanto Fund and the Shell Companies Foundation. The President of Dow Chemicals is a foundation trustee of the Rollin Gerstacker Foundation from which ACSH has received payments of over $75,000.

ACSH receives money from all the industrial sectors that contribute to the production of chemically treated foodstuffs. While receiving money from firms like International Flavors and Fragrances Inc., and McCormick and Company, both producers of artificial flavourings and colourings, ACSH published a report that denied that the ingestion of food-colouring agents could lead to hyperactive behaviour in children. Amongst medical and pharmaceutical interests, ACSH is funded by the Alliance of American Insurers, the Burroughs Wellcome Fund, Ciba-Geigy and Pfizer.

ACSH has presented work funded by paper companies and timber concerns which use vast quantities of herbicides. ACSH campaigned for Alar, while receiving a grant of at least $25,000 from the Uniroyal Chemical Company which manufactured the chemical spray for apples.

In the early 1980s, the Center for Science in the Public Interest (CSIPI) approached eight well-regarded scientists to review ACSH reports covering topics in their specialist areas. Almost without exception, the scientists concluded that the ACSH reports were biased and unscientific with many serious omissions of fact. ACSH has published two cancer reports, both of which exonerate chemicals.

On the Monsanto dioxin-containing pesticide 2,4,5-T, the CSIPI reviewer said that ACSH report failed to mention contemporary studies carried out in Sweden which indicated increased rates of cancer amongst workers exposed to phenoxy herbicides. Monsanto has been ACSH's biggest funder and, while the company might in the past have announce, for example, that 'it is cutting its toxic waste emissions by 90%,' it was donating hundreds of thousands of dollars to support anti-environmental organisations like ACSH.♦

Elizabeth Whelan has defended a range of Monsanto's products such as PCBs, 2,4,5-T, the artificial sweetener Nutrasweet, and the company's genetically-engineered hormone, rBGH, which is now being injected into dairy cows and added to much of North America's milk supply.

With ACSH, as with the NCAHF and other important organis-ations linked to the 'health fraud' movement, although science is ostensibly espoused, what is produced is a bastard progeny, the consequence of a partly covert liaison between large corporations, career academics, pay-rolled scientists and sponsored journalists.

CSICOP and the dirty business of hoaxes

In 1975 Paul Kurtz, a philosophy lecturer at New York University, launched the Committee for Scientific Investigation of Claims of the Paranormal (CSICOP). Not long after its inauguration, Kurtz held a press conference in New York to announce a campaign to purge the media of occultist leanings. He pledged that CSICOP would try to ensure that no TV programme dealing with para-science would go out unvetted by CSICOP.

♦ Sir Richard Doll, a one time consultant to Monsanto, recently became one of ACSH's scientific advisors.

SKEWED

A rationalist and atheist organisation, CSICOP campaigned initially against religion, spiritualism and what it considered to be 'irrationality'. During its first years, the organisation was riven by disputes, some of the scientists who had come into the organisation finding it too authoritarian. The McCarthyite style of CSICOP was illustrated in 1976, when Marcello Truzzi, a well-respected Italian scientist, was 'denounced' for being 'soft' on CSICOP targets. Truzzi consequently resigned.

In 1976, Kurtz set up CSICOP's first piece of combative 're-search' to disprove the work of Michel Gauquelin, a French psychologist who had shown that those born under certain configurations of Mars had certain types of personality. Unfortunately for Kurtz and CSICOP, a replication of Gauquelin's research confirmed his results. Faced with a damage limitation exercise, Kurtz and his colleagues wrote up the results of their research in the *Humanist* as if they had disproved Gauquelin's results.

The amused and cynically lazy style adopted by CSICOP became the hallmark of any 'scientific' work that followed. Studies undertaken by the organisation were never conducted with regard to correct scientific procedures; results that did not give the conclusion required by CSICOP were simply presented as if they did. To those at the centre of CSICOP, privy to the organisation's funding and long-term aims, such exercises must have seemed hugely entertaining.

In 1993, James Randi and John Maddox, together with other sceptics, travelled to France to disrupt the work and career of Jacques Benveniste, who was researching the mechanism of homoeopathy. After taking over his laboratory and pretending to replicate his research, they were still unable to disprove his results so they claimed that they had, mocked him publicly, and then pressured the French Research Council to withdraw his funding and throw him out of his laboratory. For serious scientists, the cost of such juvenile japes was often, personally, professionally and financially, very damaging.

The Politics of Medical Cynicism

Although in its early days it was difficult to see where CSICOP was coming from, by the late 1980s its direction and perspectives were clearer. The organisation involved a number of prestigious scientific consultants and, while they could be said to be defending rationality, their purpose was probably better expressed as defending industrial science and attacking alternative philosophies.

By the end of the 1980s the most serious departure from the group's original rationalist and materialistic agenda was a new and determined focus on 'health fraud.' In 1986, James Randi, a principal figure in the organisation, received a grant of $272,000 from the MacArthur Foundation to see him through five years of hoaxes and attacks upon all matters spiritual, psychic or *holistically medical*. CSICOP activists stated their new case with clarity at the Fourth Conference of European Skeptics, in August 1990.

> Of special concern in this session was the popularity among Europeans of alternative health cures, such as holistic medicine and homeopathy. In our view [Paul Kurtz reporting], adequate scientific verification has not been made to support these fields. The European Skeptics at our meeting agreed that many of these practices can be dangerous to the public health. Unfortunately, government and health professionals are hesitant to criticise questionable therapies because of the economic and political power of their advocates.

How much economic or political power did alternative health therapists or product producers have in 1990? Could it be true that it outweighed that of the petrochemical industry and other multinational industries and was enough to threaten governments? Such unsupportable and patently irrational remarks are a hallmark of propaganda and typical of the 'health fraud' strategy. What CSICOP does is to turn the arguments used by critics of the pharmaceutical industry inside out and throw them back. Around the time that Kurtz wrote this, the world pharmaceutical companies were threatening to pull the plug on public health care in America if the government attempted to force pharmaceutical prices down.

> Alain Mey, representative from France, deplored the sale of homeopathic medicines in most pharmacies in his country.

> Of special interest was the paper given by Dr. A. Gertler, head of the skeptics group in Rossdorf, Germany (formerly East Germany.) Gertler discussed the dangers of alternative medicine to the public health.

Every year the number of people affected by adverse reactions to pharmaceutical products and procedures increases. Deaths from adverse effects now represent the third highest cause of death in America. Deaths from alternative medicine do not even figure in any form of local, national or international mortality statistics.

Homoeopathy comes in for continuous attack from the major CSICOP activists. They have assigned to it the most derogatory label in the CSICOP lexicon, suggesting that its practitioners and followers constitute a 'cult'. By traducing something as a cult, they inevitably imply that supporters are 'mindless' and without individual will. In the Summer 1989 issue of *Skeptical Inquirer*, James Randi stated:

> I certainly agree with Gardner's designation of homeopathy as a 'cult.' It meets many of the criteria, including the invention of attitudes or statements on the part of those who oppose its notions and claims (sic.)

At the 11th European Skeptics Congress held in London in September 2003, almost a whole day was given over to 'debunking' complementary and alternative medicine. The contemporary CSICOP shows considerable interest in clinical ecology and environmental medicine, even publishing important anti-environmental health books. The organisation was also quick to side with those who claimed that repetitive strain injury and CFS are psychiatric in origin.

The American National Council Against Health Fraud

In 1982, US Representative Claude Pepper introduced three Bills in the House of Representatives. Each of these Bills argued for legislative codification of the aims and strategies of the defunct Co-ordinating Conference on Health Information (CCHI). One Bill called for a national clearing-house for consumer health information, another for increased criminal penalties against 'quacks.' The third called for the formation of a Federal strike force inside the Department of Justice, to be used for the prosecution of 'quacks'. In 1984 all of the Pepper Bills fell at the Committee stage.

The 'health fraud' movement in America grew out of this statutory failure. In 1984, a meeting was held in Sacramento, California, with the main object of fighting 'quackery'. The meeting took place at the Department of Health and was organised by the recently formed National Council Against Health Fraud (NCAHF). The NCAHF representative was the only person present who was not a government official. The meeting included representatives from the American Food and Drug Administration (FDA), the California Food and Drug Board, the Board of Medical Quality Assurance, a California State Board that has the power to revoke medical licences, the US Postal Service and the Federal Trade Committee.

At the first meeting, the NCAHF representative gave an account of the groups, individuals and practitioners whom they wanted to attack, including health promoters, chiropractors and 'diploma mills' that issued false health practice degrees. The later history of the NCAHF shows that these subjects were only the tip of the iceberg. Over the next five years, pronouncements by NCAHF listed a wide range of diagnostic aids, therapies and treatments not recognised by allopathic practitioners. These ranged from practitioners who used nutritional supplements and vitamins to any form of treatment described as holistic, including homoeopathy, naturopathy and clinical ecology. Diagnostic aids such as hair mineral analysis and testing for food allergies and high technology tests unavailable from public health sources were all listed for censure.♦

In the summer of 1985, there was a tidal wave of 'health fraud' articles directed against 'quackery'. The first National Health Fraud Conference, held at the National Press Club in Washington in September, followed this first propaganda offensive. The style of the NCAHF (replicated by the UK Campaign Against Health Fraud, [HealthWatch]) was to have a couple of council members covering different specialisations, so that collectively the organisation can 'authoritatively' mount attacks in any area of medicine.

The American National Council Against Health Fraud's first serious campaign was against chiropractors. To mount attacks they often used one of their council members, usually a member of the profession. Chiropractors soon came to recognise their enemy and understand their tactics, giving a recent account of the NCAHF in their on-line bulletin, *Dynamic Chiropractic*, they recount:

> The National Council Against Health Fraud (NCAHF) . . . the words alone create extreme emotions in most of the chiropractic profession. This is the group that, in 1985, presented their *Position Paper On Chiropractic*. This position paper discussed such charges as 'Hazardous Practices' and 'Hucksterism' as if they were an integral part of the chiropractic profession.

♦ Alternative therapies are not only about treatment but also about diagnosis. 'Health fraud' activists have always campaigned against diagnostic testing which might show any condition not recognized by orthodox medicine. They would stop testing on patients for vitamin and mineral status, for example, because they believe that illnesses are not consequent upon a low status and because such tests are costly to either doctors or a socialized medical health service. 'Health fraud' activists' opposition to diagnostic testing has been expressed in their campaign against patients claims to have ME or CFS.

The Politics of Medical Cynicism

Chiropractors quickly diagnosed a financial interest behind the position of some NCAHF members. Of Dr. DuVall's presentation on chiropratic at the organisation's second conference, the magazine said:

> It was almost as if Dr. DuVall would not be satisfied until the chiropractic profession modified itself to conform with the desires of the insurance industry. Could this relate to the fact that Dr. DuVall earns a substantial amount of his income by reviewing damage claims for third party payers?

In his book *The Great Medical Monopoly Wars*, P. J. Lisa suggests that the Pharmaceutical Advertising Council linked up with the FDA to organise campaigns against quackery and to promote articles in newspapers, television programmes and advertisements. He names the companies which supported these promotional strategies in the 1980s as Lederle, Syntex and Hoffmann-LaRoche, and says that Paul Chusid, a past President of Grey Advertising, which handled both Syntex and Lederle accounts in America, told him that many of the 'health fraud' campaigns originated in his office.

Ralph Nader, America's greatest consumer activist, has questioned claims that NCAHF is independent and consumer-orientated. Such claims are also undermined by the fact that three of its major activists, Dr. Victor Herbert, Dr. Stephen Barrett and William Jarvis, are also on the Scientific Advisory Board of the American Council on Science and Health and some prominent 'health fraud' figures work for industrial insurance companies, giving evidence against consumer claims for damage.

The NCAHF maintains working parties, which it calls Special Task Forces. These are meant to issue literature and call upon speakers in specialised areas of medical fraud. However, iatrogenic illness (illness induced by professional medicine), any kind of chemically induced ill health or exploitative orthodox practices do not appear as working party subjects.

SKEWED

The NCAHF resources list for 1995 advertises over 500 articles, pamphlets and booklets, the subjects of which provide a good guide to NCAHF priorities. Articles attack acupuncture, alternative AIDS treatments, clinical ecology, alternative cancer treatments, herbal medicines, nutritional theories, holistic practices, naturopathy and general 'quackery'. Although these articles come from a cross section of publications, a high proportion of them have been published in pro-NCAHF publications, such as the FDA Consumer Nutrition Forum or publications of the American Council on Science and Health.

The NCAHF bi-monthly Newsletter is a digest of press reports reminiscent of intelligence-supported digests put out by government departments in the years immediately after the 1939-1945 war. The Newsletter has frequent dismissive allusions to books that support ecology and natural health treatments, for example: 'Society to be Plagued by Crank Ecology Books.'

Leading figures of the Council appear to have a prodigious output of books and magazine articles, especially in a wide range of popular magazines. Apart from its Newsletter, the NCAHF publishes little under its own imprint, but works closely with the American Council on Science and Health publication, *Priorities and Issues in Nutrition,* and with the CSICOP publishing house, Prometheus.

One small difference between the 'health fraud' movements in Britain and North America is that in North America they have, mainly for strategic legal reasons, proliferated and set up a number of organisations involved in what they now like to call 'quack-busting.' In 2000, Stephen Barrett, an MD, psychiatrist and one of the principal 'health fraud' activists in the US, attacked Hulda Clark and her cancer clinic in New Mexico. Hulda Clark is the author of three books and founder of the Hulda Clark cancer therapy.

Barrett succeeded in getting Clark's clinic in New Mexico shut down; this stirred the wrath of Hulda Clark supporters who had been the subject of a number of court actions begun by Barrett. Lawyers acting for Clark began a $10 million case against a wide range of US 'health fraud' activists. The NCAHF was so concerned that they changed their name in an attempt to steer away from the legal rocks in their path. The writ with which they were served, however, names all quackbusters individually to avoid just this contingency. The action cites charges for constraint of trade, legal harassment and racketeering.♦

The British Campaign Against Health Fraud

HealthWatch,■ the British 'health fraud' group, is intimately related to NCAHF. CSICOP helped set up the British Campaign and leading members of CAHF and HealthWatch have always shared common views with leading members of the NCAHF.

Medical journalist Caroline Richmond called the inaugural meeting of the British Campaign Against Health Fraud (CAHF) in October 1988. The subsequent steering Committee meeting was advertised in the *Newsletter of the Medical Journalists Association* (MJA). The MJA, of which Richmond was a long-standing member, was then supported by Ciba Geigy and a number of other pharmaceutical companies. Companies used the Association's newsletter to advertise meetings, conferences and 'freebies' at which they promoted their drugs to journalists.

♦ In California, 'health fraud' activism has provoked the first Health Freedom Act, which positively defends alternative medical therapies and the sale of alternative health products.

■ When the original Campaign Against Health Fraud was first established it was actually called the Council Against Health Fraud, mimicking its US counterpart. In 1991, the group changed its name to HealthWatch. Throughout this book, the organisation will be called CAHF when it was titled this and HealthWatch when that was its title. Readers should bear in mind that both names apply to the same organisation.

SKEWED

At the organisation's public launch, Professor Vincent Marks was quoted as saying: 'Bogus explanations for ill health bring the genuine concept of scientific medicine into disrepute.' CAHF was an organisation, the article said, 'of doctors and lay members who aim to protect the public from taking cures and untested medical treatments.'

Those who represented the core of CAHF at its formation in 1989 remained involved over the next few years; others on the fringe drifted away. At a Steering Committee meeting held at the Ciba Foundation on April 3rd 1989, two joint presidents were elected:♦ Dr. Michael O'Donnell, broadcaster and former GP, editor of trade magazine *GP* and television and radio presenter Nick Ross, well-known as the presenter of the BBC television programme *Crimewatch*.

Professor Simon Wessely, the foremost proponent in Britain of the argument that ME and CFS are psychological aberrations, illnesses invented by sufferers or, in the case of children, by their parents, was both a founding and leading member of CAHF. Two other long-time members, Dr. David Pearson and Dr. Charles Shepherd, until very recently Medical Director of the UK ME Association, have both been active in support of the Campaign's aims.

Soon after the press launch, the leading Campaign activists were Dr. Nick Beard; Dr. Christopher Bass, a psychiatrist then working at King's College Hospital, London, a Committee member of the British Association for the Advancement of Science and a

---

♦ The Ciba Foundation used to be the information and propaganda arm of the drug company Ciba Geigy. At their premises in London, they hosted meetings and seminars while publicising medical events which gave a favourable impression of the drug company.

These seminars included ones on ME and Chronic Fatigue Syndrome and their psychiatric aetiology. Ciba Geigy merged with another company to become Novartis and the foundation is now known by that name.

psychiatric colleague of Wessely's; Dr. Simon Wessely; Professor Michael Baum, a well known oncologist, and his brother Harold Baum, Professor of Biochemistry at King's College Hospital; Diana Brahams, barrister and journalist; John Walford; Mark Pownall; Dr. Iain Chalmers and Dr. Vincent Marks.

In 1992, the minutes of the CAHF Annual General Meeting disclosed that in the years 1991-1992 the Campaign received a grant from the Wellcome Foundation, at that time one of the biggest Anglo-American pharmaceutical companies. Other funding bodies included the medical insurance company Private Patients Plan and the pharmaceutical company Astra.

Caroline Richmond seemed most concerned that journalists should have the 'proper' view of health matters. To her, one of the principal aims of CAHF was to inform the media about treatments which did not reach an acceptable standard. 'The campaign will give journalists and everyone in the media concerned with health, access to an independent assessment of the many claims about health that are currently in circulation.' She did not say, as she was to do later, that her principal driving force was to campaign against the practice of clinical ecology, which she saw as damaging people.

Writing as the co-chairman, Nick Ross pursued a line held in common with North American campaigners: that it is the elderly, the old and the ill that are exploited by 'health fraud.' Ross seemed to envisage the Campaign as an extension of his consumer rights and the para-police work he has done for years on television. Homing in on criminal fraud, Ross wrote: 'It is a particularly offensive form of fraud when people pose as healers and exploit that desperate need for help by offering illusions of cure that can never be fulfilled.'

CAHF newsletters provided campaigners with a forum where they could criticise what they saw as 'unscientific' ideas about health in the media. In the first newsletter, Caroline Richmond complained about the absurdity of suggesting that electricity has anything to do with illness. This is a dispute which has run and run: when new evidence was recently presented about power lines, electromagnetic fields and cancer, Elizabeth Whelan, the founder of the American Council on Science and Health, wrote a categorical denial of the suggestion in the *Wall Street Journal*.

At the Annual General Meeting of CAHF in 1990, members discussed under what circumstances and from whom the campaign might accept money. 'The Committee decided that money from any source, including the pharmaceutical industry, would be acceptable if it was given on a 'hands off' basis, provided that no single interested party contributed more than 25% of CAHF's annual requirement.'

In 1991, the Campaign, feeling that it had been penalised when earlier in the year it had been refused charitable status because of its campaigning activities, decided to change its name from the Campaign Against Health Fraud to HealthWatch. The point of this cosmetic exercise was to make the organisation appear less combative and more charitable. It also placed HealthWatch in the context of a number of other groups, mainly set up in conjunction with the police: Neighbourhood Watch, Homewatch, and Carwatch. In the following year, though its campaigning zeal had not abated and its members caused problems for a number of alternative and natural practitioners, HealthWatch was granted charitable status.

Over the last decade, HealthWatch has continued with a relatively low profile which reflects a strategy of members appearing to act individually on projects which are common to, and have the blessing of, the organisation. HealthWatch members have been either centrally or peripherally involved in attacks on vitamin supplement manufacturers, health device producers, nutritional companies, a variety of alternative cancer therapies, diagnostic analysis companies, writers and journalists, as well as on ME, CFS and Multiple Chemical Sensitivity sufferers.

The Politics of Medical Cynicism

In the year 2000 the then Chairman of HealthWatch, Thurstan Brewin, committed suicide in a Dorset hotel room.

A gathering storm

HealthWatch members and the organisation's officers tend to give a rosy picture of a small charity struggling to promote reliable information about health care and staffed by volunteers. Professor Simon Wessely's recent description of them in answer to a critic would fit a Hans Anderson fairytale:

> Clearly the . . . author knows sod all about Healthwatch. I am not sure it even still exists, to be frank . . . As I recall it consists of about half a dozen rather nice, well-meaning people largely retired from the health service. Your doppelganger makes it sound like some sinister cabal with links to the Mossad and CIA. What utter rubbish! Someone has some seriously paranoid thinking here!

But not everyone agrees with this picture of a more or less defunct group of 'rather nice' do-gooders.

In July 2001, the Earl Baldwin of Bewdley, who served on the Research Council for Complementary Medicine and was Chairman of the Parliamentary Group for Alternative and Complementary Medicine, argued in the House of Lords that, because the influence of drugs companies and their money permeated all aspects of medicine, we were in danger of inhabiting a medical 'monoculture', this, he said, was 'all the more serious when we are unaware that we are in it.' He told the House of Lords that 'drug company money has gone into HealthWatch, the body that has set itself up to expose unacceptable practice in medicine,' and as an aside he asked, 'unacceptable, according to whose agenda?'

HealthWatch was again mentioned in Hansard two years later, when the accountability of registered charities was under scrutiny.

The Countess of Mar asked Her Majesty's Government what powers the Charity Commissioners have to ensure that registered charities were accountable for their activities. She then drew attention to the activities of HealthWatch, which she said had been supported by the Wellcome Foundation and the medical insurance company Private Patients Plan, pointing out that it had 'been systematically destroying the reputations of people working in complementary medicine, particularly in nutritional medicine.'

In both these cases, the then HealthWatch Chairman, the late Thurstan Brewin, moved quickly to try to change the attitude of the two Peers, writing insistent letters claiming that the organisation was being misunderstood.

Another report

One project involving HealthWatch members, which sheds light on their aims and objectives, was a Report entitled *Allergy: Conventional and Alternative Concepts,* produced for the Royal College of Physicians (RCP). When the RCP decided to write this report in 1989, it was in order to attack alternative concepts of allergy, food intolerance, chemical sensitivity and practitioners in those areas. Despite her lack of medical training, a medical degree or membership of the Royal College of Physicians, HealthWatch founder Caroline Richmond secured the job of writing the report.

The Committee was self-appointed and consisted principally of doctors antagonistic to alternative medicine. It was chaired by Professor Barry Kay and one of its members was Professor Anthony Pinching, who later became a leading figure in the ME / CFS world. None of the participants declared any potential conflict of interest.

The report Committee finished a preliminary draft in autumn 1991, by coincidence at roughly the same time as a High Court action, Taylor vs Airport Transport Warehouse Services, was beginning in London's High Court.[*] Dr. David Pearson, a friend of Caroline Richmond, founding member of the Campaign Against Health Fraud and a self-proclaimed expert on chemical sensitivity, was the leading expert witness for the Defendants, Air Transport Warehouse Services (ATWS).

Lorraine Taylor, a van driver for ATWS, claimed that her health had been seriously damaged by the spillage of a volatile chemical being carried in the back of the van she was driving. Taylor's solicitor approached Dr. Jean Monro, one of Britain's most experienced clinical ecologists, to appear as an expert witness on her behalf. Dr. Pearson's task in giving expert medical evidence was to attest that Lorraine Taylor could not be suffering from any long-term chemical injury.

The previous year, in October, the Campaign Against Health Fraud had been involved in making a *World in Action* programme which had bankrupted Dr. Monro's small private hospital. Both Dr. Pearson and Caroline Richmond featured in the programme attacking Dr. Monro's work. Subsequently, a lawsuit taken out by Dr. Monro against the programme's production company and the television station responsible for the broadcast was settled, with a statement of retraction being read out in Court.

Dr. Pearson and Caroline Richmond were to use Lorraine Taylor's case as another opportunity to try to destroy Dr. Monro's credibility. In his evidence on behalf of the company, Dr. Pearson argued that the Plaintiff's symptoms were not a sign of any physical damage caused by chemicals but evidence only of a psychiatric condition – anxiety attacks. Further, he argued that the chemical in question, a concentrate of allyl caproate, was not toxic to a healthy person and Taylor must have been idiosyncratically vulnerable to it.

---

[*] 21 October 1991: Osmond Gaunt & Rose for the Plaintiff and Wilde Sapte for the Defendant, before Mr. Justice McPherson.

SKEWED

Lorraine Taylor's continuing medical condition, it was suggested, was a consequence of her having an 'egg-shell personality.' No medical expert came forward to define this previously unknown condition that had not at that time been accepted by the British courts.

Giving evidence against Dr. Monro, rather than *for* the transport company, Dr. Pearson argued the HealthWatch line, asserting that clinical ecology was actually a cult, which harmed patients who were drawn into it. He claimed that people who *thought* that they were chemically sensitive had been 'brainwashed' by clinical ecologists and consequently became progressively alienated from 'normal work and social contact.' It was difficult to imagine how this had happened to Lorraine Taylor because she had suffered serious symptoms of illness consistently during her year-long search for a medical expert who would support her case. During this time she had found no one who could tell her what was wrong with her.

A week before Lorraine Taylor's trial was due to begin, and after the time for entering new evidence had expired, Dr. Pearson gave the draft RCP Report, of which he apparently had knowledge through Caroline Richmond, to the defence solicitors to be submitted to the court. The Report was not finalised and had not been endorsed by the Royal College of Physicians or any of its Committees, nor had it been near any process of peer review.

When it became known that the draft report had been entered in evidence, and following pressure from a number of people, solicitors for the Royal College of Physicians wrote to the defence solicitors and thereby the court, asking that the draft not be submitted. The letter stated: 'The College is not in a position to endorse the contents or conclusions of the draft you have seen . . . we must ask that this letter be brought to the attention of the Judge.' Regardless of this letter, the draft report was tendered to the Court by Caroline Richmond under the stratagem of a subpoena obtained by Dr. Pearson via the solicitors for the Defence.

The Politics of Medical Cynicism

It is difficult to know how significantly the judge was influenced by the inaccurate draft report, which was scathingly critical of the clinical ecologists' concept of chemical sensitivity. It is, however, unlikely that the judge would have remained uninfluenced by a report backed by the prestigious Royal College of Physicians. In the event he admitted to accepting the 'devastating critique' of Dr. Pearson and found against Lorraine Taylor, basing his Judgment on the HealthWatch line that she had been harmed *by the 'suggestion' that she was affected by chemicals, rather than the chemicals themselves.*

When later the contents of the draft report became public, it faced massive criticism and had to be re-written. It was described by some Fellows of the RCP as 'wildly inaccurate' and misleading; others commented upon the selective nature of the references and pointed out the reliance on many unsupported and prejudicial statements.♦

Caroline Richmond, who had attended court with Dr. Pearson each day of the hearing, was jubilant at the verdict because of the damage that it did to Dr. Monro. In one article after the case, she wrote: 'Dr. David Pearson at Manchester University has warned that many clinical ecology patients end up as . . . psychological cripples.' She continued with a quotation from a Manchester University psychiatrist, Professor David Taylor: 'What is absolutely critical is that physicians should recognise this sort of sickness from the very outset and refuse absolutely to be drawn into the web of . . . delusion that some people need to protect themselves from unpalatable truths.' This quote is bizarre in light of the fact that Lorraine Taylor

---

♦ For the full account of how this document came to be tendered to the court, and for a complete critique of the report as it was finally published, see: Davies, Dr. Stephen, and Downing, Dr. Damian, 'Allergy: Conventional and Alternative Concepts. A Critique of the Royal College of Physicians of London's Report.' *Journal of Nutritional Medicine* 1992; 3: 331-49.

had been a fit working lone parent looking after herself and her son prior to the chemical spillage. What was the 'unpalatable truth'? That she had suddenly and inexplicably become psychiatrically ill?

Caroline Richmond was supported in her comments upon Taylor's mental state and in her critique of clinical ecology by barrister Diana Brahams, an early member of HealthWatch and wife of Malcolm Brahams, HealthWatch Chairman and solicitor in 2001. In a *Lancet* article Brahams wrote: 'The judge accepted the evidence given by the defendant company's experts – namely Dr. D. J. Pearson . . . whose "careful and impressive" evidence persuaded the judge that there was no scientific basis for the "spreading phenomenon" of chemical sensitisation.'

David Pearson is a general physician who professes an interest in what he has termed 'pseudo-allergy'. In contrast to Pearson's unevidenced beliefs, world-class experts who have made the study of chemical sensitivity their life's work do believe that there is a 'spreading phenomenon' of chemical sensitivity.

When the furore about the scientific integrity of the Royal College of Physicians Report erupted, HealthWatch members and activists were amongst the most supportive of the Report. Professor Barry Kay, who convened the meetings and chaired the Report committee, wrote an article in the *BMJ* in 1993 entitled *Alternative allergy and the General Medical Council* in which he attacked the concepts of clinical ecology and chemical sensitivity:

> This is based on the idea that some patients are unusually susceptible to their environment . . . Clinical ecologists . . . attempt to diagnose and treat a disease which conventional doctors believe does not exist . . . The GMC must face the issue of alternative allergy practice, particularly when a diagnosis is given of an illness which conventional doctors believe does not exist . . . The GMC should consider censoring all forms of diagnosis and treatment which, by reasonable standards, have

failed to show clinical efficacy. There should be a close dialogue between the GMC and the royal colleges to ensure . . . clinical trials using generally accepted procedures.

Foremost in their support of this article were HealthWatch members Charles Shepherd, Simon Wessely, Caroline Richmond and Professor John Garrow. They all clearly saw this as a prime opportunity to attack the concept of clinical ecology in general and Multiple Chemical Sensitivity in particular. Dr. Simon Wessely wrote:

I and many of my colleagues who work in general hospital psychiatry often see patients (who are) seeing alternative allergy practitioners . . . Such patients are often suffering from various psychological disorders, in particular depression, anxiety or somatization disorder. Formal studies confirm that most patients who have been labelled as having . . . 'environmental illness' fulfil criteria for psychiatric disorders . . . *providing a false diagnosis re-enforces maladaptive behaviour* . . . some of the techniques used by clinical ecologists, which centre on avoiding environmental stimuli, can worsen psychological distress and physical disability. (Italics added.)

Charles Shepherd wrote in staunch support of Professor Kay's views:

A.B. Kay deserves support in his attempt to persuade the General Medical Council to provide far more effective protection for members of the public . . . unfortunately, through gullible journalists, grossly exaggerated claims can be made for 'natural' health supplements, herbal remedies, allergy treatments, etc.

In her own support for Kay, Caroline Richmond wrote:

People with such symptoms . . . are convinced that their symptoms are caused by organic illness . . . many behave like members of cults . . . doctors must educate the Profession and the public that inchoate multiple symptoms of psychological origin are curable at little or no expense if doctor and patient collaborate in treatment.

SKEWED

The letters page of the *BMJ* is, of course, the best place to publish unreferenced discourse, affording as it does an opportunity to make grandly prejudicial remarks without too rigorous a requirement for supportive evidence. The fact that HealthWatch members so substantially supported the views expressed by Professor Kay speaks volumes about the organisation's objectives.

CASE HISTORY TWO

OP poisoning defined under the Mental Health Act

Joe[14] had helped with the dipping and contract shearing of sheep as far back as he could remember. In 1993 he fell ill with pneumonia; since then he has been consistently ill. He started to sleep during the day, had headaches and unaccountable sweats, and became very moody.

When Joe went to his GP with these symptoms, he was prescribed Prozac. According to his family, on Prozac Joe was consistently worse than he had been before. He developed shaking down his left hand side and a day did not go by when he was not in pain. At his local hospital he was subjected to numerous tests to try to discover what was wrong with him; he was tested for diabetes, Lyme disease, and many other complaints; all the tests came back negative.

After his pneumonia, Joe could not do a full day's work; he became so exhausted on occasions that he could hardly move. Exposure to certain substances, even as a smell, made him ill, like the smell of sheep dip or cleaning substances, and he could not stand some smells in supermarkets. Lacking answers from the medical profession, Joe did his own research and found that his symptoms were the same as those suffered by people with Multiple Chemical Sensitivity and organophosphate (OP) poisoning.

Joe was referred to a general medical consultant because of consistent pains in his head; he twice had CAT scans. These provoked serious anxiety when the technician told him that

---

14 The real name of this person has been changed in order to protect his identity.

he had to see the consultant immediately. Of course, he imagined the worst. When, however, he visited his doctor, he was told that although there were two shadows on his brain, they had probably been there since birth and they were nothing to worry about.

At a steeplechase meeting, Joe met someone who also suggested that he had OP poisoning. When his mother wrote to someone on his behalf, they suggested that he see a neurologist in another town. This specialist did various tests on his memory, before confirming that he had OP poisoning. This diagnosis gave Joe hope, but it was short-lived: the neurologist sent Joe back to his GP, in the hope that he would receive treatment at a local hospital. The treatment never materialised.

Joe was determined to get help with his illness. He did more research on the internet and eventually came across a doctor only a few miles away who had worked with OP sufferers. His GP declined to refer him to this doctor, so Joe went on his own, privately. Within ten minutes of the consultation, the doctor had diagnosed OP poisoning. When Joe returned to his doctor with his new diagnosis, he was sent back to his local hospital and there again his journey came to a dead end because the hospital had no treatment for OP poisoning. Joe ended up going back frequently to his doctor for pain relief.

Joe got nowhere with the NHS. Finally, because he was unable to work and claiming benefit, he was sent to a Department of Health and Social Security doctor. He could hardly walk into the room for the consultation but the doctor's report claimed that he was fit to work. Joe won an appeal against the doctors judgement but, because his illness apparently had no physical cause, his case was classified under the Mental Health Act; inevitably this has been detrimental to him.

Joe is bitter and angry at the way in which he has been treated. He sees the fact that the NHS does not believe he is ill as a fundamental injustice, and the fact that he cannot get treatment as a fundamental attack on his human rights.

> Where is the justice when no one believes you are ill when you have contracted your illness through compulsory sheep dipping. I have to live with this condition for the rest of my life and I am never going to know when I wake up in the morning if I will have a good day or a bad one. One of the worst aspects of this, is that no one believes what I say; doctors shake their heads and tell me it's a mystery. The mystery of course is lost on me, especially when I am rolling around on the floor in agony knowing that the painkillers I will have to take will not fully ease the pain.

CHAPTER THREE

The Public Health Revisionists

As the health delivery system continually fails to meet the demands made upon it, conditions now classified as illness might soon develop into aspects of criminal deviance and asocial behaviour. [15]

All claimants are sent to a psychiatrist, whose diagnosis is subject to questionable decisions. One of the side effects of Mrs. Buckland's disease is that she cannot use medication. The fact that she is not taking medication is used by the insurance company as evidence that she cannot be suffering. The company has moved the goal posts yet again. [16]

Your health is part of one of the most competitive markets in history. On a thousand occasions throughout your life money can be made from your health or fear of illness. In a capitalist society the sale of health care is no different from the sale of cars or condoms; products with a limited life are produced and have to be sold. There is an army of scientific pundits out there, like fairground barkers, all shouting desperately hard to get you into their tent.

In the nineteenth century, public health campaigners were truly champions of the people, fighting to push through measures unpopular to industry, the local authority and the State. Today in the field of public health those who shout the loudest and are heard

---

15 Ivan Illich, *Medical Nemesis; The Expropriation of Health.* Calder & Boyars, Ideas in Progress. London 1975.

16 Clive Efford, MP, speaking in the parliamentary debate on permanent health insurance in Westminster Hall, chared by Sir Alan Haselhurst, December 1999.

most clearly are mainly revisionists who, as well as selling us products, are determined to turn our attention from an unhealthy environment and divert our perception of ill-health away from industrial causes.

Arguments that the cause of CFS, MCS, ME, or GWS is psychological serve a significant purpose: in addition to simply labelling sufferers as being mentally unwell and creating a market for pharmaceuticals, they also dull the determination to inquire into other causes. This is one way in which we can identify the individuals and groups involved in defending the status quo; like no other physicians or medical scientists in history, these people all argue that it is counter-productive to look for any biological cause of these illnesses and that detailed clinical investigations are not appropriate.

At the same time, no proponent of a psychological aetiology has even hinted at the exact psychological mechanism of any of these apparently psychiatric illnesses. There are many populist ideas put forward by academic psychiatrists, such as the one that young, over-achieving middle class women are most prone to ME or susceptible to MCS because they collapse under stress and retreat into the world of imaginary phobias; such 'theories', however, fail to account for under-achieving men and combat-hardened soldiers of both sexes.

This chapter, which sifts through the arguments about psychological illness put forward by the most visible pundits, does not argue that all those mentioned in this book work for one single cause. It is, however, clear that all those who have something to defend or conserve in this situation will use the best strategic arguments available. Psychological aetiology is the *best general* argument that can be adapted by diverse chemical, pharmaceutical, professional and industrial interests to obscure a physical cause of these illnesses.

The Public Health Revisionists

The ordering of the individuals and organisations in this chapter does not relate to any particular narrative but simply illustrates various usages of the psychological aetiology argument. Because the 'Wessely school' is influential in Britain, I have looked first at Professor Simon Wessely (referring to him throughout as Professor, his present title) and then presented other individuals and institutions in no particular order.

*   *   *

In September 2001, Kimberly Kenny, the Chief Executive Officer of the American Chronic Fatigue Syndrome patient group, known as CFIDS (Chronic Fatigue and Immune Dysfunction Syndromes), sent a letter to Dr. Gro Harlem Brundtland, the Director General of the World Health Organization in Geneva. The letter raised a serious matter.

In Autumn 2001, Chronic Fatigue Syndrome sufferers in Britain and America who believed that ME and CFS were organic illnesses found that they had been outflanked. They discovered that web sites carrying the logo of the World Health Organization (WHO) but controlled by the Institute of Psychiatry at King's College Hospital in London and the Department of Psychiatry at the University of Oxford, promoted the WHO *Guide to Mental Health in Primary Care*, a reference manual issued a year earlier. Since 1969, ME had been formally classified in the WHO International Classification of Diseases (ICD) as a *neurological* disorder, yet the web *Guide to Mental Health* suggested that the WHO was apparently now classifying ME under 'Mental and Behavioural Disorders.'

In the section on Chronic Fatigue Syndrome, the *Guide* clearly stated that 'Chronic Fatigue and Chronic Fatigue Syndrome, known internationally as *neurasthenia*, may be referred to as ME.' The site attributed the cause and continuation of CFS to a number of lifestyle factors and suggested that the illness could be cured:

SKEWED

What can keep fatigue going? Too much rest. Avoiding activity. Demoralisation and depression. Various methods of rehabilitation have been shown to be helpful. These include cognitive behavioural therapy and . . . graded programmes of exercise . . . What is negative thinking? Sufferers often feel . . . that any attempt to do more . . . may lead to an increase in symptoms, which the sufferer may believe means they are doing themselves permanent damage. This leaflet outlines ways you can identify and begin to change negative thinking.

The letter from CFIDS Association to the Director General of the WHO was unambiguous:

The diagnostic criteria in the [*WHO Guide to Mental Health in Primary Care*] are not consistent with the internationally accepted published criteria . . . Rather they reflect relatively loose criteria used only by a small number of researchers and clinicians in the UK . . . CFS is not considered by leading researchers of the illness to be a mental disorder as indicated in the WHO *Guide*. Numerous biological abnormalities of the immune, endocrine and circulatory systems have been documented [which] are not referenced in the WHO *Guide* (web version.) Risk and perpetuating factors have never been proven to be associated with CFS (ME), therefore the WHO *Guide* contains misleading information when it states that lifestyle factors are responsible for the development of CFS (ME) . . . the information in the WHO *Guide to Mental Health in Primary Care* is inaccurate, incomplete and inconsistent with WHO's own guidance in ICD-10 [and] the CFIDS Association of America calls for the immediate removal of this section . . .

In response to numerous representations the WHO confirmed that the Institute of Psychiatry and King's College Hospital, a WHO Collaborating Center for Research and Training in Mental Health, were responsible. The web section on CFS was taken from a patient management package written by Simon Wessely and his colleagues. The WHO confirmed that it was not acceptable for it to support two opposing classifications of ME and the matter would be looked into. In September 2001 the WHO issued a statement which specified that 'there is now a clear distinction between chronic fatigue, fatigue syndromes and neurasthenia on the one hand, and Chronic Fatigue Syndrome and ME on the other.' In publicly emphasising its classification the WHO was leaving Wessely out in the cold and clearly withdrawing its authority from his classification of ME and Chronic Fatigue Syndrome as a psychological condition.

Professor Wessely's attempt to use the authority of the WHO to give credence to his own minority view was audacious. The classification of illness in manuals like the ICD is exceptionally important. For all legal and medical administrative purposes, the formal classification of a disease governs how and by whom the patient is treated. As well as being universally accessible on the Internet, the *WHO Guide to Mental Health in Primary Care* is the most important care guide for general practice doctors in the English-speaking world. Thus any primary health care worker consulting this Guide would be justified in referring a patient who presented with CFS to a psychiatrist.

In Britain, and increasingly in America and Australasia, Professor Simon Wessely is perceived as part of a small group of psychiatrically orientated academics insistent upon diagnosing those with ME or CFS as having irrational perceptions of their illnesses. The war between doctors and patients around these illnesses, as in other health spheres, has remained to all intents and purposes hidden from the wider public. Professor Wessely is eminently qualified, very influential in Government circles and appears personally affable. In many interviews, he presents himself as a slightly isolated pioneer, much misunderstood and inadvertently involved in a struggle to present a disagreeable medical truth to patients in the face of their consistent suspicion, animosity and ignorance.

The son of parents who settled here as refugees from Nazi-occupied Czechoslovakia, Wessely qualified as a medical doctor with a BM BCh from Oxford in 1981. Having picked up a number of academic qualifications such as an MSc, MA, BA, and becoming a member of the Royal College of Physicians in 1984 and the Royal College of Psychiatrists in 1986. He joined a Board of the MRC in 1998 and gained places of standing on many committees, boards and councils which administer psychiatric medicine and its research.

The British have a love of misunderstood boffins, especially when they appear to be dissenters, and so Wessely's membership of a small and apparently ineffectual organisation of quackbusters called HealthWatch might be seen as endearing. In reality, however, Professor Wessely is far from being a dissident, misunderstood or isolated. He plays an important part in a network of psychiatric medical professionals whose views and research are almost completely coincident with those of the governments of Britain and North America. He has access to funding, media and support, which enable him to shape and promote the prevailing view about a number of issues which are of importance to those States.

Professor Wessely is the leading CFS research academic in Britain, heading the CFS Research Unit at King's College Hospital, where he also heads the Gulf War Research Unit and pursues the role of civilian adviser in psychiatry to the British Army. Professor Wessely and his colleagues♦ make frequent and dismissive reference to the topic of chemical exposure, claiming that any illnesses which are presented as having been induced by chemicals can, in fact, only be the consequence of psychological stress.

♦ 'Members' of this roughly defined 'school' include psychiatrists Professor Anthony David of The Institute of Psychiatry; Dr. Michael Sharpe, formerly of Oxford and now at Edinburgh; Professor Richard Mayou of Oxford; Professor Keith Hawton of Oxford; Dr. Tony Pelosi of Glasgow; Dr. Stephen Lawrie of Edinburgh; Dr. Peter White of St. Bartholemew's Hospital, London; Dr. Anthony Cleare of King's College Hospital; Dr. Steven Reid, clinical Research Fellow at King's College Hospital; Alicia Deale and Trudie Chalder, both at King's College Hospital.

The Public Health Revisionists

Since the end of the 1980s, Professor Wessely has steered a fine course between carefully avoiding categorising ME and CFS patients as mentally ill, whilst nevertheless working hard to classify their illness, against the prevailing trend, as a psychiatric condition. Despite the clear and published results of his work, Wessely displays a personal diffidence, frequently making statements in interviews which appear to suggest that he may have doubts about the psychiatric origins of ME and CFS. He can appear shy and awkward in public on occasions and rarely makes clear, short and definite statements about his academic beliefs.

In a recent paper published in the November 2001 issue of *Psychological Medicine*, Professor Wessely appears to concede that disturbance of the HPA axis, a most important breakthrough for those who believe ME and CFS are primarily physical, may be important in the pathophysiology of CFS and fibromyalgia:

> *accumulating evidence of the complex relationship between cortisol and 5-HT function* [central neurotransmitter] *makes* [a disturbance between these] *most likely. The significance of these changes remains unclear . . . it is unclear whether these changes are primary or secondary to behavioural changes . . .*

Any statement like this one is, however, always hedged around by a 'chicken and egg' caveat. While something physical might be important, it could be created by a psychiatric condition.

In Britain, Professor Wessely has established an unrivalled position as a well-placed Government advisor and peer reviewer in almost all the seminal journals. He has been involved with every serious inquiry into ME and CFS over the last decades and his papers and those of his colleagues, produced in considerable number, dominate the field in any literature review.

Wessely has a controlling position at the Center of Anglo-American Research and Co-ordination of CFS, being part of a small core of British and US specialists who, one way or another, set the policy on this illness. Together with Dr. Michael Sharpe, he is a member of the US National Institutes of Health Committee on CFS. Wessely is also a member of the six-man advisory Committee to the University of Washington Chronic Fatigue Syndrome Co-operative Research Center (CFSCRC).♦

The Advisory Committee consists of 6 investigators who serve as consultants to the Center. This committee meets yearly in Seattle to advise the Center Director and Associate Director on the progress and content of research programs.

Professor Wessely was one of the first researchers to gain big grant money from the US Department of Defense to begin research which would conclude that Gulf War Syndrome was a physically non-existent syndrome and that symptoms were produced primarily by stress, being communicated from one veteran to another by false illness beliefs. Researchers wanting to explore the chemical aetiology of GWS were from the beginning frozen out of the grant awards in just the same way that those wanting to research the effects of organophosphate pesticides had been sidelined.■

In the late 1980s, Wessely collaborated closely with Caroline Richmond, the Campaign Against Health Fraud founder, who played a leading role in helping him publicly demolish the scientific categorisation of ME and re-determine it in the minds of the public as a sham illness. Over ten years, he helped, supported and advised

---

♦ Other members of the CFSCRC Advisory Committee in 2000 were Dr. Michael Sharpe; Dr. Mark Loveless, Associate Professor of Medicine, Division of Infectious Diseases, Oregon Health Sciences Center; Dr. Michael Irwin, Associate Professor of Psychiatry, University of California, San Diego; Dr. Helen Mayberg, Associate Professor of Neurology, Psychiatry, and Radiology, University of Texas Health Sciences Center, San Antonio; Dr. Gregory Gardner, Assistant Professor of Medicine, University of Washington.

■ In Britain, the case of Goran Jamal stands out, while in the US, Robert Haley has had to depend upon the largesse of Ross Perot to privately fund work on the chemical cause of GWS.

The Public Health Revisionists

Elaine Showalter, a feminist literary critic, to assemble the arguments in her book *Hystories*, which in two populist chapters recounts the hysterical origins of Gulf War Syndrome and Chronic Fatigue Syndrome. His collaboration with Caroline Richmond and later with Elaine Showalter enabled them both, despite their absolute lack of scientific knowledge or training in medicine, to speak at conferences and seminars on ME, CFS and Gulf War Syndrome. Showalter has become deeply involved in Wessely's foray's into military funded research into GWS.

In July 2000, Showalter spoke with Wessely on GWS at the Royal College of Physicians Edinburgh Conference. In 2002, she worked with Wessely during the NATO-Russia advanced research workshop on social and psychological consequences of chemical, biological and radiological terrorism, held on 25-27 March at NATO Headquarters and Co-Chaired by Wessely. Wessely's Report of this workshop gives a glowing appraisal of Showalter's contribution. 'Professor Showalter (Princeton, USA) concluded the workshop by looking at the way in which terrorism has become part of our culture. She drew attention to the little studied role of popular literature in defining our responses. Like Hollywood, these reflected our views, but also shaped them. It took a literary critic to remind an audience of many psychologists and psychiatrists the importance of [the American flag as] a "comfort blanket." '

Wessely's research results and publicly expressed views have stirred the ire of patient self-help groups. He has stated publicly that members of patient support groups for ME and CFS are fooling themselves, refusing to face up to the reality that their members are mentally ill.

Perceiving the world and its problems, Wessely sometimes appears to view social tragedies with a detached professionalism, evidence of his theory that experts should avoid stoking popular fears. Stating his views recently about the protracted troubles in the six northern counties of Ireland (*Guardian* 20 October 2001) he was, like a government spokesman protecting the legitimacy of the State, strangely dismissive of any personal trauma: 'Thirty years of IRA activity has caused inconvenience, but civil society has taken it in its stride.' His response as well to the twin towers destruction, and the following deaths from anthrax, was very professional. At the height of the anthrax scare, Wessely was reported in the *Guardian* on October 19, 2001 as saying that people need not fear anthrax because 'biological agents are ineffective as weapons of war.' Fears of anthrax could be associated, he suggested, with 'outbreaks of mass sociogenic illness' which were 'already appearing.'

Professor Wessely sometimes seems to forget or mis-remember his committed views about mental illness. Accounting for this, he recently told a journalist that he did 'not fully appreciated the power of words.' The February 5, 1999 issue of the *New Statesman* carried an article by Ziauddin Sardar entitled 'Ill-defined notions.' Featuring Professor Wessely, the article commented: 'Even though 400 veterans have actually died and some 5,000 are suffering from illnesses related to Gulf War Syndrome, the syndrome does not officially exist . . . Wessely has been arguing that ME is a largely self-induced ailment that can be cured by the exercise programme on offer at his clinic . . . Wessely, who occupies a key position in our socio-medical order, denies the existence of Gulf War Syndrome, just as he denies the existence of ME. Clearly, he is a follower of Groucho Marx: "Whatever it is, I deny it." Not surprisingly, lots of people hate him.'

Wessely works in the most prestigious London units involved in psychiatric research; he is based at King's College Hospital, now part of Guy's, King's and St. Thomas' School of Medicine (GKT). The GKT complex also encompasses the Institute of Psychiatry (IOP). The whole of Wessely's department in the Institute of Psychiatry is committed to, and working on, issues relating to the psychiatric aetiology of illness. Wessely states his interests as being in somatiz-ation and clinical epidemiology, especially in relation to Chronic Fatigue Syndrome and what he terms 'post conflict syndrome and military health' which principally means Gulf War Syndrome.

The Institute of Psychiatry receives funding from, amongst other sources, Unilever, a massive chemical-based company; SmithKline Beecham and Pfizer Limited, both producers of antidepressant drugs; Novartis Pharmaceuticals (previously Ciba Geigy); NPS Pharmaceuticals; Lilly Industries Limited, the manufacturers of Prozac; Hoescht Marion Roussell; Glaxo SmithKline; Bristol Myers Squibb Pharmaceuticals; Bayer; Zeneca Pharmaceuticals; and Wyeth Laboratories. It also receives funding from US and British government departments and a number of British Health Authorities.

In 1999, the Institute of Psychiatry held 211 research grants, with an annual value of £14.5 million. The Institute received almost £3M from pharmaceutical companies in 1998 and 1999, the second highest source of funding, behind the MRC and just ahead of the Wellcome Trust and the DoH.♦ The core of the 'Wessely school' activists also work in the same institutions as Wessely and, over the years, both Wessely and a number of his close colleagues have received grants from the Linbury Trust.■

British teaching hospitals, like British universities, are now awash with conflicting interests. At the same time, these institutions are so closed to public scrutiny that it is difficult for them to be studied or criticised.

Until 1999, Professor Wessely's work appeared to be empty of conflicting interests. For some years, he did not disclose his role as

---

♦ In the years around 1999, professor Wessely held a number of official positions at the MRC, the Institute's largest funders.

■ The Linbury Trust, one of the Trusts belonging to the Sainsbury family, was a part funder of the Chief Medical Officer's Inquiry into ME and CFS, which is examined in Chapter 5.

supervising director of PRISMA, the multinational health care company, nor has it been completely clear how deeply Professor Wessely is involved in the work of British and North American defence departments.♦ Today it is hardly possible for an academic or a clinician to work for both employer and employees, as Professor Wessely has done in relation to GWS, or in insurance covered treatment management and with patients, without being accused of having conflicting interests. However, the issue of conflicting interests is, in post-industrial society, so complex that a major review of ethics is clearly needed.

Military Matters

Professor Wessely has been employed or grant-aided by both the British Ministry of Defence and the US Defense Department; he is also locked into a number of NATO discussion groups. These relationships make his research work on Gulf War Syndrome quite different from the work of his more independent colleagues and clearly involve conflicts of interest.

Professor Wessely was one of the co-chairs of the 'NATO-Russia advanced research workshop on social and psychological consequences of chemical, biological and radiological terrorism,' held in March 2002 at NATO Headquarters. Viewing Wessely's Report of this Workshop, it is easy to see where the psychological aetiology of unexplained illness fits into the analysis of 'post war' and 'post disaster' situations and how it is in the interest of both industry and the military to keep making the point that many of the casualties of civil and military incidents present with primarily psychological symptoms.

In his report of the Workshop, explaining Gulf War Syndrome, Wessely makes one of his confusing statements about the relation-

---

♦ Wessely is adviser on psychiatry to the MOD.

ship between psychological and organic aetiology.

> The 1991 Gulf War also had long-term effects on members of
> the Armed Forces of the Coalition nations that participated . . .
> The key lessons were that the fear of exposure to CBW weapons
> was a major factor in the subsequent health of individuals, but
> this interacted with unexpected side effects of the measures
> taken to protect the Armed Forces against these weapons . . .

This statement, involves a classic Wesselyism: it suggests that, on
the one hand, the primary problem amongst soldiers who reported
ill health was *fear* of exposure to CBW weapons while, on the other
hand, it suggests that soldiers had illnesses which were provoked by
side-effects of vaccines and other medicines given to troops. The
difference in real life between the two parts of this statement is that
while the first part has been the subject of long and expensive
research by Professor Wessely, the second research path has been
starved of funds and is rarely verified in polite academic circles.

One explanation of chemical sensitivity given at the Workshop
is perhaps the most bizzare ever recorded. Dr. Omar Van der Bergh
of Belgium does not even bother with obsfucating Wesselyisms.
According to Wessely's Report, Dr. Van der Bergh suggested that
chemical sensitivity was simply a Pavlovian response, a response
which had been observed after many toxic exposures. This is a
brilliant piece of deductive reasoning, simplicity itself: people who
react physically to repeated exposures to chemicals, are in fact
reacting to psychological not physical 'trigger mechanisms'; whenever they experience exposure to chemicals they think either consciously or unconsciously, 'I should act as if that chemical is having
a physical effect upon me.' Taken to its logical conclusion, this idea
could resolve the world's food problem: if infants are given one
good meal early on, they would just have to be reminded of this, by
smell or perhaps by a photograph, for their metabolic nutritional
processes to be set in motion – Pavlovian Nutritional Therapy.

The Workshop aired all the usual explanation of toxic industrial incidents, the history of which some participants wanted to re-write. 'Professor Ben Nemery (Belgium) showed that events can also develop in hours. In his review of the Coca Cola incident in Belgium, *now seen* as principally an episode of mass psychogenic illness . . . [we were] impeded by the lack of an acceptable linguistic term which both acknowledged the psychological origin of symptoms, without denying its seriousness and reality. He proposed the term Catastrophic Reaction Syndrome an acceptable term.' This term, however, is obviously insufficient because it fails to differentiate between those physically affected and those affected psychologically; perhaps a better term might be 'Imagined Catastrophe Reaction Syndrome.'

With Professor Wessely's engagement with the NATO and the US and UK military paymasters, theories and conclusions about anything involving chemicals in relation to soldiers, might be considered to involve conflict of interests. Clearly, working for the employers of soldiers is quite different from working for either the soldiers themselves or any group which they form and which is in conflict with these employers. The resolution to Gulf War Syndrome and other related cases could ultimately involve substantial pay-outs by various governments.

Professor Simon Wessely and PRISMA Health

PRISMA Health♦ was founded in 1999 and began establishing its programme in Europe and North America. It is an odd organisation. In the year 2001, its web site said that it had established operating

♦ At first glance, PRISMA Health could easily be confused with PRISMA – Providing Innovative Service Models and Assessments – a pan-European organisation funded by the European Commission's Information Society Technologies Programme. Interestingly, this PRISMA is carrying out a study of new technology and health care inside the British NHS.

programs in the UK, Denmark, the Netherlands and Canada; but despite advertising an office in London, in Autumn 2001, this office had no phone number listed in any UK directory. The head office and the corporate staff of PRISMA are in Essen, Germany, in the centre of one of Europe's largest and most productive economic regions.

PRISMA literature suggests that the organisation provides a private health care programme for individuals with chronic conditions, however, it appears to deal only with corporate clients or their insurance companies. The areas of chronic fatigue and chronic pain are areas in which insurance companies have previously been loathe to get involved. PRISMA claims to be able to treat, at considerable expense, conditions which 'traditional healthcare has been unable to treat.' PRISMA says that part of the company's groundwork has involved getting medical insurance companies on side to fund their individually-tailored programmes for people with chronic ill health. This description was taken from the PRISMA web site in 2001:

> PRISMA Health AG is an international group of companies dedicated to the resolution of long-term disabilities. Most of our clients have been unable to carry out full-time employment or lead normal lives for many years. Many of our clients suffer from a severely disabling condition for which no clear organic or orthopaedic cause can be identified for example chronic pain, fatigue and depression. These clients usually require a specific and interdisciplinary treatment program designed to resolve their specific difficulties to help them lead a normal life. In many instances, we find that the traditional healthcare providers have no resources to treat these chronic conditions effectively.

> Prisma Health provides such an interdisciplinary resolution program for these clients. It is offered in unique home-based manner as this has proven to be much more effectively (sic). The program has been developed and researched over the last 20 years by disability experts from the McMaster University in Canada. This university is worldwide known (sic) for its innovative and

successful rehabilitation approaches in for example chronic pain.
Many university specialists have been working closely in the
treatment and research of over 2000 clients.

Professor Wessely is the only medically trained supervisory board
member of PRISMA; he adds his specialisation in 'medically unexplained illnesses' to those of other board members in banking, law,
corporate administration and finance.

President of PRISMA in the year 2000 was George F. Thoma, a
German managing partner at Shearman & Sterling, one of the biggest global law firms, employing over 860 lawyers, 30% of whom
practise outside the US. Representatives of the US government and
the most prestigious private industry of North America like
Monsanto, have visited the company's offices in New York – in the
year 2001 a glass tower block in Manhattan – since the company
was founded in 1873.

George F. Thoma is quoted in all the international lawyer index-
es as a man to watch. A member of the Mergers & Acquisitions
Group in Shearman & Sterling since 1991, Managing European
Partner from 1994 until 2000, and from 2000 a member of the
firm's Executive Group, Thoma practises primarily in the areas of
corporate law, mergers and acquisitions, corporate restructuring and
privatisations.

Although the PRISMA web site information describes Thoma's
practice as broadly based and concentrating on capital markets,
merger and acquisition transactions, this gives only half the picture
of this man, who has committed part of his busy life to building a
company that will ensure medical care reaches those with chronic
illness.

Thoma was the leading lawyer in deals such as the Daimler
Benz-Chrysler Corporation merger. Shearman & Sterling and
Thoma acted for VEBA on its $14 billion merger with VIAG. The

team also advised DaimlerChrysler Aerospace in connection with its merger with Matra Aero Spatiale and Casa to form the European Aeronautic Defence and Space Company (EADS).

Thoma, who has worked for banks, chemical companies and pharmaceutical companies, worked inside the Treuhandanstalt♦ helping to privatise the East German shipyards and became the principal counsel and co-ordinator representing the Treuhandanstalt for the privatisation and corporate reorganisation of the chemical, mining and public utility industries in former East Germany.

Also in mergers and acquisitions at Shearman & Sterling is Stephen Volk, a member of the Council on Foreign Relations, the US east coast establishment strategy group which is close to the President and the intelligence community and which has guided North American foreign policy over the last century. Another long-standing member of Shearman & Sterling is Clark T. Randt, a recent US ambassador to China and Yale University friend of President Bush.

With offices in a large number of countries, Shearman & Sterling is ideally placed to advise on foreign policy, having worked on such issues as the efforts by the Government of Kuwait to collect war reparations from Iraq for environmental damages following the Gulf War, the matter of the Government of Kazakhstan in its

---

♦ The Treuhandanstalt (or Treuhand) was originally established by the government of the German Democratic Republic to act as the nation's privatisation agency before unification. At first this organisation was relatively small. In June 1990, the department was handed over to the West German government. 'At the height of privatisation in 1992, the Treuhand had approximately 4,000 employees, working out of one central and three branch offices.' The main criticism of the Treuhand-anstalt is that its expenditures for restructuring firms were enormous. It was estimated that the organisation spent about $222 billion during its life span. (*The Treuhandanstalt: East Germany's Transition to Market Economy* by Sarah Corrie and *Whither the Treuhandanstalt in Dimensions of German Unification*, A. Bradley Shingleton, Marion J. Gibbon and Kathryn S. Mack (ed.))

development of oil and gas reserves in the Caspian Sea and the matter of the Government of Mexico in relation to environmental aspects of the North American Free Trade Agreement.

Lawyers working for Sherman & Sterling are also well placed to advise on environmental issues and chemicals, the company having worked with Merrill Lynch Partnership Management in designing and implementing an environmental compliance programme for its real estate portfolio properties in the United States, with Lazard Frères and the global underwriters on environmental issues in the privatisation of the Hungarian national oil company, and for different companies on product liability defence cases, energy regulation and environmental cases, including mass-disaster cases, property damage claims and environmental and toxic tort cases. The company worked for SmithKline Beecham in its $189 billion merger with Glaxo Wellcome, creating the world's largest pharmaceutical company.

It is indeed gratifying to see that even in a capitalist global economy, there are individuals like Thoma, happy to join with curiosity led academics to launch high risk venture capital – indeed almost charitable – projects which will enable people suffering from illnesses like MCS, CFS and GWS, to get effective insurance backed treatments.♦

♦ Prisma Health, the multinational company which is based on the idea that all fatigue illnesses are psychological in origin, slipped into the world with powerful friends and little ballyhoo. However, one of the principle companies trying to develope a physically based treatment for immune compromising fatigue illnesses, Hemispherx Biopharma (HEB), was not so lucky. With their product Ampligen undergoing a five year Phase III trial, Manuel Asensio a 'short-seller' trader, chose the company as a target. Asensio tried to bring down the value of HEB by arguing that CFS was psychological and that in their literature HEB had quoted a too high incidence of the illness; he also argued that Ampligen was of no therapeutic value. The accusations led HEB to file a case against Asensio in 1998. In February 2000, HEB sought $80 million from Asensio to cover the losses caused by his (cont.)

Insurance: PRISMA's British Programme on CFS

A key principal of the PRISMA program is that 'a dedicated Field Consultant' carries out the treatment mainly within the client's home. The Field Consultant co-ordinates an individual program with a multi-disciplinary team of professional specialists.

Professor Wessely worked out the programme that PRISMA is selling to insurance companies for people with Chronic Fatigue Syndrome. Interestingly, he says nothing in his introduction about patients suffering from any kind of psychological difficulties, although he lays emphasis on antidepressant drugs, the prescription of which one imagines must be preceded by some kind of psychiatric evaluation (from the 2001 PRISMA web site.)

> Because well-designed clinical trials have found that patients with fibromyalgia (an illness similar to CFS) benefit from low-dose tricyclic antidepressants, doctors often prescribe these drugs for people with CFS with generally positive results.
>
> Some researchers believe that these drugs improve the quality of sleep. Patients also have benefited from other kinds of antidepressants, including the newer serotonin re-uptake inhibitors. Therapeutic doses of antidepressants often increase fatigue in CFS, so doctors may have to escalate the dosage very

---

♦ (cont.) attack on the company. Asensio won a first trial, but lost a second judgement precipitated by his court room behaviour; no damages were, however, awarded to HEB. In defence of his argument that CFS was a psychosomatic illness, Asensio drew upon Elaine Showalter's book *Hystories*, and in defence of his argument that the incidence of fatigue illnesses had been grossly exaggerated, he presented a much criticised study, the results of which were in conflict with contemporary data, by Runi Price et al., published in a 1992 issue of *Public Health Reports*. Independent observers might wonder why, if he was so alarmed about companies trading on treatments for CFS, Asensio has not taken on PRISMA. After all, PRISMA must have stated a high incidence of fatigue illnesses, otherwise they would not have found capital backing. Further, the PRISMA CFS management programme involved CBT, GET and antidepressant pharmaceuticals, each of which have, in various research studies, been shown to be of little or no value in treating CFS.

slowly, or prescribe the so-called more active antidepressants. In addition, some people with CFS benefit from the benzodiazepines, a class of drugs used to treat acute anxiety and sleep problems. Patients often try more than one drug before finding one that works and can be tolerated.

Even though no specific CFS treatments exist, symptomatic treatment still can be quite helpful. Non-steroidal anti-inflammatory drugs may benefit the body aches or fever associated with the illness, and non-sedating antihistamines may help relieve any prominent allergic symptoms. Learning how to manage fatigue enables people with CFS to improve their level of functioning and quality of life despite their symptoms. A rehabilitation medicine specialist can evaluate individuals and teach them how to plan activities to take advantage of times when they usually feel better.

Emotional support and counselling can help patients and their loved ones cope with the uncertain prognosis and ups and downs of the illness.

In this manifesto, Professor Wessely advocates the administration of antidepressant drugs despite the fact that a number of surveys and some research suggest that these drugs were ineffective in cases of ME and CFS. Later in the company's web site Introduction, Human Resource Director Jan Paul Schinkel makes mention of another major plank of Wessely's treatment for CFS.

The outcome of our program is largely dependent on the skills of our staff, particularly in cognitive behavioural therapy.

PRISMA, is an interesting company, launching itself into a very distressed insurance market, which had previously had little success in controlling policy holders choice of treatments, the great majority of which have turned out to be too expensive. If PRISMA is financially successful – although it is possible that this is not a principle consideration – it could eventually have a treatment monopoly in all European and North American countries.

The Public Health Revisionists

PRISMA could be the face of the future, a massive multi-national health-care service, working only through large insurance companies for corporate or State employers. Perhaps further into the future, such companies will cater for the health not only of company employees but also for some communities, villages and towns. But is PRISMA a public company set up to treat the general population with chronic illness or is it something else entirely?

With thousands of veterans suffering from Gulf War Syndrome, could the North American and British States use a treatment company that would keep control of them, offering them orthodox psychiatric care without addressing either the matter of chemicals or an organic aetiology of the illness? Which insurance companies is PRISMA linked to? Does the US Defense Department or the British Ministry of Defence intend to refer people to PRISMA through the NHS? The answer to some of these questions was partially answered in 2002, when Dr. Michael Sharpe confirmed in his contribution to the UNUM company report, *UNUM Provident: Trends in Health and Disability 2002*, that 'Funding of rehabilitation by commercial bodies has begun in the UK (with organisations such as PRISMA) and is likely to continue.'

The British Psychiatric Aetiology Adherents and Insurance Companies

Professor Wessely's board role in PRISMA would appear to indicate that he is associated through that company with multinational insurance companies and as in other spheres, he is determining the perception, diagnosis and medical and management of ME/CFS, as well as the amounts which this illness costs the State and private companies.

Insurance companies in general, and the companies which they ultimately act for, appear to stand to profit from the theories and the practice of the psychiatric school, and certainly such organisations could be hindered by further research into the physical nature of fatigue illnesses. The bigger the parameters for unexplained illnesses and the greater the number of illnesses which can be shown to be psychiatric in origin, the less money the insurance companies need to pay out. Even if this saving is happening by accident, expert advisers who claim that ME and CFS are mental health problems, together with those experts who claim that exposure to chemicals can not cause serious physical illnesses, are saving insurance companies billions of pounds.

It is not surprising then, that a number of Wessely School followers are also advisers to insurance companies and consequently expert witnesses in assessments or court cases. These physicians and psychiatrists tell the insurance companies what they want to hear. With the help of these physicians and psychiatrists the insurance companies can 'knock back' thousands of claims.

If we accept this analysis, industry will not just be willing to help doctors, psychiatrists and consultants who proffer claim-blocking advice, but also those who support inexpensive treatments such as the prescription of antidepressants and those who advise against sophisticated tests and diagnostic tools. Further, as we have seen in the rest of this book, industry will definitely favour a diagnosis that has no rational basis because there is then no one to claim against – if you get Gulf War Syndrome from talking to someone else who has it, or from toilet seats, then it is hard to claim compensation.

* * *

In December 1999 there was a parliamentary debate about permanent health insurance at Westminster Hall, chaired by Sir Alan Haselhurst. The debate was sponsored by Mr. Clive Efford, the MP for Eltham, on behalf of one of his constituents, Mrs. Buckland, who suffered from lupus, a disease which has 30,000 sufferers in Britain, ninety per cent of whom are women. The condition produces chronic fatigue, but unlike ME it is a well defined disease that can be clearly diagnosed.

Mrs. Buckland had taken out an insurance policy with UNUM, an American owned company established in 1848, with present day assets of $15.5 billion, and a market leader in 'group long-term disability insurance' in Britain.

Mr. Efford gave a very clear narrative account of Mrs. Buckland's case, which he said highlighted tactics other MPs might be familiar with. So extreme were the practices of this company, said Efford, that a 250 member support group has been set up for people who said that their legitimate claims have been denied; the group estimated that 4,000 people are in similar situations throughout the country. When faced with a court case, such companies often settled before the case could be brought before a judge and before the medical opinion of experts would be subjected to cross-examination, which could exposed the companies fraudulent practices.

Mrs. Buckland's symptoms could change from hour to hour and from day to day; she might have aching joints, sudden seizures and loss of the use of her hands, chronic fatigue, which could last for several weeks, numerous severe headaches each week, or pain when walking up even slight inclines.

Mrs. Buckland's illness was confirmed in a letter from a consultant rheumatologist in December 1997. Her employers submitted a claim to UNUM in February 1998. Under the terms of the policy, Mrs. Buckland should have received payment in the following March, but instead she was visited by a UNUM counsellor who, in her words, 'was not interested in my problems but was merely looking for reasons for UNUM to reject my claim.'

SKEWED

In April 1998, a letter to UNUM from another consultant rheumatologist set out the condition from which Mrs. Buckland was suffering and confirmed it as systemic lupus erythematosus. In May 1998, Mrs. Buckland was granted disability living allowance. Later that month, UNUM declined her benefit and any liability. Again in May 1998, Mrs. Buckland's employer wrote to UNUM outlining its concerns about the decision and the disregard for her medical condition.

Mrs. Buckland's employer appointed a professional insurance marketing services company to prepare an appeal. This company visited UNUM, and on their behalf Mr. Williams reported: 'We were advised that Mrs. Buckland would have to return to work and become ill again before the claim could be considered.'

The appeal when it went ahead was supported by two consultants, a certified counsellor from Lupus UK and a letter from Mrs. Buckland's general practitioner regarding her fatigue. A letter from the advisors contacted by Mrs. Buckland's employers quoted Sir Richard Baylis, an eminent endocrinologist with experience of cases involving the claims of lupus sufferers, who offered his assistance and suggested also that another doctor, the author of *Understanding Lupus*, could provide evidence. Following the Appeal, in August 1998, UNUM requested that one of the consultants prepare a report on the effects of stress on lupus sufferers. The consultant responded by saying that significant scientific evidence already confirmed such effects.

In October 1998, UNUM sent Mrs. Buckland to a Harley Street consultant psychiatrist, who asked her first whether she was happy and later what books she read, before concluding by sympathising with her in her 'battle' with UNUM.

In January 1999, UNUM rejected Mrs. Buckland's appeal, giving the remission of the illness as the reason for the rejection. Later that month, Mrs. Buckland visited her GP, who had received a letter from UNUM recommending that they would make a payment if she agreed to therapy and the prescription of antidepressant medication. Mrs. Buckland's GP rejected the need for antidepressants and told UNUM that she had extreme reactions to any medication.

Mrs. Buckland told her Member of Parliament, in briefing him for the debate, 'My life has been completely changed by my illness and everything I have worked so hard for will now be lost because of the unbelievable treatment I have received from UNUM.'

It was Anthony D. White, MP for Great Yarmouth, who addressed the matter of ME in the Debate. He offered the evidence of Dr. E. Dowsett, one of the most renowned doctors in the field of ME. Dowsett had told him that, occasionally, during the first 20 years of her practice, she was asked by insurance companies to provide comprehensive medical reports on patients with ME. However, from 1994 the procedure began to change, the comprehensive assessment being replaced with a pro forma offering two choices. The first choice, a good prognosis, was indicated if the patient had been offered psychiatric assessment, cognitive behaviour therapy (CBT), graded exercise therapy (GET) and suitable drugs. The second, poor prognosis, was indicated if the patient believed that their illness had an organic basis.

Patients, Dr. Dowsett said, were expected to fill out these pro forma themselves. Several patients were forced to attend psychiatric clinics and take part in cognitive behaviour therapy, graded exercise therapy and take psychoactive drugs. They were told that, if they did not, they would lose their pension rights.

Anthony White, went on to cite two cases that had been brought to the All-Party Parliamentary Group on ME. The first was that of David Little, who had worked as a financial adviser with Allied Dunbar. In 1986, he took out a health insurance policy with his company that was underwritten without any exclusions. Almost a decade later, he became ill and, in October 1996, he was diagnosed with ME.

SKEWED

Mr. Little began to manage his illness by taking plenty of rest, and in April 1997 he returned to work. Disability payments were agreed on a proportionate basis while he was rehabilitating. In December 1997, he suffered a further relapse, after which he was unable to work. At first, Allied Dunbar made full payments under Mr. Little's insurance agreement. However, in July 1998, he was asked to see an independent consultant who concluded that he was unlikely to be able to return to work full-time, but that he should be able to manage part-time work. As a consequence of this interview and despite the fact that the Benefits Agency had assessed him as completely unfit for work, Allied Dunbar disqualified Mr. Little's disability claim, offering him only a further six months' rehabilitation payment.

Mr. Little complained to the Personal Investment Authority ombudsman, who, despite having received evidence of the organic aetiology of the illness, turned down his appeal on the ground that ME might not exist as an illness, and that if it did exist, it was of a psychological nature and Mr. Little was therefore in need of psychotherapy.

Since the loss of his insurance benefits, Mr. Little has separated from his wife and family as a result of financial pressures, and was at the time of the debate on the verge of losing his home.

The second case highlighted by Anthony White, MP, was that of Ms. Kidd. Ms. Kidd's story was similar to that of Mr. Little's. A partner in a firm of solicitors, she became ill with ME in 1991 and stopped work in September 1992. Her insurers, Swiss Life, paid her under the terms of a private health insurance policy from April 1993. Swiss Life's own medics confirmed her condition. Despite this and the fact that her illness left her bedridden for much of the time, Miss Kidd saw a wide range of medics and complementary medical practitioners in a bid to find a cure.

The Public Health Revisionists

In 1999, Swiss Life changed its attitude. The company forced Ms. Kidd, under threat of stopping her payments, to see a psychiatrist with known views on the causation of ME. Ms. Kidd did attend the interview with the psychiatrist but was later refused sight of the report. She was then subjected to a month's covert surveillance which naturally caused her great worry and some fear. Swiss Life, which operates a group policy for the firm for which Ms. Kidd worked, refuses to communicate directly with Miss Kidd, although she was a partner in that firm.

At the time of the Parliamentary Debate, Swiss Life had informed Ms. Kidd's firm that they have evidence that her claim was false and requested a meeting with a representative at which she would not be present. Should the company withdraw Miss Kidd's benefits, she will be forced to fight the insurance company through the courts; a terrible prospect for someone suffering from ME, as the stress and exertion involved will undoubtedly lead to a deterioration.

Anthony White, MP, summed up what appeared to be wrong in the two cases of ME that he cited: 'Insurance companies that take unilateral decisions on the diagnosis and care of people suffering from ME, about the aetiology and treatment of which there is controversy, are, to say the very least, not following good practice. For someone with ME, the most damaging feature [of dealing with their case] is that stress may severely disrupt recovery; indeed, it may exacerbate the condition and cause regression.'

* * *

Those insurance companies most involved in the area of 'medically unexplained symptoms' are: UNUM, Swiss Life, Canada Life, Norwich Union, Allied Dunbar, Sun Alliance, Skandia, Zurich Life, Permanent Insurance, and as re-insurers, the massive Swiss Re. A number of the Wessely School act as advisers to insurance companies. Psychiatrist Peter White, one of the Wessely School and a member of the CMO Working Group (see later chapters), has had an involvement with Swiss Re. The psychiatrist Dr. Michael Sharpe has had an involvement with Allied Dunbar and UNUM.

In May 1995, Professor Wessely and his colleague Dr. Sharpe spoke at a UNUM-supported symposium organised by the Industrial Relations Service (IRS) and the insurance industry on Chronic Fatigue Syndrome and its management, *Occupational Health Issue for Employers*. At this symposium they advised employers how to deal with employees who were on long-term sickness absence with CFS and ME.

Advance notices and booking forms for the meeting stated that 'ME has also been called the "malingerer's excuse." ' The title of Dr. Sharpe's presentation was 'Treatment – the options,' and he spoke about antidepressant drugs, exercise and cognitive psychotherapy. Simon Wessely's presentation was called 'Stress and Chronic fatigue Syndrome – the facts and the myths,' and covered topics including 'What is the current evidence about the cause' and 'What role does psychology play.' The presentation by Trudie Chalder, one of Professor Wessely's colleages, was entitled 'Management of CFS – A practical guide'; it included a section called 'Selling the treatment to the patient.' From many of the things said by Dr. Sharpe at this conference, it was clear not only that he was promoting what would be considered by some unproven psychological treatments, like CBT, for uptake by insurance companies, but that he saw his role as helping doctors in the insurance industry to 'correct' any mis-perceptions they might hold about ME/CFS being a physical illness.

Dr. Michael Sharpe was one of those responsible for the recommendation to insurers that claimants with a diagnosis of ME/CFS could be subject to covert video surveillance. In UNUM's *Chronic Fatigue Syndrome Management Plan*, ME/CFS is described as 'Neurosis with a new banner'; this same Plan also states: 'UNUM stands to lose millions if we do not move quickly to address this increasing problem.' There would appear to be a conflict of interest in some circumstances between a doctor's role as a physician to a patient and his role as an insurance company strategist working to deny certain illnesses and to 'catch out' those who are purported to be feigning illness.

In 2002, Dr. Sharpe wrote a contribution to the UNUM company report, *Trends in Health and Disability 2002*. For the first time, this Report confirmed the involvement of PRISMA in the delivery of cognitive behavioural therapy to NHS patients with CFS/ME. Sharpe also advises in the Report that a psychiatric classification provides an alternative diagnosis of somatoform disorder for patients with 'medically unexplained symptoms' such as CFS, and that such a classification has important treatment implications.

Many insurance companies use an organisation called Managed Medical Care to assess patients who are chronically ill. This organisation relies upon a computerised test called the 'Blankenship evaluation' to determine the status of any claimant who has ME or CFS. Without a proper examination by a doctor, this coding device determines who will go forward with their claim and who will not. These 'functional capacity evaluations,' or FCEs, are used by several insurance companies.

There has recently been international publicity about UNUM which further exposes their strategy not to pay claims to policyholders. In one case, a claim brought by Dr. Joanne Ceimo from Arizona, who was unable to work as a cardiologist following a neck injury, UNUM faces $84.5 million damages for 'mistreating an injured policy holder,' including $79 million in punitive damages.

In another action, California Judge O'Malley Taylor criticised UNUM, saying: 'There is clear and convincing evidence that [UNUM's] bad faith was part of a conscious course of conduct firmly grounded in established company policy.'

SKEWED

A federal lawsuit filed in 2001 in New York sought to represent tens of thousands UNUM policy-holders as part of a class action against the company. Hundreds of individual policy-holder lawsuits preceded this action against UNUM. In early 2003, the state of Georgia fined the company $1 million over its claims handling practices. The company's own former medical director has stated that UNUM's primary policy was to deny disability claims and that company medical advisers were encouraged to use language in their patient reports that would support claim denials. If too many medical opinions favoured the policy-holder, the doctors would be reprimanded or sacked.

In 2002, a Florida federal court awarded $36.7 million to ophthalmologist John Tedesco when UNUM refused to pay his benefits after he was diagnosed with Parkinson's disease. The case which is, however, of most interest to people with ME/CFS is that of Dr. Judy Morris. Just before filing her lawsuit against UNUM, Dr. Morris, an ME/CFS sufferer who can no longer work in the field of Accident and Emergency medicine, attended a conference in Boston and spoke to Dr. Sharpe. Morris had found that it was Sharpe's advice on CFS which UNUM used to support the view that CFS is a psychiatric condition and upon which UNUM relied to support the contention that psychotherapy can effectively cure it.

At the conference Morris told Sharpe that his research was being used by UNUM to deny payments on legitimate CFS claims. Dr. Morris later received an e-mail from Sharpe telling her that UNUM's employees were 'not the monsters she was making them out to be.'

Dr. Morris obtained two opinions from experts about her condition, one of whom, Dr. Richard Glew, an infectious diseases specialist, concluded that Dr. Morris was unable to work. The other expert, Professor Nancy Klimas, an immunologist from the University of Miami in Florida and a leading researcher in ME/CFS, tested Dr. Morris' blood and concluded that there were marked

T-cell activation, abnormal CD4 subsets, decreased NK cell function and markedly increased general immunological activity, and that these results were 'completely consistent with CFS, clinically, historically and immunologically.'

UNUM was sent this objective evidence and in addition was informed by Dr. Morris' GP that the CDC did not consider CFS a psychiatric problem. Despite this evidence, UNUM witnesses still maintained that if Dr. Morris would have CBT, she could 'begin focusing on her many accomplishments rather than on her perceived failures [and] she will begin the path to recovery and return to work.'

State Benefits

The situation where claimants are assessed by psychiatric consultants also affects all kinds of State Benefit schemes. However, perhaps because National Insurance contributions can be more exactly counted as an individual public contribution, State agencies are a little more open to scrutiny than are private companies. It has therefore proved easier in at least one case to get decisions on ME/CFS cases reversed.

In 1993, Monica Dale became ill with ME, and applied for her retirement pension. Although she was not examined or her state of health evaluated by a medical expert advising the NHS Pension Agency, Monica's application was turned down. By her own standards and those of her husband, Monica was seriously ill. Fortunately she had a sympathetic GP and she appealed, was examined by a London consultant, who understood ME and CFS, and her appeal was granted.

Her case attracted the attention of Radio 4 and she took part in an item for the *Money Box* programme; also interviewed on this programme were the Pension Agency's Chief Executive and a representative from the Royal College of Nursing. During her interview, Monica made a point of raising the matter of being turned down for a State Benefit without being examined by a doctor. In August 1996, she wrote an article in *Nursing Times*, entitled *The Birth of a Campaign*, and put a letter in the Action for ME magazine *Interaction*. After raising the issue publicly, she was flooded with requests from people wanting help.

Eventually, Monica and her husband forced a meeting with the NHS Pension Agency, the DSS, the Treasury and the public service union, Unison. Monica and her husband were, after a fight, invited to the meeting. The object of the meeting was to discuss the problems people with ME had with pensions. As a result of this meeting a DSS working party was formed, which eventually produced the Report *Prognosis and Chronicity*. Using this document, the Pension Agency had a framework within which to work when deciding upon good or poor prognosis in ME cases.

As a result of this working party report, the Pension Agency agreed to re-assess over 200 cases. Despite the difficult nature of this task, all the cases were subsequently granted their ill health retirement pension. Since the framework used for making decisions on permanency came into effect, the pension application process with ME has become much clearer and smoother, allowing hope that, even if the first application is turned down, the process as a whole is not rejected. Hundreds of people with ME who apply for ill health pensions in the NHS are now getting them, thanks to the changes that the Dales helped bring about.

Reflecting on her condition and on the changes which she has helped introduce, Monica Dale is very modest about what she and her husband were able to do. She gives clear reasons why others don't often get involved in fighting for their cases:

> When you are too ill to work, fighting for your rights is an
> everyday battle which takes over your life. The devastation the
> illness causes is largely hidden. Financial problems, having to

move, living day to day coping with all the problems ME physically causes, these things assume the most important role.

Being constantly told how well you look is hard to swallow, when it's taken all your strength to get to the shops to buy food which needs the least preparation. Eating is very hard some days. Friends think you are putting it on and those who are not true friends fall by the way-side not understanding what is going on, wondering why we can't snap out of it, someone jealous that you appear to be lazing in bed while they work their fingers to the bone in an over stretched health service, or school. Marriages, families, relationships, children, all suffer. Suicides have happened, many regularly have suicidal thoughts. Life is one black hole. ♦

Monica Dale has seen countless insurance company cases and she is amazed and disgusted at the problems which companies face claimants with. She has talked to people who have been the targets of secret filming, who have been followed by people with video recorders, snooped upon and filmed through their windows. All this, she says, 'build's up a picture of a criminal being watched for the next law breaking activity they might undertake.' She sees serious problems in psychiatrists assessing physically incapacitated people for insurance companies.

After her experience in helping people push through their legitimate claims, Monica Dale and her husband set up Campaign Advice Support and Help (CASH), which helps people with ME facing problems with their private health insurers.

Industry fronts and insurance witnesses in North America

The American Agency for Toxic Substances and Disease Registry (ATSDR), which is part of the Department of Health and Human Services, based in Atlanta, Georgia, was set up to monitor exposure

♦ In an e-mail to the author.

to, and the adverse human health effects of pollution in the environment. In August 1998, ATSDR released for public comment a pre-decisional draft report of their Interagency Workgroup on Multiple Chemical Sensitivity, entitled *A Report on Multiple Chemical Sensitivity*. The Report was intended to provide a public health evaluation of the extent and nature of MCS and recommend future actions for Federal agencies.

Many of the lay responses to the Report were critical, loud and angry. Irene Wilkenfeld, co-ordinator of the Safe Schools project in Lafayette, was both critical and knowledgeable. Irene had suffered Multiple Chemical Sensitivity for the last twenty-eight years and worked for the last thirteen years as a consultant specialising in the detoxification of classrooms. After an introduction in which she familiarised the Workgroup with the concept of hubris, she launched into a critical attack on the draft:

> I read your callous, deceptive Draft Report with stunned dismay and I find it to be a powerful instrument of harm. Its flip scepticism, stonewalling and dismissiveness do a gross disservice to the American people in general, and to MCS patients, in particular. This report is a source of misinformation and misinterpretation that will no doubt squander any opportunity for significant research funding into this emerging public health crisis. This report will one day be condemned for its intellectual arrogance, wilful neglect and institutional sabotage.

The first issue that she approached was bias, accusing the report of failing to disclose the serious 'conflicts of interest' held by the man whom the Workgroup had hired to be the report's primary author, Dr. Frank Mitchell.

At that time Frank Mitchell was Chair of the Scientific Advisory Board of the Environmental Sensitivities Research Institute (ESRI), an organisation whose sole purpose is to *block* recognition of MCS. As Irene pointed out, although it must surely have been known to the Workgroup, ESRI is an organisation funded by chemical manufacturers, the particular but covert brief of which is to argue against the concepts of Multiple Chemical Sensitivity.

When Albert Donnay, the founder of Multiple Chemical Sensitivity Referral and Resources (MCSRR) found out about Mitchell's role in the report, he made a formal request that Mitchell's ESRI affiliation and key role as the report's author be disclosed. The Workgroup, however, denied any conflict of interest and continued to list Mitchell as a 'consultant'. Donnay pointed out that Dr. Mitchell, who had recently retired as Chief Medical Officer of ATSDR, was not hired as a consultant. The fact was that Mitchell's old boss, Workgroup co-chair Dr. Barry Johnson, had arranged for him to be re-hired by ATSDR through a Postgraduate Research Program normally reserved for 'academic' scientists.

Mitchell's role in the Drafting of the Interagency Workgroup report on MCS led to a GAO and NIH Inspector General's investigation when it was found that he had slipped into the role without a written contract and without filing any conflict of interest disclosure statement or even crediting his funding source.

Unsurprisingly, a report that had been written, even in part, by Mitchell was unlikely to come to any conclusion other than that MCS had a psychological or psychiatric aetiology. The Report suggested that 'psychological factors should be carefully evaluated in the diagnosis and treatment of patients who have MCS.' Irene Wilkenfeld begged to disagree; she thought that psychological factors should only be evaluated after all physical evaluations have been made: if then there was still no cause found, it might just be correct to look at the person's psychological disposition. She made the point that it was 'just plain shoddy science to label everything you don't completely understand as "psychosomatic." '

The revelation that an ESRI stalwart had been writing for the US government on chemical sensitivity brought the organisation into the public view and gave critics another opportunity to look at the personalities involved. For one of the organisation's most prominent individuals, its founder and major proponent of the psychological cause of 'environmentally' induced illnesses, Dr. Ronald Gots, the adverse publicity was beginning to mount up.

Dr. Ronald Gots is a medically qualified doctor with a PhD in pharmacology; his publicity credits him with authorship of four books and 60 articles on toxicology, pharmacology and expertise in legal claims. He is an important person in an array of organisations. He has been Principal of the International Center for Toxicology and Medicine and President of the National Medical Advisory Service, Inc. (NMAS), which provides expert witnesses and lawyers to defend corporations in product liability lawsuits. He is founder and executive director of the Environmental Sensitivities Research Institute (ESRI) and a leading advisor for RISE; he is also a member of the International Center for Toxicology and Medicine (ICTM) and a board member for the American Council on Science and Health. The ICTM, ESRI and NMAS have at some point all operated from the same office and at least two of them have had the same fax number. Gots is also a council member of the International Society of Regulatory Toxicology and Pharmacology (ISRTP).

Gots used his position in these organisations to lobby against the New Mexico Legislature's appropriation of funding for MCS research and education. He visited Santa Fe in 1996 in an attempt to oppose the legislative and educational momentum that was occurring there in relation to MCS. Gots has also advocated the denial of Medicaid coverage for diagnosis and treatment of MCS and he is sharply critical of non-profit disability organisations which sponsor MCS support groups.

Dr. Ronald Gots is especially interesting as a figure in the battle around chemical sensitivity, because the centre of his work in a number of different forms involves giving evidence on behalf of insurance companies facing claims for chemical sensitivity or other damage. Dr. Gots' critics suggest that he has not cared for patients of his own for 20 years but has testified against the claims of MCS patients for over a decade.

His evidence is always that MCS, and anything associated with it in the minds of clinical ecologists, is an imaginary or psychoneurotic phenomenon and not an organic or physical illness. Gots testified on behalf of one corporate defendant: 'The MCS theory has been subjected to peer review evaluation and it has generally been rejected as junk science.' He appears to hold MCS patients and their physicians in contempt, infamously suggesting on one occasion that MCS is 'a peculiar manifestation of our techno phobic and chemo phobic society.' Despite heavy battles with clinical ecologists and critical appraisals of his work by at least one judge, Dr. Gots manages to stay afloat.

Dr. Gots and insurance

Paul Benedetti, a feature writer and investigative reporter with the *Hamilton Spectator* in Ontario, Canada, who has won awards from the National Council Against Health Fraud, wrote the ACSH report on chemical sensitivity. The Report was edited by Stephen Barrett, MD. In the report, considerable stress is placed on the position of insurance companies.

> In the United States and Canada, advocacy groups are fighting hard for recognition of 'multiple chemical sensitivity' ('MCS') as a specific disease. These groups and the patients they represent are demanding that insurance companies cover the cost of expensive and unproven treatment by clinical ecologists. They are also seeking payment through worker's compensation and Social Security Disability programs and pressing for special workplace and housing conditions.

A 1997/1998 ACSH statement further outlines the problem:

SKEWED

Unless the problem is properly addressed, the millions of dollars now changing hands through claims and lawsuits will become billions, wreaking havoc with many industries and insurance programs and ultimately raising costs to all consumers. The American Council on Science and Health believes that false claims related to 'multiple chemical sensitivity' and its associated pseudo-scientific practices constitute a serious problem in our society.

The ASCH Report states that clinical scientists 'suspect that the majority of "MCS" patients suffer from psychological disorders such as depression, anxiety reactions and somatization (bodily reactions to stress.)' This is typical ASCH reporting, 'clinical scientists' in this context can mean no more than a handful of scientists in the whole of North America.

Expert witnesses like Dr. Gots, who is an Advisor to ASCH, act out their position on MCS in the courts. In court, however, the expert witness is likely to have the details of his life's work exposed in a way that does not occur when he writes a book or appears on television.

The State Farm (SF) insurance company used subsidiary assessor companies to deal with their claims. When SF received a claim for personal car accident damages, they would send that claim to an assessor company to carry out a 'paper review' of the injuries. In State Farm's case, such reviews were carried out without reference to the injured claimant.

In 1998, a judge presiding over an insurance claim case described the Medical Claims Review Services run by Dr. Gots, which did paper reviews for State Farm, as a 'completely bogus operation,' and suggested that it was a software company which 'prepared "cookie cutter" reports of stock phrases, assembled on a computer, supporting the denial of claims by insurance companies.'

Gots' background in MCRS and the issue of State Farm review companies came under scrutiny following appeal cases in the US courts of people who had been denied claim payouts. Looking at medical review companies that worked for SF, it became apparent that doctors did not *write* the review reports and rarely even signed them.

A previous State Farm Superintendent said that not only did SF know that there was a pattern of negative opinions but it wanted it that way. He said that there was only one purpose in using a paper review and that was to increase profits by reducing costs. The State Farm manual actually stated that if adjusters want to deny a claim, they should hire a paper review company.

After a period of denials, Dr. Gots eventually agreed that 10 to 15 per cent of MCRS reports (that is hundreds of reports) were never looked at by a doctor. The American NBC programme *Dateline* obtained 79 reports and in all of them there had been the recommendation to cut back or deny care to accident victims.

Gots links with the insurance industry are surprisingly transparent. In 1989, before he had carved out an interest in the environmental health business, he wrote an article in an insurance industry trade publication urging the industry to use 'paper reviews.' The use of negative paper reviews, filled by apparently independent companies was, he said, one way to combat the 'vast economic interests' that were constantly pressing for 'exaggerated medical losses.'[17] ♦

Books and Papers

The publishers of Gots' penultimate, book *Toxic Risks: Science, Regulation and Perception*, claimed that it explored 'the practical problems created by widespread misunderstanding of the limits of

---

17 *Cutting Claims with Fraud? Records Sealed In Major Insurer's Case*. Edward Walsh, Washington Post Staff Writer. Sunday, July 4, 1999.

♦ The 'vast economic interests' are those mythical ones which greenwashers and 'health fraud' activists are always pretending are praying on global corporatism.

the scientific knowledge base inherent in most environmental issues.' The book was reviewed in the *Journal of Occupational Medicine* as 'of little value to public health professionals and scientists,' and 'replete with sweeping generalizations, over-statements, and exaggerations.'

Gots wrote his next book, *Chemical Sensitivity: The Truth About Environmental Illness*, published in 1998, with Stephen Barrett, perhaps the most notable 'health fraud' campaigner in the US. The CSICOP publishing house Prometheus published the book, a full frontal attack on clinical ecology. Writing about the book, Barrett says that symptoms of environmental illness are brought on 'by psychological factors rather than physical ones.' The book, he says, debunks claims related to 'sick building syndrome,' 'mercury-amalgam toxicity,' 'yeast allergy,' and 'Gulf War Syndrome.'

Nearly everyone outside pro-industry groups reviewing the book pointed to the fact that the references were limited and selective and the book was full of generalisations. Just after it was published, a lay reviewer from Seattle posted this erudite paragraph on the Internet:

> This book is misleading and full of bad information. Written from the perspective of the chemical industry, it misinforms readers about Multiple Chemical Sensitivity. The authors, with well-known connections to industry, are understandably inclined to perpetuate the major polluters' myth that the MCS pandemic (including Gulf War Syndrome) is purely psychiatric in origin. No surprise that all of the recent medical studies showing multiple physical abnormalities in MCS patients are downplayed. I recommend the reader instead buy Bonnye Matthew's new book *Defining Multiple Chemical Sensitivity* to find out exactly why these industry doctors are so opposed to people finding out the truth.

One of the persistent themes in the writing of Gots and Barrett is financial damage which might be done to industry were MCS to be recognised. *Chemical Sensitivity* is to some extent a handbook for insurance company experts to argue from and by its very publication it acts as an apparently authoritative text that can be referred to in court. One favourable review of the book from Barrett's colleagues in a NCAHF Newsletter draws attention to this very point:

> Particularly revealing is the information on the political activities of practitioners and patients, and the implications their purported claims have for insurance companies who are pressured to pay for dubious treatments. In 1977, a federal tax court ruled that, Theron Randolph, MD, a leading proponent of clinical ecology, could deduct the extra cost of 'organically grown' foods as a medical expense!

Gots and mould

Gots attacks all aspects of chemical sensitivity, especially those which are currently before the courts. It has been recognised for some time by specialists in environmental illness that moulds can be an important factor in health. Moulds have been associated with cases of 'sick building' syndrome and are presently the subject of a number of court cases in which property owners in the United States are suing building owners or builders for sensitivity damage.

In the year 2000, Dr. Gots and four of his colleagues from the International Center for Toxicology and Medicine, Inc. wrote a paper entitled Health Effects of Mycotoxins in Indoor Air, which was published in the *Journal of Applied Occupational and Environmental Hygiene*. Dr. Brautbar, a clinical Professor of Medicine at USC School of Medicine specialising in toxicology, began his review of this paper with a number of simple questions. Firstly, 'Does the *Journal of Applied Occupational and Environmental Hygiene* have a conflict of interest statement as is the custom in most scientific peer reviewed journals?' and 'Has such a statement been submitted by Dr. Ronald E. Gots?'

SKEWED

Secondly, Dr. Brautbar questioned Dr. Gots' funding; the source of funding for this review of the literature must be, he said, clearly declared. 'Is Global Tox Inc. funding the study?' he asked and 'What is the connection between Global Tox and Dr. Gots?' When Brautbar gets on to the substance of the paper, he criticises the outdated toxicological 'dose' argument at the centre of it. This argument, an early chemical industry ploy, does not address the idea of low dose sensitivity induced by contact with some chemicals:

> The argument of 'dose' is taken from Paracelsus who advocated that 'the dose makes the poison.' This statement suggests that all toxins require a (quantifiably high) dose to cause harm. We all know today, 2001, that this archaic statement is irrelevant. For example, it is well documented that very minute amounts of isocyanates can cause in some patients severe reaction (asthma), demonstrating that 'the dose makes the poison' is irrelevant in the case of isocyanates. We know that for latex allergy, minute amount of latex can cause a severe anaphylactic reaction in the appropriate individual. Where is 'the dose makes the poison' here?

Brautbar also takes Gots to task over two other perennial arguments in relation to chemical sensitivity, firstly that there is no literature about risk and inhaled micro-toxins, in this case moulds, and secondly, Gots' view that if there are no 'official' exposure standards, there is no problem.

> According to Dr. Gots and his group, since there are 'no known exposure standards for molds,' it is not possible to draw a conclusion. However, the fact that there are no exposure standards does not mean that mold exposure is safe. The history of benzene and health effects is a living witness to the myth and saga of exposure standards. Benzene was known to cause haematological toxicity, and despite the fact that even the American Petroleum Institute issued a position paper in 1948, that the safest levels of exposure to benzene is no exposure at all, levels for exposure from a regulation point of view kept changing from 100 ppm all the way down to what is proposed now by ACGIH to 0.1 ppm. It took industry over 50 years to admit that benzene causes leukaemia, despite the many case

reports and case studies available to industry. If we adopt this methodology suggested by Dr. Gots, we will have to see many sick patients become sicker before industry admits to the health effects of molds.

Think tanks – no thanks

Policy Foundations and Research Institutes, 'think tanks' as they are often called, bourgeoned in America following the emergence of the New Right in the late 1970s and early 1980s. The Competitive Enterprise Institute, the Cato Institute, the Hudson Institute, the Heritage Foundation, the American Enterprise Institute, the Reason Foundation, are examples.

Some of these organisations have scholar-in-residence programmes staffed mainly by former government officials, or they have magazines and in-house or freelance journalists on their books who argue consistently for the freedom of corporations to compete. Most of them uncritically support the view that government is intrusive and harmful and that corporations are boundlessly good.

The Reason Foundation runs the Reason Public Policy Institute (RPPI), which is described as a non-partisan public policy think tank that promotes choice, competition, and a dynamic market economy. A proportion of its funding comes through the circulation of *Reason* magazine. It has a business advisory board which includes executives from cigarette, chemical and pharmaceutical companies, including Eli Lilly, the manufacturers of Prozac, Pfizer, manufacturers of antidepressants, and the tobacco company Philip Morris. Its corporate funders also include Cargill, the world's biggest agribusiness, and the pesticide manufacturers Bayer and Dow Chemicals.

The RPPI argues that climate change is not caused by human agencies and they argue for the lifting of American gun controls. On pesticides the Foundation finds little argument with individuals like

SKEWED

Denis Avery, whose Center for Global Food Issues is still arguing that DDT is safe. On cigarette smoking, the RPPI argues for the freedom to smoke and against the idea that lung cancer is entirely caused by cigarette smoking.

On Gulf War Syndrome the arguments of *Reason* Magazine are expressed through its science correspondent, Michael Fumento. He argues that the science of GWS has been manipulated to serve the best interests of liberal groups that seek favour, for some uncertain reason, with veterans and who are also influenced by scare stories in the media. Fumento argues that signs of a mysterious illness that has been called Gulf War Syndrome are nothing other than the signs of an everyday life in contemporary America. Any symptomatic picture that has emerged from the research, Fumento says, shows only that veterans are somatising. Fumento, however, rarely gives references for the research he is addressing or discloses any interest conflicts.

The views and work of the Cato Institute have much in common with those of the Reason Foundation; it also supports the free market, private enterprise and de-regulation. Founded in 1977, the Institute's 2001 budget was $13.8 million; it has approximately 90 full-time employees, 60 adjunct scholars and 15 Fellows.

With policies in mind to de-regulate the pharmaceutical market, the Cato Institute advocates 'moving pharmaceutical and medical device approval into the private sector.' This would mean ex-pharmaceutical company executives and serving staff, without the involvement of government agencies, having meetings to decide which drugs might be licensed. To the Cato Institute this idea means that drugs would be developed, licensed and made accessible to consumers more quickly than is the case at present.

The Cato Institute accuses those objecting to such policies of privatisation of 'constraining industry.' According to the Institute and other similar think tanks, those who worry about the adverse reactions of drugs, chemical sensitivities or allergies, are at best hysterical and at worst subversive. They are people who behave irrationally, shifting the blame for their problems away from themselves and onto industry or government:

> Worrywarts have shifted their phobias to obscure and distant threats posed by things like global climate change, alien invasions, cloning and second-hand smoke.

This is the common line pursued by supporters of psychological aetiology of illnesses like ME and CFS; it can be found in similar form in a thousand disguised circumstances. The argument, which is unsupported by any evidence, assumes a growing community of irrational individuals with irrational phobias born of mental disorders, who want to demand financial recompense for imaginary damage inflicted on them by the industrial military complex. The often used propaganda ploy can also be recognised here, when worry about alien invasion is equated to worry about second-hand smoke.

Michael Fumento and Elizabeth Whelan

Unsurprisingly, Michael Fumento agrees with Drs. Gots and Barrett about Multiple Chemical Sensitivity. In an article entitled *New Syndrome? Or More Silliness?* he writes:

> Mainstream medicine has a name for it: hogwash. But to a small army of lawyers, doctors, and reporters, multiple chemical sensitivity (MCS) is a vicious epidemic, 'the ultimate 20th century illness.' And because of that small army, it needs to be taken seriously, even if you are convinced it's hogwash. If MCS advocates get their way, perfume and cologne will be banned in public buildings, insecticide spraying will be severely limited, *and litigation will break the back of many a corporation.* (Italics added.)

Fumento is a Resident Fellow at the American Enterprise Institute, author, journalist, and attorney specialising in science and health issues. He made a name for himself campaigning against the American AIDS establishment and media science commentators who consistently prophesied that HIV would spread exponentially throughout the heterosexual population. When Fumento was proved right and neither an American nor a European AIDS pandemic occurred in the heterosexual population, he extended his campaign against media myths, amplification and populist science pundits to cover health risks related to chemicals.

Wherever the chemical industry is criticised, there you will find Michael Fumento, arguing its protection as if it were an endangered species. The only real problems, according to Fumento, are high public spending, liberal politicians, big government, a too popular press and irrational and ignorant citizens. Fumento's statements about scientific issues are never supported by a comprehensive review of the literature and his populist stories often get increased mileage from the same mechanism of media amplification that he attacks.

Fumento can often be found on the same subjects and in the same papers as Elizabeth Whelan, founder of the American Council on Science and Health. Fumento's analysis of the US Love Canal dump, which he shares with Elizabeth Whelan, bears an unstudied similarity to Professor Simon Wessely and colleagues' analysis of the Camelford aluminium sulphate dumping incident that occurred in Cornwall in 1988.

In 1896, William Love partially excavated a canal nearly two miles long on the outskirts of Niagara Falls City, in a failed attempt to connect the upper and lower Niagara Rivers. During a period from 1942 to 1953, the Hooker Chemical and Plastic Corporation buried 22,000 tons of chemical waste along 19,000 cubic yards of this trench. After Hooker vacated the site, having apparently agreed that the land was not to be excavated, the City School Board bought it for $1 and subsequently built houses on it. Eventually a school was also built on the site.

The Public Health Revisionists

In 1977, tests revealed toxic chemicals seeping into the basements of homes near the canal. In 1978 authorities declared a health emergency, closed the school and evacuated 235 families. The following year, New York State authorities evacuated families with pregnant women and with children under 2 years of age from the most heavily contaminated southern half of the Love Canal neighbourhood. In May 1980, the federal government offered evacuation to everyone in Love Canal. In the late 1990s, after spending large amounts of money, the Environmental Protection Agency (EPA) declared the site safe and the area was re-populated.

Two separate conflicts have arisen over the Love Canal incident. Firstly, there is a considerable amount of resentment amongst those who support industry towards the Niagara Falls City Authority, who took a legal action against the new owners of the old Hooker Chemical Company and towards the EPA. Industrial interests claim that the EPA is a government bureaucracy that spends public money unaccountably.

It is, however, a second conflict which is most deep set and serious. Greenwashers insist that *no one on the original site ever suffered ill health from toxic chemicals*. They don't deny that the chemicals were there, or that they could have come to the surface when the site was built on. However, they say a single journalist created the myth of toxicity and ill health; his exaggerated 'muck raking' stories powered a hysterical bandwagon. Both Fumento and Whelan denounce the toxic threat at Love Canal as imagined and not real:

> **Fumento:** The second part of the Love Canal myth is that residents began suffering a health disaster in the late 1970s. As I documented in my book *Science Under Siege*, nobody at Love Canal complained of any exceptional illnesses until a muckraking environmentalist reporter for the local paper began a series of articles telling the people that they were sitting on a toxic waste site. Lo and behold, from then on every illness in the

town was blamed on the ingredients brewing beneath the surface. It even made national news when one family's dog began inexplicably vomiting.

Fumento: Only later did the truth begin to seep out. Study after study conducted by the federal government and the State of New York Department of Health found that Love Canal residents had no more illness than would be expected in any other area of similar size. Believe it or not, dogs that don't live on top of toxic waste dumps also vomit.

At more or less the same time, Elizabeth Whelan wrote:

Whelan: The modern-day Love Canal saga might be traced back to 1976 when residents adjacent to the canal began to complain of chemical odours from the landfill created by a previous corporate resident, Hooker Chemical. A local reporter began writing about suspected cases of toxic waste-induced illness in the area, and by 1978, Love Canal became a national media event with articles referring to the neighbourhood as a 'a public health time bomb.'

Whelan: Was there ever any real health problem at Love Canal? Yes, there was, in the sense that there was an enormous amount of media-induced stress placed on residents who were terrified that they and their children would become ill. But no – there was never any documented evidence that exposure to chemicals at the site caused death or disease.

Twenty years after the fact, both Fumento and Whelan not only write categorically that no one's health was affected by chemicals but are also sure that the whole myth was drummed up by a journalist and campaigned upon by hysterical tenants:

Fumento: The media descended upon the town and relayed to the outside world every sneeze, every cough, and every ache and pain experienced by Love Canal residents, making it clear that they could only be caused by toxic waste, which included the dreaded dioxin.

Whelan: Indeed, Love Canal has become one of the key buzzwords in the alarmist environmental vocabulary. The

> misrepresentation of health risks due to exposure to low levels of 'toxic waste' is the more serious issue . . . Nearly 20 years have passed since those blue-ribbon panel findings – and there is still no evidence of an increased incidence of disease or birth defects associated with exposure to the Love Canal chemicals.

Rachel's Environment & Health Weekly (*Rachel's*), well known for its independent research and perhaps the principal environmental report in America, tells a different story. Peter Montague, *Rachel's* founder and editor, says that two hundred and forty eight different chemicals were identified at the Love Canal site, 30 of them embryotoxins, and 18 suspected teratogens. At least 34 of them were known to cause cancer. For 100 of the 248 chemicals identified, no toxicological data could be found.

While Fumento and Whelan portray inhabitants of the Love Canal site as hysterical dupes, driven by a media frenzy into demanding a move from the site, *Rachel's* describes the collective struggle of the inhabitants as 'one of massive citizen struggle, and of victory against tremendous odds.' *Rachel's* also tells a quite different story about the public health research carried out on the site. While Fumento says that none of the New York Authority research concluded that there were any 'out of the ordinary illnesses' on the site, *Rachel's* insists that some research undertaken by New York State Health Department is still secret, and health researchers who disagreed with the way the research was handled at the time were purged from the Department, demoted, transferred, or harassed.

The only New York State Health Department statistics to see the light of day were reported in *Science* magazine and showed that lung cancer among Love Canal men was up 70% compared to the average of New York State (excluding NY City) and among Love Canal women it was up by 100%.

In 1980, health researchers began formal studies of the children living within a few hundred yards of Love Canal and pregnancy outcome of women in the same area. The results of two studies of the children of Love Canal, published in 1985, reveal ill effects among those who lived near the Canal as compared to those who lived further away.

One study surveyed two groups of children: 239 children who were born to mothers exposed to Love Canal chemicals while pregnant, and 707 controls, children from the same city whose families were similar to the Love Canal families in every respect except where they lived. The two groups were specifically matched for socio-economic status, smoking, alcohol consumption, and medication taken during pregnancy. Although the studies did not include the 235 families who were the first to be evacuated from Love Canal, because the resources to trace these families were not available, and although children who had died were excluded from the study, the results were clear. Low birth weight babies were 2.3 times more likely to occur among homeowners living near Love Canal compared with the control group (11.1% as against 4.8%) and serious birth defects were twice as likely to occur among those living near the Canal (12.1% vs. 6.2%.)

A second study of child health involved 523 Love Canal children and 440 control children from the same city, matched in every respect except where they lived. The study found seizures 2.5 times as prevalent among Love Canal children as among controls; learning disabilities were 1.5 times as prevalent; hyperactivity was almost 3 times as prevalent; eye irritation was twice as prevalent; skin rashes occurred twice as often; abdominal pain was twice as prevalent; incontinence occurred three times as often. Thus, by seven health measures, living near Love Canal was associated with ill health among children.

Rachel's concludes from these studies and the ones which were not published that communities need access to research facilities and the capability to carry out their own environmental research:

'With control over their own experts, citizens have a chance of learning what's happening and what they must do; without it, citizens can be duped by the state.'

Britain's Love Canal

The similarity of view between Fumento, Whelan and Professor Simon Wessely is sometimes striking. In 1988, a water supply company worker mistakenly tipped 20 tonnes of a chemical cocktail into the water system of the small Cornish town of Camelford. In the following two days, many of the inhabitants imbibed large quantities of the chemicals.

The first health consequences were symptoms such as vomiting and diarrhoea; as time went by, people suffered personality changes, with loss of short-term memory, irritability and sensitivity to a large number of other chemicals. The incident caused an unquantified number of human deaths and a massive incidence of long-term adverse health effects in both human and animals.♦

Some years after the incident, a study commissioned by lawyers acting on behalf of the Camelford plaintiffs and funded through Legal Aid, showed conclusively that those exposed residents suffered considerable damage to cerebral function, with evidence of organic brain damage. The personal tragedies caused by the toxic contamination at Camelford were heartbreaking.

Like Fumento and Whelan writing about the Love Canal incident, British 'health fraud' activists and greenwashers decided, retrospectively, that the incident and its serious adverse effects on human health had been a mirage. Depending upon fading memory,

---

♦ A draft report of this incident should be available in Spring 2004, from The Committee on Toxicity of Chemicals in Food, Consumer Products and the Environment: Subgroup Briefed to Consider Health Effects of The Lower Moore Water Pollution Incident.

they revised the history of the incident. According to Professor Wessely, writing in 1995, symptoms of ill health in Camelford could have been due to heightened perception of normal bodily sensations *being attributed to* an external cause such as poisoning.

This theory of *wrongly perceived* illness belief is what Whelan and Fumento suggest is happening – propelled by a hysterical media, people with existing mental health problems, living in different places, 'come out' at times of an environmental crisis, crying, 'Help me, I'm ill and I'm sure it's because I have been poisoned by aluminium sulphate, or by chemicals in the Love Canal, or something.'

Like Fumento and Whelan, Wessely and his colleagues seem to believe that those who become involved with the idea of environmental illness are often 'infected' by contemporary fears about the environment and chemical toxins. For these writers and academics, chemical illness always has to be irrational and 'unreal', for were they once to admit to it in any circumstance, the financial, industrial and political implications could be considerable.

Bernard Dixon, an editor of the *New Scientist* in the 1980s♦ and closely associated with the Campaign Against Health Fraud, showed his belief in the Wessely line most clearly in a 1995 *BMJ* article, 'Still Waters', which assesses a Wessely and David paper about Camelford also published in the *BMJ*. Dixon states baldly and utterly irrationally that 'mass hysteria was largely responsible for the furore.'

Wessely and his colleagues campaigned with the same degree of determination, not only against Gulf War Syndrome, ME and CFS, MCS and toxic exposures like Camelford, but also against recog-

---

♦ Dixon was also a member of the British branch of CSICOP that helped set up HealthWatch and on the steering committee of the Media Resources Service, an extension at that time of the Ciba Geigy (now Novartis) drug company.

nition by the Courts of pesticide exposure damage. Notable amongst these cases are those caused by organophosphate pesticides. The organophosphates, developed by Bayer in the years immediately before the 1939-1945 war, were from the beginning established as damaging to the human nervous system. The Wessely school, however, argues adamantly against this established scientific knowledge.

Professor Anthony David, one of Wessely's colleagues and a staunch member of the Wessely school, sat on the Royal College of Physicians' and Royal College of Psychiatrists' Working Party which produced the Colleges' report on organophosphate sheep dip. The report stated that the ill-health suffered by farmers and others after chronic, low-dose exposure to OPs was likely to be due to 'severe anxiety or depression, which have intuitively *been attributed by the sufferers to* OP exposure.' (Italics added.)

Did the Gulf War happen?

Gulf War Syndrome became such a big problem for the British and North American Governments mainly because the admission of the syndrome would have opened the floodgates to liability claims for chemical damage. If experts agreed or admitted, even tentatively, that some Gulf War veterans had been adversely affected by chemical sensitivity, the whole carefully built edifice created by the chemical companies since the 1970s would collapse. The claims on the State, industry and the medical establishment would be immense. Consequently, the same pattern of denial has been acted out with Gulf War Syndrome (GWS) as with other chemical crises.♦

♦ 'With about 300,000 troops in the gulf, the military has been criticized for failing to follow a 1997 law that requires medical screenings of troops before and after deployment. The military is conducting neither physical or mental examinations, nor blood sampling, as Congress required. "What's so difficult about all of this?" asked Rep. William Janklow, a South Dakota Republican. "We're talking about elementary data? What is so mysterious about giving everyone a physical (cont.)

SKEWED

Initially, when the complaints are fresh in the public mind denial involves a lot of operatic ballyhoo and distractive shouting, with important people pointing in many different directions. There follows a period of quiet while the public is assured that research has been commissioned and will be carried out by the best and most independent scientific brains in the country; no mention is made of vested interests. Finally, some ten years after people became sick, when, the authorities hope, the worst cases have died, the steady drip, drip of denial begins.

The momentum of denial is carried forward by well placed academics, science pundits and journalists, who covertly introduce concepts like stress, hysteria, media-hype into the analysis of the phenomena. In relation to Gulf War Syndrome, as in depleted uranium weaponry, the whole process of the denial is actually a continuation of the war itself, in this phase conducted by the British and North American States against their own citizens, who are seen to be putting in jeopardy the State's apparent moral legitimacy.

Of course, denying soldiers comes hard even to the most fawning servants of vested interests, not as simple as denying the existence of Chronic Fatigue Syndrome. The physician has to agonise over the best approach to adopt: 'What? You sweat all the time, your short-term memory has gone, you have bouts of shaking, you can't sleep, yes I can see your hair has fallen out, some days you're so tired you can't stand up. Look, don't worry about it; all these symptoms are completely imaginary. How about some Cognitive Behaviour Therapy, that will cure you of imagining you're ill. No . . . please, you don't have to put your hands round my neck for graded exercise. . .'

♦ (cont.) exam?" Republican Christopher Shays, who leads the subcommittee and has been investigating gulf war illness for a decade, said Congress intended otherwise "From my standpoint, you're not meeting the letter of the law, clearly you're not meeting the spirit of the law." ' [Merit of physical exams of troops after military deployments discussed, by David Goldstein. *The Kansas City Star*. 2003.]

The Public Health Revisionists

With soldiers, most journalists and politicians find that some glad-handing and promises of understanding are best used to sweeten the unpalatable truth that the suffering soldier is a hysteric.

Having been a serving conscript himself, Michael Fumento offers his service record with each bowl of bile he serves up about Gulf War veterans:

> . . . studies published in major medical journals repeatedly show that Gulf vets have no more deaths, cancers, birth defects, miscarriages, or hospitalisations when compared to vets who didn't deploy to the Gulf. This isn't to say they never have health problems. One researcher who claims GWS is real nonetheless admitted he had identified no less than 123 symptoms! These range from the utterly mundane – such as hair loss, graying hair, and weight gain – to the utterly preposterous, such as semen that burns flesh like 'napalm'; vomit that glows in the dark, and two vets who claim that they are literally shrinking.♦ In other words, this 'syndrome' simply comprises people getting the same illnesses at the same rate that we would expect any group of 700,000 Americans (and their spouses and children) to get. Add an element of hysteria, which accounts for the claims of glowing vomit, flesh-ripping semen, and the incredible shrinking men. Hysteria also causes myriad psychosomatic illnesses such as labored breathing and aching joints.

This is all high quality stuff, right down to the throw away 'semen that burns flesh like napalm.' After all, no one is going to argue around this, or ask to see the exhibits, semen is pretty sensitive stuff. And it would take a brave American to begin talking about napalm; didn't American forces use napalm to maim, damaged and burn the skin off Vietnamese peasants?

Beneath all the colourful circus hype, Fumento is committed to propagating the idea that GWS has a psychiatric rather than an

---

♦Here we find the same argument strategy being used as with ME and CFS, where stress is placed on the number of allegedly absurd claims. These claims throw all others out of kilter. Clearly it is only a short step between complaining of GWS, believing you are shrinking and believing in alien abduction.

organic aetiology; speaking of one study that argued for GWS, he says: 'What the study showed was that troops who had the most complaints also claimed to have had the greatest exposure to pesticides, vaccinations, and what-have-you. This is *exactly what we would expect from ailments that are psychosomatic.*'

About one scientist who argues that Gulf War Syndrome is a chemically induced condition, Fumento notes that he is 'the best-known propagator of the junk science surrounding the previous incarnation of GWS, namely Agent Orange. Yet to this day, scientists continue to monitor the Vietnam vets with the highest Agent Orange exposures and find they have no more medical problems than persons with no exposure.'

Agent Orange, the defoliant dropped by the ton on Vietnamese villages, was produced by Monsanto and Dow, and contained dioxin, one of the most deadly chemicals known to man. Scientists, chemical companies and the American State have good reason to disguise the results of research into Agent Orange. The living proof of the terrible health damage caused by this chemical is in Vietnam, where babies are still being born with deformities over thirty years after the war.

Predictably, the Cato Institute takes the same line on Gulf War Syndrome as the Reason Foundation. In 1997, when President Clinton announced a new scientific panel to review the evidence on Gulf War Syndrome, Michael Gough, director of science and risk studies at the Cato Institute, also addressed the question of Agent Orange as an example of how research is manipulated in the public interest. Like Fumento, Gough suggested that when the hype and the spin had died down, there was absolutely no adverse effect on Vietnam veterans recorded by any trustworthy scientific studies.♦

♦ The chemical companies, claimants and the courts took quite a different view when in 1988 they came to a collective settlement which set up a fund for vets, entitling some of them to millions of dollars.

The Public Health Revisionists

In order not to insult the vets, Gough uses a sophisticated political argument on GWS. It is, he says, not that war veterans should be refused compensation for illness, but that science should not be dragged into service in contentious political situations: 'Congress should bring down the curtain on the charade that science will guide the decision to compensate veterans. If it decides to compensate veterans for diseases that they and their champions associated with the Gulf War, it should concede its motivations: compassion for veterans, gratitude for their service or simple congressional vote grubbing.'

While this could be read as a straightforward attempt to persuade politicians of the benefits of *realpolitik*, such arguments would close the door on research and forever disguise the cause of GWS. It would hide the fact that chemicals are responsible for what Gough is happy to call 'an unspecified disease in search of an unidentified cause.'

While 'health fraud' activists and greenwashers quickly had to attach their psychological views on Chemical Sensitivity to claims of GWS, even Barrett and Gots realised that they could not simply accuse veterans of being mentally ill. They chose instead to suggest that the soldiers had been conned into *believing that they were ill* by other mentally disturbed MCS patients and their unscrupulous physicians. 'Ever vigilant for new recruits, MCS advocates have embraced "Gulf War Syndrome" as their own. But the Presidential Advisory Committee on Gulf War Veterans' Illnesses has found no connection,' say Barrett and Gots in their book on environmental illness. Barrett and Gots describe GWS as if it were a conspiracist's charter, the product of deranged patients, corrupt scientists and unscrupulous clinical ecologists:

> The concept of a 'Gulf War Syndrome' is appealing. It comes at
> a time when public distrust of Government is at an all-time high.
> It turns on conspiracies, a favourite theme of television

producers. It provides the media with an endless parade of self-perceived victims. It provides a feeding trough for serious scientists, since funding is abundant, and for every charlatan with a newsworthy theory. It is a field day for politicians who solemnly promise to 'get to the bottom' of the problem. The big losers in all of this are the ailing veterans whose confusion about what happened prevents them from getting on with their lives.

Veterans are tacked onto this paragraph which first attacks television producers, the media, self-perceived victims, serious scientists, charlatans and politicians. What it says about these people is unsustainable and, again, the world is turned upon its head for ideological purposes. *If only there were* large numbers of television producers who believed in conspiracy, serious scientists who had abundant funding, medical practitioners with radical views and politicians who even *promised* to get to the 'bottom of the matter.' In the main, of course, this vast army of professionals willing to expose GWS exists only in the ideologically fulminating minds of people like Gots and Barrett.

One of Professor Simon Wessely's consideration of GWS, published in the *BMJ*, was the crystallisation of his long-held view that Gulf War Syndrome and illnesses which are often presented as chemically induced are actually caused by 'contagious hysteria.' In this study, Wessely concludes without a flicker of irony that the most significant indicator of a veteran presenting with GWS is their having spoken to someone else who believes that they have GWS: 'The strongest association was knowing another person who also thought they had Gulf war syndrome.' One wonders if this association was more significant than the fact that they had served in the Gulf War. Papers like this of Wessely and similar papers written by his colleagues are devoid of science and their results are utterly spurious, yet paper after paper remain substantially uncriticised by the academic and scientific community.

Repeatedly straining credibility

The Cato Institute and a number of other industry-based groups have opposed proposed ergonomic regulations that the US Occupational Safety and Health Administration has tried to introduce. The regulations, based, according to a Cato policy commentary, on 'junk science' would particularly protect information technology workers from Repetitive Strain Injuries (RSI). Industry involved academics are arguing that RSI, together with chemically induced illness and those of unknown origin like ME and CFS, has both a psychiatric aetiology and a hysterical dimension.

Professor Edward Shorter, chairman of the Medical History Department at the University of Toronto and a historian of psychiatry, frequently makes statements about 'hysterical' medical conditions. He agrees with the 'health fraud' line that people with psychiatric difficulties often seek diagnostic labels for their difficulties in order to ensure that people pay attention to them: 'And if you have basically hysteria (sic) and you can dignify it with something that makes it sound like you have a serious illness, then you get more respect from people.'

In a newspaper interview, Shorter regurgitated the sceptic's popular history of Chronic Fatigue Syndrome and used it as evidence against the reality of RSI. Like many academics, Shorter talks a good illness, especially with respect to psychiatric aetiology. His throwaway popular style makes him entertaining without the need for references or proof. Here is one journalist's account of Shorter's history of CFS:

> Chronic tiredness, joint pain, dizziness, anxiety and depression that never seem to go away are familiar to many people. The French call it *personalité fragile*. English doctors once called it hysteria. Whatever the symptoms, sufferers have always sought to find a recognized diagnosis to explain their woes. 'The current burst of hysterical illness started in the 1960s [with

Chronic Fatigue Syndrome] and it built momentum from there.'
Dr. Shorter says these are all media-spread illness attributions.
Chronic Fatigue Syndrome was hard to discredit because some
researchers found sufferers also carry Epstein-Barr virus. Wider
studies show almost everyone carries the virus. 'But now, even
chronic fatigue is starting to go the way of the dodo bird, and
now multiple chemical sensitivity is the new biggie.'

Although Shorter gets even this 'pop' history hopelessly wrong, like
Wessely, Showalter and others, he uses the same tabloid style, and
suggests that hysterical stories are manipulated and amplified by the
media to consolidate the irrational narratives of people with
psychiatric conditions.

There's no evidence at all that Multiple Chemical Sensitivity
(MCS) is a real disease. These are just examples, but there's a
whole world of epidemic disease attributions that is just filled
with curiosities. There are people who believe they are allergic
to dental amalgam. There are people who think that they have
problems with the tempero-mandibular joint in their jaw that
disables them. There's the whole fibromyalgia crowd that is sort
of blended together with the whole chronic fatigue illness
attribution now. This really does go on and on.

Any seasoned observer of the 'health fraud' movement would sense
that Shorter was building up to some comment on alternative and
complementary medicine. Sure enough, he ends the interview by
warning people who think they may have RSI against visiting
alternative healers, who would probably, he quips in his exacting
academic style, diagnose sensitivity to gasoline. Rather, that is, than
hysteria.

Quackers

Having appeared in the mid 1980s, 'health fraud' organisations have
by now developed a complete language and structural response to
anyone who doesn't visit a 'proper doctor' or consumes the
prescribed quantity of non-recreational drugs. The problem with

this developing language is that it has become peculiarly illogical, the arguments it constructs irrational and cranky. It is a professional language, with strategic professional goals, virtually meaningless to the average layperson trying to decide for the first time whether or not they should visit an alternative practitioner. Like the North Americans and the Koreans shouting at each other over a border for half a century, 'health fraud' activists shout their propaganda into the darkness.

Dr. Stephen Barrett is one of the most vociferous US 'health fraud' activists. He is a retired psychiatrist, who – according to him and his colleagues – is a nationally renowned consumer health advocate and quackbuster. He is, so his publicity says, editor, co-author or author of forty-four books, including epics like *The Health Robbers* and *The Vitamin Pushers*.

Barrett is the Vice President and a Director of the National Council Against Health Fraud and runs Quackwatch, a web site that attacks alternative and complementary health practitioners and those involved in clinical ecology. Barrett is also a member of the trinity of US organisations that support the 'health fraud' movement in America; he is a 'Scientific Advisor' to the American Council on Science and Health and is a 'Fellow' of the Committee for the Scientific Investigation of Claims of the Paranormal (CSICOP).

Barrett has written copiously opposing clinical ecology and environmental illness and wrote his last book, *Chemical Sensitivity*, with Dr. Ronald Gots; since then, the two of them have been picking up publicity from popular magazines and trade papers. After their book came out Gots and Barrett were interviewed in 2001 by Debbie Carvalko for her article: *Do Common Chemicals Cause Disease? Debate Rages*; they made a good double act:

> 'I wouldn't say it's not real,' adds Dr. Ronald Gots, a principal at the International Center for Toxicology and Medicine in Rockville, Maryland and board member for the American

Council on Science and Health. Over the past 20 years, Gots has personally examined or studied the records of at least 300 MCS sufferers. 'But the literature has increasingly developed to show that there is a psychological component for many of their symptoms. I do think there are emotional explanations for most of these individuals' problems . . . It is toxicologically impossible for minute exposures to chemicals to cause the vast and intense array of multi-system symptoms that MCS proponents cite,' Gots says.

Barrett argues that MCS symptoms are psychosomatic, triggered by *abnormal thought*. 'There is no such thing as MCS. What you have is a phenomenon where people have symptoms they are connecting to chemical exposures,' insists Barrett, a retired psychiatrist who runs Quackwatch, a Pennsylvania-based medical watchdog group. (Italics added.)

Barrett says, 'Many experts have studied "MCS" patients and concluded that their basic problem is psychological rather than physical. The best current data suggest that certain psychological factors predispose individuals to develop symptoms and to seek out someone who will provide a "physical" explanation of their symptoms. Many of these patients suffer from somatization disorder, an emotional problem characterized by persistent symptoms that cannot be fully explained by any known medical condition, yet are severe enough to require medical treatment or cause alterations in lifestyle. Some are paranoids who are prone to believe that their problems have outside causes. Others suffer from depression, panic disorder, agoraphobia, or other anxiety states that induce bodily reactions to stress.'

Stephen Barrett sometimes writes about MCS as if it is solely a problem of people claiming illegitimate benefits of various kinds, supported by physicians who do not mind supporting bogus claims:

Chemical sensitivity (or 'multiple chemical sensitivity') is a term used to describe people with numerous troubling symptoms attributed to environmental factors, from simple house paint to complex building structures, and materials in offices and schools. Many such people are seeking special accommodations, applying for disability benefits, and filing lawsuits claiming that exposure to common foods and chemicals has made them ill. Their efforts are supported by some physicians who use questionable diagnosis and treatment methods, while critics charge that these medical approaches are bogus and 'chemical sensitivity' is not a valid diagnosis.

Again, when discussing the matter of children allegedly railroaded into CFS by their parents, money becomes one of the most important issues in Barrett's mind:

> Barrett says he believes adults with the disorder often share one goal: money. Many seek disability benefits or sue chemical companies. Like Barrett, most medical doctors say they believe when a child is affected, it's because an adult – often the mother – has, intentionally or not, 'taught' the child to hyper-react to chemical exposure. 'Kids do what is expected,' says Barrett.

Summing up his book *Chemical Sensitivity: The Truth About Environmental Illness* in *Nutrition Today*, Barrett tries to make fun of the symptoms of chemical sensitivity:

> The complaints associated with chemical sensitivity include depression, irritability, poor memory, fatigue, drowsiness, constipation, sneezing, wheezing, skin rashes, headache, chest pain, pounding heart, swelling, upset stomach, paralysis, AIDS-like illnesses, psychotic experiences, and just about every other symptom noted in medical textbooks.

Barrett put the great majority of MCS diagnoses down to false reports 'from misled, obsessive patients' supported by 'opportunist doctors.'

John Renner

John Renner died following emergency heart surgery in September 2000. He was one of the most important 'health fraud' activists in America and the damage he did to alternative and complementary medicine will long outlive him. William T. Jarvis's obituary of John Renner, draws a good picture of the mind of a quackbuster, which seemingly criticises without discrimination anything which is not orthodox and which stems from the patient's own evaluation of their illness, rather than from that of a doctor:

> John was among the first to realize that what is generally described as 'unconventional,' 'complementary,' 'alternative,' 'integrative,' 'holistic,' or 'innovative' medicine is actually a manifestation of self-care by patients who are trying their best to take charge of their health problems. Most self-care involves the use of health products – over-the-counter medicines, dietary supplements, and the like. These may be found at drug stores, health food stores, supermarkets, discount stores or sold through pyramid-like marketing schemes, mail order houses, telemarketing boiler rooms, and television infomercials. Patients also engage in what John termed 'extended self-care' when they seek the services of nonmedical providers such as chiropractors, massage therapists, herbalists, nutrition consultants, reflexologists, palm readers, and astrologers to solve physical, emotional, or social problems. Sometimes patients turn to 'medical renegades and rascals' (terms John taught us to use) in their desperation or search for speculative therapies.

Even in an obituary, Jarvis, the founder of the NCAHF, cannot resist using 'health fraud' propaganda. For example, the first sentence does not bear serious analysis. Some 'complementary,' 'alternative,' 'integrative,' 'holistic,' or 'innovative' medicine, far from being 'a manifestation' of self-care, were most probably pioneered by a disillusioned orthodox doctor. While other so called 'alternatives', like Traditional Chinese Medicine, are ancient orthodox systems.

The last sentence of the obituary contains clear proof that 'health fraud' activists are talking to themselves: Jarvis throws a little destabilising semantic nonsense into the mix. Is a nutritional consultant or a chiropractor 'a non-medical' provider; non-pharmaceutical maybe, but non-*medical*? And then comes the real rapier thrust – comparing palm readers to herbalists and massage therapists? The truth is that in any serious organisation the authors of such assertions would be a laughing stock; in the 'health fraud' movement they are the leading lights.

The Public Health Revisionists

Jarvis met Renner and Victor Herbert in 1983 at a conference entitled 'Fact, Fiction and Fantasy in Health Information for Patients,' at St. Mary's Hospital in Kansas City. Renner became an ex-officio member of the board of NCAHF a year later. In 1985 he established the Kansas City Committee on Health and Nutrition Fraud and Abuse. Soon afterward, he opened the Consumer Health Information Research Institute (CHIRI) in Kansas City.

All the funding organisations for Renner's groups were ultimately linked to the $12 million (1983) Speas Foundation. A large percentage of the Foundation's money is invested in drugs, chemicals and medical interests. These interests include Eli Lilly and Merck, as well as a number of other companies, all of which have been involved in FDA and PAC (Pharmaceutical Advertising Council) anti-quackery campaigns. The Speas Foundation gets its money from the Speas Company, a processed food manufacturer.

Promoted as an authoritative commentator on health issues, Renner had filed for bankruptcy in the early 1970s, leaving creditors wanting for over a million dollars. The Kansas City Group was responsible for campaigns against a number of herbal and natural treatments, most particularly a series of preparations designed by Dr. Kurt Donsbach under the label of Herbalife. The strategies used against Dr. Donsbach were almost entirely covert. They included Fraud Unit investigators from the Sacramento Department of Health posing as Herbalife distributors.

Until his death Renner was the President of the Consumer Health Information Research Institute and in 1988 was awarded the FDA Commissioner's Special Citation 'for exceptional efforts in combating health fraud.'

Inevitably, Renner adhered to the theory that CFS is mostly in the mind. He wrote two papers with Susan Abbey MD, a Canadian psychology researcher. One of the papers, entitled *Chronic Fatigue Real and Unreal: The Facts*, was presented by Abbey and Renner at the second conference of NCAHF in 1986, amongst other presentations with titles like: *Psychic Surgery and Other Medical Miracles, Current Experiences with the World of Fraud, Investigative Techniques Used to Detect Health Fraud.*

A case too far

2001 was a bad year for the NCAHF in the US courts, a number of alternative medicine producers and practitioners fought back against the legal chicanery organised by quackbusters. The National Council Against Health Fraud (NCAHF) decided to sue around forty three 'Alternative Medicine proponents' in California, suggesting that they were engaging in 'health fraud', doing what 'wasn't scientifically proven.' The first case that came to trial was NCAHF vs. King Bio, a manufacturer of around 50 homoeopathic products.

A California Superior Court ruling by Judge Fromholz, in December 2001, threw considerable doubt on the credibility of Barrett and other National Council Against Health Fraud 'experts'. The NCAHF had brought their action attacking the homoeopathic products of King Bio Pharmaceuticals, Inc. and its president Frank J. King on the grounds that they were advertising falsely. That is, they were using false, deceptive or misleading statements or re-presentations in the labelling or advertising of their homoeopathic products. NCAHF argued and attempted to offer testimony to the effect that the claims stated in the defendants advertising were scientifically unsupportable.

The trial began in October 2001. NCAHF presented two experts, Wallace I. Sampson, MD, and Stephen Barrett, MD. The defendants brought Jacquelyn J. Wilson, MD, as an expert witness. Granted a motion of no case to answer after the presentation of the NCAHF case, the judge found in favour of King and against the NCAHF.

The Public Health Revisionists

Because the NCAHF appeared from the beginning to have significant difficulty in disproving the claims of King Bio Pharmaceuticals, they tried to shift the burden of proof to the company, saying that the company should have to prove that their products worked. The court was having none of this and Judge Fromholz in his ruling made it plain that the court found that there was no case in California to support the shifting of the burden of proof to the defendant in a case of this type. The judge made it clear that the logical end-point of NCAHF's burden-shifting argument would be to permit anyone with the requisite filing fee to walk into any court in any state and file a lawsuit against any business, casting the burden on that defendant to prove that it was not violating the law. Such an approach, the judge said, would itself be unfair.

In reviewing the evidence presented by both parties, the Judge had some scathing things to say about the NCAHF witnesses. Of Wallace I. Sampson, MD, the judge said:

> The thrust of his testimony appeared directed to the conclusion that the evidence supporting claims of efficacy for homeopathic drugs does not meet the standard that he believes applies to valid clinical studies. All of Dr. Sampson's testimony was quite general in nature. Dr. Sampson, a retired medical doctor with an oncology specialty, has had only limited involvement in clinical research studies. He has little expertise in research methodology and does not instruct in that area. He admitted to having had no experience with or training in homeopathic medicine or drugs. He was unfamiliar with any professional organisations related to homeopathy, including the Homeopathic Pharmacopoeia Convention of the United States.

> While he stated that he teaches a university course on 'alternative medicine,' Dr. Sampson admitted that the course does not instruct on how such methods may be practiced, but rather is a course designed to highlight the criticisms of such alternative practices. Therefore, the Court finds that Dr. Sampson has relatively thin credentials to opine on the general questions of the proper standards for clinical or scientific research or other methods of obtaining valid evidence about the efficacy of drugs.

SKEWED

The Court further finds that Dr. Sampson lacks experience in the field of homeopathic drugs, which renders his testimony of little or no weight in this case. In addition, Dr. Sampson admitted to having done absolutely no investigation concerning Defendants' specific products.

Moving on to Stephen Barrett, MD, the judge was equally, if not more, dismissive of his evidence. Because of overlap with Dr. Sampson's evidence, Barrett's testimony was limited by the Court to the sole issue of FDA treatment of homoeopathic drugs. The Judge made it clear that the relevancy of this issue was questionable at best.

Dr. Barrett was a psychiatrist who retired in or about 1993, at which point he contends he allowed his medical license to lapse. Like Dr. Sampson, he has no formal training in homeopathic medicine or drugs, although he claims to have read and written extensively on homeopathy and other forms of alternative medicine. Dr. Barrett's claim to expertise on FDA issues arises from his conversations with FDA agents, his review of professional literature on the subject and certain continuing education activities. As for his credential as an expert on FDA regulation of homeopathic drugs, the Court finds that Dr. Barrett lacks sufficient qualifications in this area.

Dr. Barrett's purported legal and regulatory knowledge is not apparent. He is not a lawyer, although he claims he attended several semesters of correspondence law school. While Dr. Barrett appears to have had several past conversations with FDA representatives, these appear to have been sporadic, mainly at his own instigation, and principally for the purpose of gathering information for his various articles and Internet web sites. He has never testified before any governmental panel or agency on issues relating to FDA regulation of drugs. For these reasons, there is no sound basis on which to consider Dr. Barrett qualified as an expert on the issues he was offered to address.

The court further found that both Dr. Sampson and Dr. Barrett were biased heavily in favour of the NCAHF and thus the weight to be accorded their testimony is slight in any event. Both were long-time board members of the NCAHF; Dr. Barrett had served as its Chairman. Both participated in an application to the U.S. FDA during the early 1990s designed to restrict the sale of most homeopathic drugs. Dr. Sampson's university course presents what is effectively a one-sided, critical view of alternative medicine. Dr. Barrett's heavy activities in lecturing and writing about alternative medicine similarly are focused on the eradication of the practices about which he opines.

Both witnesses' fees, as Dr. Barrett testified, are paid from a fund established by the NCAHF from the proceeds of suits such as this case. Based on this fact alone, the Court may infer that Dr. Barrett and Sampson are more likely to receive fees for testifying on behalf of NCAHF in future cases if the Plaintiff prevails in the instant action and thereby wins funds to enrich the litigation fund described by Dr. Barrett. It is apparent, therefore, that both men have a direct, personal financial interest in the outcome of this litigation. Based on all of these factors, Dr. Sampson and Dr. Barrett can be described as zealous advocates of the Plaintiff's position, and therefore not neutral or dispassionate witnesses or experts. In light of these affiliations and their orientation, it can fairly be said that Drs. Barrett and Sampson are themselves the client, and therefore their testimony should be accorded little, if any, credibility on that basis as well.

The judge had quite a different approach to the defence witness Jacquelyn J. Wilson, MD (called out of turn, during the prosecution case because of scheduling difficulties.) She was, he said, a board certified medical practitioner with particular experience in homoeopathic medicine. Dr. Wilson testified that she has trained in homoeopathic medicine and received certification to practise in the field from at least one State agency. She lectured and consulted on the subject of homoeopathy and was a member of the Homeopathic Pharmacopoeia Convention of the United States.

Dr. Wilson had, the judge said, treated many patients using homoeopathic drugs. Based on this background, Dr. Wilson was, unlike Drs. Barrett and Sampson, qualified as an expert on issues relating to homoeopathy generally. She testified that the Materia Medica contain several types of valid scientific evidence respecting the effectiveness of homoeopathic drugs. She also testified about the general manner in which homoeopathic drugs are recognized and regulated by the FDA.

The NCAHF had, the judge said, failed to show that the defendants knew or should have known that any of their statements were untrue, false or misleading. The judge found against the NCAHF on every issue that it brought before the court, saying that there was no evidence to support the accusation that King Bio Pharmaceuticals had broken any part of the law, being neither 'unlawful', 'unfair' nor 'fraudulent' with respect to their advertising and labelling. The Plaintiff's advertising, the judge said, was unlikely to mislead a reasonable person.

In April 2003, the decision was appealed by NCAHF but given short shrift by the California Appeals Court. The court found that quackbusters had no business interfering in California's health care system. The Court also declared that Stephen Barrett and Wallace Sampson MD were 'biased and unworthy of credibility.'

Amongst other things, the Appeal Court said that 'The trial court concluded NCAHF failed to prove a false or misleading statement. King Bio's expert testified the products were safe and effective. The products were included in the Homeopathic Pharmacopoeia and complied with FDA guidelines. NCAHF presented no evidence that King Bio's products were not safe and effective, relying instead on a general attack on homoeopathy, made by witnesses who had no knowledge of, or experience with King Bio's products, and who were found to be biased and unworthy of credibility.'

The Court also said: 'We conclude there is no basis in California law to shift the burden of proof to a defendant in a representative false advertising and unlawful competition action. We conclude further that the Legislature has indicated an intent to place the burden of proof on the plaintiff in such cases. Finally, we conclude federal authority is not apposite.'

This court ruling on NCAHF tactics and their representatives specific testimony critical of homoeopathy, inevitably casts massive doubt over *all* other pronouncements of both the organisation and one of its leading members. How should we perceive Barrett's view, which he holds in common with other Anglo-American 'health fraud' activists, that environmental illness, CFS, GWS and other illnesses, are all in the mind?

The handmaiden

Elaine Showalter is an American academic, an Associate Professor of English at Princeton University, and a post-modern feminist literature critic. In the late 1990s, she caused a splash on the chat show circuits after she departed from her own area of expertise to publish a book entitled *Hystories: Hysterical Epidemics and Modern Media*. The book strung together a random collection of scientifically unsupported phenomena, including Chronic Fatigue Syndrome, Gulf War Syndrome and alien abduction, and tied them together with a fantastic post-modern theory of hysteria. Showalter explained to a journalist:

> 'I'm really talking about the structural similarities of these epidemics,' she explains. 'Somebody has symptoms, they're vague but they're real symptoms. This person goes around looking for help, and eventually finds somebody who says to them, "I think you've been abducted by aliens" or "I think you have Chronic Fatigue Syndrome." Then you embark on a process of becoming that kind of patient. They say their goal is to find a cure. But the syndrome becomes a way of life.'

> Why aren't CFS sufferers content to be diagnosed with psychogenic disorder? 'I don't know' she says. 'There are some people who work on this who say it's part of the syndrome to hate psychiatry – I think that's extreme. But I think they need to have a legitimate, organic illness as a cover. This is just terribly important to their self image.'

SKEWED

The core message of Showalter's book is twofold. She accuses her 'hysterics' of escaping into imagined tales of physical phenomena upon which they lay the blame for their poor life prognosis. People, she says, should take responsibility for themselves and their difficulties, preferably resolving internal conflicts with psychoanalysis. She also suggests that in modern society the media amplifies the seeds of hysteria, duplicating with gathering intensity and conviction the claims of the mentally unstable. Showalter, who has been funded by the Avalon Foundation, researched *Hystories* over a staggering ten-year period, mainly on summer visits from America to London's Wellcome Institute, where she enjoyed the intellectual companionship of Professor Simon Wessely.

Academia inevitably found Showalter's book entertaining and it remained the hot topic of conversation at dinner parties and chat shows for a couple of weeks until the breeze of fashion turned minds to something new.

The most substantial criticism of the Chronic Fatigue Syndrome chapter of *Hystories* came from an Associate Professor in the Department of History at Villanova University, Mary Schweitzer. Schweitzer had been on medical leave with ME for two years prior to the appearance of Showalter's book in 1997. At the start of her review, Schweitzer points out that writing about serious illnesses like CFS or GWS needs a slightly more rigorous intellectual approach than that with which Showalter's post-modern and subjective training equipped her. Rather than draw on a comprehensive literature review, Showalter seemed to have:

> lifted [quotes] seemingly at random from a few existing trade books on the subject, articles in such sources as 'USA Today,' 'The Independent,' 'McCall's,' and 'Newsweek,' and a single symposium held in London in May, 1992 (p. 130.) The lone exception to this pattern came in frequent references to Showalter's London mentor, psychiatrist Simon Wessely. While including mention of Wessely's publications, however, she

134

omitted all mention of existing published works in scholarly
journals disputing Wessely's thesis.

As far as she was able in a short review, Schweitzer raises all the
pertinent questions about Showalter's view of CFS and places the
book within its sociological context, hinting at a much broader
purpose for its writing:

> Why would a Princeton scholar ignore the abundant and growing
> scholarly literature on the physical basis of the symptoms of
> CFS? Why did her construction of an outbreak of 'hysterical
> epidemics' on the eve of the new millennium require the
> inclusion of this disease, about which she apparently knows so
> little? Why choose to interpret the narratives of patients and
> doctors as a 'protolanguage rather than a disease,' privileging an
> English professor's narrow textual analysis over the testimony of
> the medical profession itself – and patients? The answer lies in
> the very sociological factors Showalter claimed to depict. There
> is, in a sense, a 'hystory' spreading in epidemic fashion with
> regard to CFS, but it is Showalter who is helping construct the
> text. Paradoxically, as evidence mounts within the medical
> research community that CFS is a seriously debilitating
> neurological illness, with unknown but possibly contagious
> origins, efforts to portray CFS and its sufferers as a type of hoax
> have increased in the popular press.

Dr. Gots, Mr. Stossel and junk journalism

In Britain and North America there are journalists who dip critically
in and out of the environmental movement, often doing a great deal
of damage. In 1996, ABC television produced a programme entitled
Junk Science; the presenter was John Stossel. Stossel already had a
name for being pro-industry, having reported on and promoted food
irradiation and pesticides while downplaying the dangers of
asbestos and electromagnetic fields.

Junk Science became infamous because it simply presented the
chemical industry point of view on clinical ecology and Multiple

Chemical Sensitivity. In fact *Junk Science* was very similar to *The Allergy Business*, another programme critical of clinical ecology made in England for *World in Action*. *Junk Science* used covert techniques, bogus patients and hidden recording in a manner which is now common to programmes about clinical ecology, alternative cancer treatments and alternative medicine generally.

Stossel's programme targeted Dr. Grace Ziem, an occupational illness physician who specialises in Multiple Chemical Sensitivity and who was, at the time, also president and medical director of MCS Referral & Resources (MCS R&R), an organisation founded by Albert Donnay devoted to the diagnosis, treatment, accommodation and prevention of Multiple Chemical Sensitivity disorders. Ziem, a Harvard and Johns Hopkins-trained physician with a PhD, has cared for hundreds of chemically injured patients. She told the press that Stossel sent her two phoney patients – a member of the ABC News staff and her sister-in-law. They both lied about their medical history and symptoms and presented as being concerned about MCS.

Stossel's phoney patients were suspected early on by Dr. Ziem who with her staff noticed several inconsistencies during the patients' extensive initial workups. Dr. Ziem's suspicions were confirmed by a colleague at the Mt. Sinai School of Medicine in New York City, who told MCS R&R that Stossel's assistant producer had disclosed the deception to him in the course of inquiring about Dr. Ziem's medical practice. 'That Mr. Stossel would send me phoney patients' said Dr. Ziem, 'reflects his chemical industry agenda to discredit the physical basis of MCS disorders, the suffering of MCS patients, and the efforts of physicians such as myself to diagnose and manage MCS disorders through the careful avoidance of aggravating chemical exposures and other medical treatments.'

Stossel brought Dr. Gots, who had been involved in a long-standing dispute with Albert Donnay, forward as a witness against

MCS and clinical ecology. Following the programme, Donnay accused Gots of failing to review any of the literature which disputed the contention that MCS has a psychological basis: 'It is really grossly misleading for Mr. Stossel to give credence to Dr. Gots' claim that MCS is either a psychogenic illness or an iatrogenic (doctor-induced) fear of chemicals.' Donnay pointed out that in an extensive bibliography on MCS, compiled by MCS Referral & Resources, the overwhelming majority of current peer-reviewed studies of MCS support a physical basis for the disorder.

Donnay also pointed out that although the programme cited Dr. Ronald Gots as 'a toxicology expert' who had 'worked for industry and government,' Gots was actually a pharmacologist with no formal training or certification in toxicology. Donnay brought up Gots' background as a witness for insurance and chemical companies. Stossel's programme also made use of Michael Fumento, introducing him as a researcher into MCS for twelve years, even though Fumento is simply a journalist.

In a document headed *16 Misleading Statements*, Donnay points out that Stossel had determinedly mixed up allergy with chemical sensitivity, suggesting that the programme was about 'people who say they are allergic to almost everything.'

Stossel had also characterised Ziem as a 'clinical ecologist' who was 'often in court,' and as a 'frequent witness in law suits.' Donnay pointed out that Dr. Ziem testifies in court less than once a year on average, and only in cases involving her own patients. In making Dr. Ziem out to be a charlatan, Stossel had described the bogus patients as being given only a brief physical examination and then a 16-page questionnaire to fill in. Donnay pointed out that like all new patients, the two 'actresses' were first asked to complete a questionnaire before being given a comprehensive physical examination, which in this instance lasted four hours.

During the programme, Stossel maintained that it was clinical ecologists who were putting the idea of sickness into the minds of patients and suggested that doctors like Dr. Ziem were making their patients sick through the power of suggestion. Donnay pointed out that while the view that physicians create fears of MCS in their patients are current amongst a small group of commentators, there is absolutely no published evidence to support such a claim.

As has happened in cases of propaganda programmes in Britain involving bogus patients, Dr. Ziem not only gave the patients a complete physical examination but also followed up the visit with a letter to both women telling them that they did not have MCS.

Caroline Richmond

Like Elaine Showalter, though in a different academic league, Caroline Richmond was for a number of years an acolyte of Dr. Wessely. Both women appear to be feminists who eschew any hint of class or political economy. Richmond was Britain's first 'health fraud' activist, styling herself on Elizabeth Whelan, the founder of ACSH.

In mid-eighties Britain, Caroline Richmond joined up with Dr. Wessely to successfully fuse two little known campaigns on the psychological cause of chemical sensitivity and the labelling of people with ME as psychologically ill. The objective which emerged from this union was to disassemble ME, making it appear to be an illusion conjured up by sufferers.

Caroline Richmond called the first meeting of the British Council Against Health Fraud in October 1988. In a preview of the Wessely-Showalter relationship, Richmond later put a *fin de siècle* spin on her campaigning in an interview with a journalist: 'My main problem was that there was a sort of anti-science feeling in the air which I suppose is what happens at the end of the century and I know people were being harmed.' She also suggested, some years after setting up the campaign, that her principal target had been clinical ecology.

Richmond's previous work uniquely fitted her for the role of 'health fraud' activist. After gaining a degree in Zoology and working in the laboratories at University College Hospital in London, Richmond did a number of laboratory jobs, including one at the Medical Research Council's Clinical Research Centre and the Department of Therapeutics at the City Hospital in Nottingham. In 1978, having decided to be a journalist, she went to United Trades Press (UTP), which produced a large number of trade magazines like: *Soap*, *Perfume and Cosmetics*, *Dairy Industries*, *Food Manufacturer*, and *Flavouring and Ingredients*. This job put Richmond in touch with many of the industry activists she was later to pull together in the Campaign Against Health Fraud.

In 1985, Richmond registered for an MPhil in the Department of History and Philosophy of Science at London University. The Unit of History of Medicine (UHM) where she took her course, was an Academic Unit of the Wellcome Institute, which at that time was a part of the Wellcome Trust, which gained its research money from the drug company the Wellcome Foundation. In 1985, the Wellcome Foundation and the Trust were, in conjunction with US subsidiary Burroughs Wellcome, beginning the marketing campaign for AZT.♦ Richmond herself was grant-aided by the Wellcome Trust from 1986 to 1988.

♦ During the AZT campaign, the century long relationship between the Wellcome Foundation and the Welcome Trust fell apart. A number of commentators were of the view that the dirty tricks used by the drug company were unacceptable to the more refined moneymen in charge of the Trust. The Trustees had to go to court to sever the two organisations, an act expressly against the wishes of Henry Wellcome's will.

SKEWED

Sir Walter Bodmer, at that time Head of Research at the Imperial Cancer Research Fund,♦ was one of Richmond's lecturers. Bodmer was also Chairman of the eight-person Committee on the Public Understanding of Science (COPUS), an influential and populist offshoot of the British Association for the Advancement of Science. Within two years of joining the Wellcome Institute, in 1987, Richmond was elected to COPUS, despite the fact that she was neither a clinician nor a practising scientist.

In August 1990, two years into running CAHF, Richmond was so well accepted within medical and scientific circles that she gave a scientific press briefing on Chronic Fatigue Syndrome as part of her role on the Press Briefing Committee of COPUS.

On December 12, 1985, a few months after beginning her MPhil, Richmond attended a press conference at the House of Commons held by the newly formed Food Additives Campaign Team (FACT), which was subsidised by the Greater London Council as part of its policy to provide a public service in relation to health and nutrition.

The FACT team included Geoffrey Cannon, a renowned nutritionist, his partner Caroline Walker and Dr. Peter Mansfield. The press conference was called to launch the publication *Additives – Your Complete Survival Guide*. As well as support and affiliation from a large number of reputable organisations, the group had cross-party support in the Commons. FACT considered its principal

---

♦ Bodmer was involved in setting up the bogus research which suggested that women who went to Bristol Cancer Help Centre were three times more likely to die of cancer than those who didn't go. This project also involved member of the Campaign Against Health Fraud. Since then he has been a member of the General Motors panel which gives cancer research awards, along with Sir Richard Doll and Hans-Olov Adami, both of whom are industry-supportive epidemiologists. He has also been a member with Sir Richard Doll of the review body, which has concluded that electromagnetic fields do not cause cancer.

opposition came from the Ministry of Agriculture, Fisheries and Food (MAFF), which had frequently used threats of the Official Secrets Act to stifle debate about the substances added to foods.

Members of FACT were surprised when they read Caroline Richmond's report of their press conference, which was not only slighting in its tone – 'The press conference was great fun' – but dismissive of both FACT and any adverse effect of food additives. She had, she said later, written the piece after being assured by MAFF 'that food additives are probably harmless, have been screened, and are continually being monitored by government scientists world-wide.' From the time of the FACT conference, this superficial approach to health risk and the chemical industry, together with a sometimes slighting personal tone, became the hallmark of much of Richmond's writing.♦

A summary of her arguments in the mid-1980s provides an understanding of the developing approaches of the 'health fraud' activists and greenwashers – hyperactive children and others who complain of being affected by chemicals, her arguments go, rarely have any kind of chemical-related condition. Children who are hyperactive sometimes have serious psychiatric disturbances. Parents of hyperactive children are often to blame for their children's condition because they allow them too much time in pushchairs and in front of the television. Self-help groups, organised by parents and concerned individuals, only make things worse; doctors and other professionals in state agencies like MAFF know best and parents should accept their views. The inquiring press is also to blame,

---

♦ Richmond made one of her well-known infamous remarks at this Royal Society of Health meeting. After seeing a newspaper photograph of an ailing Caroline Walker, Richmond told Geoffrey Cannon, Walker's partner, that she was a poor advertisement for Cannon's ideas about nutrition. Caroline Walker died tragically young two years later after a battle against cancer. Other information about Richmond can be found in the author's *Dirty Medicine: Science, big business and the assault on natural health care*, Slingshot Publications, London 1993.

because journalists often exploit the vulnerability of depressed people by whipping up scares about such things as allergies. Fringe concern, outside the main establishment opinion, about such things as additives usually comes from unreasonable people best called 'health freaks.'

These arguments provided a template for the arguments that were to be prominent over the next ten years: the same stories were used over and over again, substituting only the type of chemical and the type of health concern. In December 1987, the *BMJ* gave Richmond space to attack those who believed in alternative treatments and diagnostic techniques not accepted by orthodox medicine.♦ In the issue of December 19, she was given over a page to describe a CSICOP-style hoax which she played on a woman campaigning on behalf of allergy sufferers.

When Mrs. Amelia Hill of Action Against Allergy received the manifesto of a new allergy campaigning organisation, the Dye Related Allergies Bureau (DRAB), she advertised the organisation in her quarterly bulletin. A small number of allergy sufferers from different parts of the world wrote to DRAB asking for more information. These people did not receive a reply; in fact the address given to Hill and reproduced in her newsletter belonged to personal friends of Richmond.

As Richmond explained in a later issue of the *BMJ*, it had all been a set-up to show how silly were those who thought that industrial or chemical processes caused allergies. 'I wrote the manifesto for the Dye Related Allergy Bureau (DRAB) as a spoof on the literature put out by those who wish to protect us from food additives, fluoridation in drinking water and the like.' It is difficult to believe that the *British Medical Journal* did not know the scurrilous purpose of this article.

♦ For another strange link between Richmond and the *BMJ*, see page 248.

The Public Health Revisionists

In articles written by Caroline Richmond prior to the setting up of CAHF, she names a number of the individuals whom the organisation was to target in 1989. In 1987 she promoted the joint British Nutrition Foundation and Royal College of Physicians' (BNF/RCP) report on food intolerance, taking the opportunity of the launch of the food-industry-compiled allergy database to target allergy sufferers.

> However, many adults who read bizarre books bought in health food stores and elsewhere have often been persuaded that everyday annoyances such as bad memory, headaches and irascibility are caused by foods. They often stop eating certain foods and do not realise that any perceived improvement is almost certainly a placebo effect.

For her 'expert' opinions in the article, Caroline Richmond drew on a variety of people who were, a year and a half later, to form the backbone of the Campaign Against Health Fraud. One of these was Dr. David Pearson, who pursued his often-repeated view that most people who think that they are suffering from food allergy actually have a psychological problem: 'Most people who present themselves to allergy clinics *believing* they are suffering from food allergy are wrong.'

Professor Maurice Lessof, the man who chaired the joint BNF/RCP committee, and whose research had often been subsidised by food and chemical companies, provided Richmond with a quote which turned clinical experience and good sense on its head: 'More problems are now caused by the improper use of diets than by food allergy.'

Dr. Tim David enlarges upon Richmond's argument that parents and not chemicals are mainly to blame.

> The relationship between azo dyes and so-called 'hyper-activity' is almost certainly a myth, nurtured by health food magazines and newspaper articles. Manchester paediatric consultant Dr. Tim David says that most parent-diagnosed 'hyperactive' children are not; they are simply more energetic than their parents would like.

Summing up her arguments, Richmond suggested that a vicious circle is created by 'fringe practitioners using absurd tests' who over-diagnose and convince people that they have illusory allergies. In turn, these badly misled patients 'raise NHS bills even further by presenting themselves as allergy patients.'

These 'template' arguments, or as Americans call them 'cookie cutter arguments,' are identical to those used by the chemical companies against MCS and similar to those used by Wessely to dispute the physical existence of ME and CFS. The argument that patients should not be given tests which encourage them to believe they have physical illnesses is particularly relevant today when psychiatrists are arguing that to test people for ME or CFS only encourages their wrong belief that they are ill.

CASE HISTORY THREE

An insurance company gets expert advice

Until ten years ago, John Hill was a physically strong man, with a personality to match. A carpenter and joiner who had served a six-year apprenticeship, as was the practice in the 1950s, he was an honest and hard working family man with a great sense of humour. To John, carpentry was not only a job, it was something for which he had a passion; the family home is full of beautiful pieces of furniture.

One day, in the early nineties, John took a job building a piggery and repairing and maintaining the property of a local farm. After a time, the farmer asked John to help run the grain dryer.

An organophosphate was used for the first time on the farm, initially in the grain dryer. John became involved in diluting the pesticide, filling a tank with it and then filling a spraying unit. John carried the mixture in open buckets across the farmyard, filling the tank as the grain went through the dryer.

John walked with a limp because of a childhood hip condition, consequently he often spilled the pesticide down his clothes, in which he continued to work. The failure of his employer to properly inform him about the chemicals he was using or provide him with personal protective equipment resulted in the organophosphate mixture being inhaled and soaking into his skin on a daily basis. John worked in these conditions from June to September. After a while, when he returned home, he began complaining of feeling unwell and suffered faintness and breathlessness.

John's condition gradually became worse until he found himself collapsing at work, passing out for indefinite periods, often until his workmates found him. Because of the severity of his symptoms, John eventually had to stop working. He has not been well enough to work since, a difficult situation for a family man who had worked consistently since the age of fifteen.

Following his exposure to organophosphate, John became clinically depressed, paranoid, forgetful and aggressive; he would disappear for hours at a time without letting anyone know where he was, sometimes during the night. He developed a deep sense of paranoia and confusion about everyday life; these feeling were exacerbated by long periods of insomnia.

Physically, John was left with severe bouts of diarrhoea and incontinence, suffering shortness of breath and dizziness. He lost the sensation in his extremities, his feet felt like sponges when he walked and he lost the sense of touch in his hands. These symptoms and others were accompanied by rapid weight loss.

John had many appointments with his local GP, who eventually diagnosed 'farmer's lung,' a condition with no cure. As a lay person without a medical background, John's wife was at a loss to know how to help him or how to cope with his worsening mental health problems. Eventually, at the end of her tether, she insisted on a referral to a psychiatrist, who prescribed antidepressants.

John's symptoms persisted and he and his wife embarked upon a civil action against his employer to gain compensation. During this period of diagnosis and the subsequent court case, John visited the Poisons Unit of a nearby Birmingham hospital to see a neurologist and psychiatrist and attended at hospitals in Peterborough, Glasgow, London, Taunton, Southampton and Newcastle. John was tested for a variety of symptoms and given numerous explanations; many of the tests were extremely unpleasant and even painful. It was, however, difficult to get a medical diagnosis which put the blame for his condition on OPs.

John's prognosis caused concern within various organisations. He spent hours with the Health and Safety Executive – firstly the Medical Executive and then the Legal Executive. Finally, the HSE suggested that John needed a solicitor and they began legal proceedings against his former employer to determine liability. The employer was found guilty on three counts of negligence. Following this decision, John and his wife took their civil action against his employer to court.

From this point onwards their lives became traumatic. They were expected to travel the length and breadth of the country at a day's notice so that John might be examined by numerous doctors for the National Farmers Union's insurance company. For every examination for the defence, a comparable examination was undertaken for John's representatives. This procedure was coupled with many appointments with solicitors and legal representatives. This investigation into his case, culminated in a five-week court case at the High Court in London.

During the court case all the medical opinion seemed to agree that John had a physiological illness and that the symptoms were not of psychological origin. The general medical conclusion was that John had suffered exposure to organophosphate pesticide. One specialist, Professor Swash, who appeared for the defendants, disagreed with this evidence, intimating that John might be a malingerer. Some time was taken up during the court case, trying to establish what a malingerer was in the context of the case and whether or not Professor Swash had actually meant that John Hill was deliberately misleading doctors by making up symptoms. Swash went to some lengths to suggest that it was very difficult to tell in such cases whether the claimant was making up symptoms or whether the symptoms were psychosomatic. Adopting a Wesselyite approach Swash took some of the responsibility off Hill, telling the court that he was probably repeating what he thought was expected of him after a number of doctors had told him that he was suffering from OP poisoning.[18]

John won his civil action and he remains the only person in Britain to win a civil action for health damage caused by OPs. Five years since the court case and ten years on from the exposure, however, John's health has further deteriorated. He still has little or no feeling in his hands or feet and a triple heart by-pass has not improved his blood circulation. These symptoms suggest the onset of non-Hodgkin's lymphoma – a disease which doctors suggested might be John's final prognosis. He still has restless nights, breathlessness, overwhelming bouts of tiredness, memory problems and struggles with simple calculations and spelling; he can only walk a few steps with the aid of a walking stick and relies heavily on a wheelchair to maintain independence.

Despite these almost overwhelming problems, John retains a positive outlook on life. His sense of humour remains intact and he takes each day at a time.

---

18 Prof. Michael Swash MD, FRCP, FRCPATH, is one of Britain's most esteemed neurologists, whose area of expertise is multiple sclerosis. He is a staff member at the GKT (King's College London) Centre for Neuroscience Research. Other colleagues in the Centre's Group are Prof. Simon Wessely and Prof. Anthony David. In October 2002, Prof. Swash gave an Oxford Clinical Neuroscience Lecture at Witts Lecture Theatre in the Radcliffe Infirmary, entitled *Hysteria, Simulation, and Malingering*.

CHAPTER FOUR

Myalgic Encephalomyelitis: A Disposable Illness

There is a growing public awareness that medical experts can and do disagree, that they are not infallible by virtue of their special access to some rigorous scientific testing process, that their 'objectivity' is not guaranteed . . . and that non-technical and political assumptions influence their advice and decisions.[19]

Like every doctor who had served in the Forces, Henderson had experience in plenty of malingering; just as in private practice he came across countless cases of psychosomatic illness produced by an inability to face some difficult situation.[20]

In the nineteen eighties it was difficult to understand why 'health fraud' activists spent so much time attacking allergy practitioners, retrospectively it seems relatively straightforward. Increasing levels of allergy appeared to be related to the increased use of chemicals in food and everyday ambient toxins; it was allergists who were moving into the new field of chemical sensitivity. In Britain, those who were to become members of the Campaign Against Health Fraud began campaigns against the idea of allergy, against patients who complained of allergy and most particularly against therapists and doctors who were diagnosing and treating allergy.

---

19 Evelleen Richards, *Vitamin C and Cancer: Medicine or Politics?*, MacMillan 1991.

20 The Ballad of the Running Man, Shelley Smith, Harper and Row, New York, 1961.

The way 'health fraud' activists explained these attacks on allergy practitioners and others was to suggest that clinical ecologists were turning allergy medicine into a business, expanding its scope out of all proportion to the numbers of people who they considered were sufferers.[21] As always with the 'health fraud' movement, this argument turned reality on its head: it was actually the chemical and drug companies which were really increasing the levels of sickness in society. Orthodox medicine, however, was not about to admit to the cause or find treatments for this increase.

It was strategically important to the 'health fraud' movement to deny the existence of increasing allergy because this condition and those practitioners who treated it were the key to other conditions like chemical sensitivity, which the movement did not want to include in their clinical canon.

Throughout the 1980s and 1990s, clinical and scientific work showed that many of the people diagnosed with MCS, ME and CFS also had a history of problems with allergy. In 1986, at a time when it was thought that all ME/CFS patients were affected by the Epstein Barr virus, G. B. Olsen and J. F. Jones concluded that 'eighty percent of [ME/ CFS] patients demonstrate clinically significant IgE mediated allergic disease, including . . . food and drug reactions.' Their work indicated that patients had '. . . a high association with hypersensitivity states . . . percent positive responsiveness to allergens is consistent with the high degrees of allergy observed in these patients.'

Even the most orthodox of researchers, who essentially believed in a psychological aetiology for CFS, like Stephen Straus in America, were arguing in 1988 that there was a correlation between food

---

21 The latest (June 2003) information on allergy comes from the Royal College of Physicians Working Party, chaired by Professor Stephen Holgate, in *Allergy: The Unmet Need*. This report not only says that the NHS 'is failing to meet the most minimal standards of care,' but also that one in three people now suffer from allergy and about 12 million people in Britain are likely to be seeking treatment.

intolerance or allergy and ME/CFS: 'Many patients report inhalant, food or drug allergies. Allergies are a common feature of patients with the Chronic Fatigue Syndrome. Among the features of this syndrome is a high prevalence of allergy, an allergy that appears to be substantial.'

In 1991, Straus made the position absolutely clear: 'There is little doubt that classic allergy and atopy are inexplicably prevalent in CFS. In a recent study, a high proportion of patients with CFS were found to be reactive to a variety of inhalant or food allergens when inoculated epicutaneously in the classic manner.'

In 1992, W. K. Cho and G. H. Stollerman remarked that classic immune responses to food might create a failing immune system response in people who have CFS: 'The immune reaction may not be stoppable even after an insult is over.' Amongst many evidenced scientific statements, in September 1996, the US National Institute of Allergy and Infectious Diseases at the National Institutes of Health issued a statement about drug sensitivities and CFS: 'Many CFS patients . . . report . . . the onset of new allergies after becoming ill with CFS. Allergies are common in people with CFS . . . the high prevalence of allergies in the CFS population . . . many patients are extremely sensitive to these drugs.'

Despite the clinical science, or perhaps because of it, British and North American 'health fraud' activists ploughed on campaigning against the growing number of practitioners who diagnosed allergy. If their argument was going to be that ME and CFS were all in the mind, they had better begin at the beginning and also brand food intolerance and allergy as psychological illnesses. And, anyway, the multinational food companies which consumed mountains of chemicals in colourings and additives had, like the pharmaceutical companies, to be defended.

Throughout the late 1980s, the Campaign Against Health Fraud (CAHF) consistently attempted to de-rail the mounting clinical opinions about allergy.♦ Dr. David Pearson, who became one of the most determined anti-clinical ecologist members of CAHF, had spent a number of years working in occupational health in America, an area that was a cauldron for anti-environmental thinking. Pearson was publishing papers as early as 1983, which purported to show that allergies were not real organic phenomena but had a psychiatric aetiology. Pearson and psychiatrist colleagues performed challenge tests on individuals who claimed to suffer from allergies, subjecting them to testing with quantities of food additives or chemicals. According to Pearson, only 5 out of the 35 patients claiming allergy produced reproducible symptoms in a double blind test.

Caroline Richmond herself wrote frequently about the psychiatric aetiology of food intolerance, allergy and ME. On a number of occasions, she obscured the nature of chemical sensitivity by confusing it with allergy '. . . total allergy syndrome, and allergy to the twentieth century, will soon be out of style, replaced by twenty first century disease. The attraction of allergy to the hypochondriac is its personal uniqueness: if I say I've got an allergy you can't say I haven't, whatever your private opinion may be.'

What is ME?

The symptomatic picture for ME closely resembles, and indeed overlaps with that of multiple chemical sensitivity, and because many people who developed ME or fatigue related illnesses also had allergic reactions they have often sought help from alternative and complementary practitioners. From the moment of this liaison between ME sufferers, clinical ecologists and chemical sensitivity, ME patients fell into a war zone.

♦ It is now accepted that by a number of indicators, the United Kingdom has one of the highest levels of allergic reaction in the world (*Allergy, the Unmet Need*, Royal College of Physicians, 2003.)

Myalgic Encephalomyelitis: A Disposable Illness

However, while the struggle around MCS and allergy was relatively covert, a secret war within medicine so to speak, the war which developed over ME and then Chronic Fatigue Syndrome, with its accusations of mental illness from psychiatrists and angry counter-offensives from sufferers, was to be fully and publicly declared.

ME was formally classified as a disease of the nervous system in the World Health Organization International Classification of Diseases 8 (ICD 8), approved in 1965 and published in 1969. It is listed by the WHO both in the tabular list and in the Code Index. ME continued to be classified as a disease of the nervous system in ICD 9, approved in 1975 and published in 1979, again both in the tabular list and in the Code Index. Finally, ME continues to be listed as a neurological disorder in the ICD 10. The WHO has said that there are no plans to reclassify ME in the psychiatric section in the next ICD revision (10.2), due in 2003.

ME and many fatigue disorders ♦ both have features of auto-immune disorder, features of allergy and multiple chemical sensitivity, which is now officially recognised in the International Classification of Diseases. Data presented at the American Association for Chronic Fatigue Syndrome (AACFS) Fifth International Research and Clinical Conference in Seattle in January 2001, showed that MCS was present in 42.6% of ME/CFS patients compared with 3.8% of controls.

Recent papers have demonstrated that the RNase L antiviral pathway is dysfunctional in ME/CFS, and it has been shown that chemicals also affect this same pathway; in other words, ME/CFS can be either virally or chemically induced. Researchers in the US have also suggested that the huge increase in chemical use can chronically depress the immune system, resulting in diseases such as ME/CFS.

♦ Although the term ME/CFS is often used in this section, CFS actually includes many unidentifiable and different subsets.

SKEWED

Recent studies have demonstrated circulating plasma RNA in Gulf War Syndrome. At the AACFS Conference a study was presented which had been conducted to determine the presence or absence of RNA in ME/CFS patients and to determine if the amplified sequences of RNA were similar to or different from those found in Gulf War Syndrome. All chronic illnesses studied (including Gulf War Syndrome, CFS/ME, AIDS and multiple myeloma) show prominent RNA not observed in normal controls.

There is an increasing literature on the issue of ME/CFS being frequently diagnosed as multiple sclerosis; as recently as August 2001 one paper listed the similarity of signs and symptoms (numbering 28) and discussed the similarities of magnetic resonance imaging (MRI) scans in ME/CFS.

Despite the constant reporting of ME as a physical and organic illness, 'health fraud' activists and greenwashers have refused to drop their insistence that patients *only think that they have* ME and are actually suffering from a functional somatic or psychiatric disorder.

Dr. N. Afari, Associate Director of the University of Washington's CFS Research Center, stated that the disorder appeared to be increasing, and that genetic abnormalities may team up with environmental influences to produce ME/CFS, and that environmental influences which researchers are investigating include the frequent pairing of ME/CFS with food and chemical sensitivities.

In April 1994, UNUM, one of the largest disability insurers in the United States, reported that in the five years from 1989-1993, men's disability claims for CFS increased by 360%, whilst women's claims for CFS increased 557%. No other disease category equalled these rates of increase. In order of insurance costs, CFS/ME came second in the list of the five most expensive chronic conditions, being three places above AIDS.

Changing language

MCS represents a real contemporary problem to chemical companies, the medical profession and the industrial military complex. As far back as the 1960s, however, the increasing advent of ME and Chronic Fatigue illnesses, the origins of which were not understood and for which there were no treatments, also represented a political and financial disaster in the making.

Anyone versed in politics knows that one of the most certain strategies for controlling and discomforting a colonised enemy is to banish indigenous languages and enforce upon the people an alien language. Failing that, social and political cohesion might be eroded by introducing the language of the colonisers to the most important social, cultural and geographic landmarks.

In North America in the 1980s, a serious and apparently post-viral fatigue illness that resembled ME was first noted in a community on the banks of Lake Tahoe in Nevada.[22] The illness usually developed in people who had first become ill with a cold or flu, and because many of the sufferers tested positive for the Epstein Barr virus, it was first called Chronic Epstein Barr Syndrome. Soon, however, it began increasingly to be reported in differing areas amongst men and women of different social classes.

Three years after the beginning of the epidemic, which was to affect hundreds of thousands of Americans, doctors, scientists, the Centers for Disease Control (CDC) and the American health insurance industry recognised that the name that they gave to the illness was very important. If the name was specific, clearly linked to a viral, post-viral or even chemical cause, then the insurance companies could face meltdown and the medical profession would have

---

22 Hillary Johnson, *Osler's Web, Inside the Labyrinth of the Chronic Fatigue Syndrome Epidemic*, Crown Publishers Inc. (Random House), New York 1996.

another AIDS scenario on its hands. A generally named illness, on the other hand, officially without a specific cause, would pose less of an economic threat.

In the United States in 1988 (coincidentally the year that the Campaign Against Health Fraud was set up in England), an eighteen-strong panel of medical scientists and clinicians, charged with formulating a new case definition and new name for the illness that originated at Lake Tahoe, failed to agree. Two of the most clinically experienced members♦ refused to sign a final document and withdrew from the panel because the proposed definition and new name were too different from the historical cases of ME with which they were familiar.

The final statement of Holmes et al re-defined ME, the Lake Tahoe illness, together with a number of other fatigue states, as Chronic Fatigue Syndrome. This new definition was perfect for the insurance companies but from this point onwards, those who had the serious and debilitating illness known as ME were lost, as were the origins and causes of their illness. The North American Centers for Disease Control and the medical insurance industry had escaped from having to acknowledge the serious nature of an increasingly reported and specific disorder, together with the consequent need to supply a treatment for it. Under cover of the most ubiquitous term 'fatigue', they had wiped out an illness by classifying a symptom.

Three years after the North American announcement, at a meeting in Oxford, an unaccountable group of Wessely school supporters adopted the new US definition for Britain, adapting it slightly to define a psychiatric illness of which on-going fatigue was a prominent symptom. Twenty six medical scientists and clinicians,

---

♦ The two members were Dr. Alexis Shelokov (USA) and Dr. Gordon Parish (UK). Dr. Parish is the custodian of possibly the world's largest reference library of the pre-1988 literature on ME, known as the Ramsay Archive, which is now housed in Scotland.

nine of whom were members of the Wessely School, including Wessely himself, and two of whom were leading members of the Campaign Against Health Fraud (Dr. Wessely and Dr. David Pearson), signed the paper that changed the name of ME in England.

By subsuming ME into the general term of Chronic Fatigue, in three years, the psychiatric establishment led by an Anglo American group which included Professor Wessely, had dispossessed a large number of people not only of their illness but also of any benefits, specific treatments or insurance cover which had previously been due to them. From 1991 onwards, anyone in Britain who developed a seriously debilitating post-viral illness would suffer an invalidated illness to be deemed a product of psychiatric disorder, the primary symptom of which, according to the Oxford criteria, was simply 'fatigue' and was specifically devoid of any '. . . *clinical signs characteristic of the condition.'*

Following the 1988 Holmes et al definition and the 1991 Oxford definition, in 1994 the US CDC produced a revised case definition – known as the Fukuda criteria –, which emphasised unequivocally that there should be no physical signs present, stating: 'The revised case definition for the chronic fatigue syndrome is modelled on the 1988 chronic fatigue syndrome working case definition. We drop-ped all physical signs from our inclusion criteria (and) we agreed that multiple symptoms criteria increased the restrictiveness of the 1988 definition. Whether to retain any symptom criteria other than chronic fatigue generated the most disagreement among the authors.'♦ The point of not including physical symptoms was ob-

---

♦ *The Chronic Fatigue Syndrome: A Comprehensive Approach to Its Definition and Study.* Keiji Fukuda et al. *Ann Intern Med* 1994:121:953-959. Michael Sharpe was one of the named authors and Simon Wessely was the named adviser / representative from the UK, being a member of The International Chronic Fatigue Syndrome Study Group of the National Institutes of Health, Bethesda, Maryland, under whose auspices the Fukuda criteria were produced.

viously to keep all references for the illness away from physical realities and body states which might be clinically tested. CFS was to be an amorphous fatigue illness with fairly obvious psychological markers. It is clear that these new definitions only applied to chronic fatigue, because ME *always* had physical signs; both observable by doctors and experienced as symptoms by patients. Critics of the psychiatric aetiology see this as yet another part of the subterfuge paving the way for the elimination of ME and re-classifying it subsummed within CFS as a psychiatric disorder.

From 1994 onwards, it would suit a number of doctors and psychiatrists to argue that there should be no complex diagnostic tests given to people who reported to their doctors with 'fatigue', once they had been primarily investigated and it was established that they had 'CFS'.

Nothing could have more seriously hampered research into ME and the group of illnesses which became CFS than the change of name. Suddenly *all* illnesses which had fatigue as a component were thrown together. The first US definition of CFS expediently concentrated on 'fatigue' as the primary symptom occurring as a post-viral effect and persisting for at least six months, with a sore throat and tender lymph glands in the neck. This undifferentiated label represented so many sub-groups as to make research into cause, diagnosis and treatment of any subset a sheer impossibility.

Within a short time of the re-classification of ME, the voluntary agencies and the charities that dealt with ME sufferers were inundated with new members who were suffering from a wide range and different levels of tiredness-linked illnesses. This had two immediate consequences; first, the most chronically ill ME sufferers were pushed from the central focus of campaigns by more able bodied 'fatigue' sufferers; secondly, by changing the name of the illness and thereby enrolling a greater number of affected individuals, the research waters became impossibly muddied and full of people whose illness had different causes, different symptoms and a variety of outcomes.

Those who had ME and believed it was a singular physical illness thought that there should be a more rigorous definition, not a broadening of the illness criteria. New definitions, they said, should have been based upon a pattern of core symptoms and upon observable physical signs, which, however discrete, are invariably present. This was not at all what the psychiatric school wanted; they preferred to obfuscate the symptomatology, bringing everyone together under the banner of 'somatization disorder.' Once this broad category had been defined and achieved, there would be no need for further tests or clinical analysis: anyone who complained of chronic fatigue lasting more than six months could automatically be given graded exercise therapy, cognitive behavioural therapy and antidepressants.

The 1994 definition of Chronic Fatigue Syndrome made it inevitable that the illness meant different things to different people. To the majority of researchers and scientists in North America, it means the organic illness which was first recognised in 1985 and now affects upwards of 2 million Americans. To a small minority of 'health fraud' activists and greenwashers in the US and Britain, CFS has a psychiatric origin and includes the British disease ME which they claimed did not exist independently.

During the summer of 2000, the US Department of Health and Human Services (DHHS) Chronic Fatigue Syndrome Co-ordinating Committee appointed a Name Change Workgroup to consider a name other than CFS, on the basis that it is necessary to have a name which more accurately reflected both the severity of the disease and the organ systems affected by it. This move came about because even the DHHS realised that this broad semantic categorisation included illnesses which demonstrated dysfunction in the neurological, neuro-endocrine and immunological systems.

SKEWED

The lack of scientific definition, especially for research purposes, is clearly stated in a 2001 article in the *Annals of Internal Medicine*: 'Most studies are limited by methodological problems such as case definition and the selection and recruitment of case-patients and controls.'

The drive against science, implicit in the nomenclature debate, did not stop in 1994. In a 1999 *Lancet* article by Prof. Wessely and Dr. Sharpe, it was argued that having reviewed the literature on syndromes such as irritable bowel syndrome, Chronic Fatigue Syndrome, pre-menstrual tension syndrome, fibromyalgia, temporomandibular joint pain, tension headaches, atypical chest pain, multiple chemical sensitivity and globus hystericus, the authors concluded that the similarities between all these syndromes outweigh the differences. Sharpe and Wessely claimed that all such disorders were psychiatric in origin and that they should all be defined in one diagnostic category as 'functional somatic syndrome.' Were this suggestion to be adopted, ME, and as importantly MCS, would both dissapear, defined finally as states no different from pre-menstrual tension.

The Wessely school, which had started out ten years previously with seemingly confused and marginal objectives focused on allergy and ME , had by the mid 1990s almost managed to change reality to fit its own philosophy. Despite having virtually obliterated ME, Wessely, particularly, took every opportunity to continue hammering nails in the coffin. Behind the attempts to impose a hysterical and Victorian history upon ME, is a continued attempt to further diminish the recognition of ME, even historically, as a real physical illness. In 1993, Wessely pointed out that 'Neurasthenia would readily suffice for M.E.' Psychiatrist Ian Hickie in Australia and others in North America would also be happy with this definition. Such a change would leave no lingering evidence of ME as a physical illness and would further transfer treatment of an illness suffered by millions entirely into the hands of psychiatrists.

Myalgic Encephalomyelitis: A Disposable Illness

Despite the name change from ME to CFS, the psychiatric lobby has still had serious difficulties in completely obliterating ME. Sufferers, obviously, and those who know that it is a recognised illness, and especially that 25% of chronic sufferers, continue to use its proper name. Dr. Charles Shepherd, the Medical Director of the UK ME Association and member of HealthWatch, tried to explain the subterranean life of the nomenclature in an interview in the magazine *Top Santé*. Asked 'Is ME the same as Chronic Fatigue Syndrome (CFS)?' he replied 'Yes, but patients prefer the term myalgic encephalomyelitis (ME) because it sounds serious.'

Changing reality

In order to re-distribute power or change social meaning, it is not enough to simply change the names of things or even change the language; you have to condition subjects into accepting the reality of the changed situation. You also have to police the continued use of newly imposed definitions. How would 'health fraud' activists and greenwashers enforce their new definitions? In North America, from the time of the consensus statement on CFS in 1988, sufferers from the illness were increasingly denied treatment or even a sympathetic hearing from their doctors.

Caroline Richmond and Simon Wessely appear to have been knowledgeable about the game plan from at least 1985. As early as that, they were determined to argue, despite the emerging clinical evidence, that ME had no organic basis and that sufferers were simply malingerers. When Wessely published articles in the mainstream medical journals on ME/CFS claiming psychiatric attributions, Caroline Richmond gave them maximum publicity in the medical trade papers.

In the November 1988 issue of *GP*, Richmond reiterated her theory that many people who visit their doctors do not have physical symptoms, or at least do not have physical symptoms which doctors recognise.

SKEWED

Patients who have physical symptoms with no organic cause (somatisers) have always been with us, but recent years have seen a new boom in allergy to the twentieth century. Then it was food allergy. In the 1980s it has been Candida Albicans sensitivity, hyperactivity (in children, but it is the mother who complains), severe pre-menstrual syndrome, myalgic encephalomyelitis, and vitamin and mineral deficiency.

It is only those who are 'chronic somatisers' who 'embrace each newly described disease of fashion as the answer to their long-standing, multiple, undiagnosed complaints.'

Dr. Stewart, a Toronto psychiatric researcher quoted by Richmond in this article, suggests that patients who present with symptoms that have no apparent physical basis should be humoured. 'Each patient needs to be convinced that his or her symptoms are being taken seriously. A balance must be drawn between making the appropriate investigations while avoiding over-investigation.' Most effective, the psychiatrist maintains, is 'psychotherapy, with anti-depressants if necessary, or tranquillisers.' Whatever happens to such patients, they must not be sent to alternative practitioners. 'The GP is an ideal person to manage patients with environmental hyper-sensitivity as he or she can reduce repeated investigations and con-sultations with multiple specialists.'

One of the illnesses which Richmond was determined had no organic base was ME. In the May 1989 issue of the *BMJ*, Richmond wrote one of her many articles about ME. The article gives intellect-ual gloss to her belief that not only is there a series of non-organic illnesses which go through cyclical fashions and which have hist-orical counterparts, it also allows her to give symptomatic pictures for a series of illnesses which she says have no physical basis. Fol-lowing this article, the *BMJ* received 43 letters all expressing great-er or lesser disgust with the inferences which Richmond drew. Two of the letters were printed.

Myalgic Encephalomyelitis: A Disposable Illness

Little more than 70 years, [after the first world war] and with the advance and development of psychology in medicine, patients with chronic health problems are often told that they are opting out or avoiding work and that they are suffering from personality disorders rather than organic illness . . . People . . . are virtually put on trial because they have presented with certain symptoms, and they must then try and justify that they are sane, that they are not trying to upset the state economy by giving up their jobs, and that they do not have shady and ulterior motives for being ill, or stand to gain by their illness.

* * *

. . . this should not obscure the fact that ME is a serious illness in which immunological abnormalities such as deficiency of T cell subsets which are increasingly being shown . . . There is no doubt that ME sometimes behaves like multiple sclerosis, a disease which also has no specific diagnostic test. No one would dream of saying that patients with multiple sclerosis were suffering from 'the vapours' or a 'wandering womb.'

Like Wessely, Shaus, Shorter and Showalter, Richmond has often presented an off-the-cuff historical analysis of ME and CFS. She gives no substantial references for this socio-cultural mish-mash but expects readers to simply agree with her that descriptions of nine-teenth century women's hysteria were the same as contemporary reports of ME and CFS:

Myalgic encephalomyelitis is a new name for an old disease . . . it's a British disease, unknown in the new world . . . The dedicated hypochondriac . . . scenting a new career as a patient . . . wants to see the 'top man' on the subject . . . Hysteria was originally a disease of spinsters, whose dry wombs wandered round their bodies in search of moisture. Then, as now, ladies suffering from the vapours retired to their boudoirs. Taken from the French verb **bouder**, to sulk, a boudoir is a lady's sulking room. The illness behaviour of patients and the diagnostic behaviour of doctors are susceptible to fashion, and they are a part of it . . . neurasthenia, melancholy, the vapours . . . now they have lost their organic associations and imply states of personality or mind. Will the same thing happen to . . . total allergy syndrome [and] myalgic encephalomyelitis?

SKEWED

Although not a doctor or clinical researcher, Richmond is quick to make erroneous and unsupported observations about ME and CFS patients:

> There is no evidence to suggest that ME patients are immunocompromised and they don't succumb to more infections than other people, although they are more likely to regard them as life events . . . many patients have succeeded in getting disability pensions . . . Advice should be given to enable them to cope with their symptoms, gradually increase exercise tolerance and return to normality.

> Many patients arrive in the consulting room with a firm attachment to a dramatic diagnosis made, not by a neurologist or a virologist, but by themselves . . . many patients have . . . read some ill thought out advice leaflets . . . Fortunately this deadlock has now been broken by two recent papers which argue for a . . . more constructive approach.

In the last quote, Richmond was promoting Wessely's most contemporary paper, *Postviral fatigue syndrome: time for a new approach*, in the *BMJ*.

Richmond's writing is difficult to take seriously because it is completely lacking in academic *élan*. Such writing, however, serves a purpose in stoking the fires of populism and circulating ideas that resonate long afterwards in the reader's mind. So it was that throughout the 1980s and 1990s, in the minds of the public, chemical sensitivity, clinical ecology, ME and Chronic Fatigue all became associated generally with slightly lunatic ideas, held by medical fraudsters, charlatans and the mentally ill:

> Myalgic encephalomyeltitis . . . sounds really serious and is guaranteed to impress the friends and relatives of sufferers . . . None of them seemed to find it remarkable that they are suffering from a disease called '<u>me</u>'.

In her book *Hystories*, Elaine Showalter attacks CFS just as Richmond had attacked ME, regardless of the name and definition which had taken place between 1988 and 1994. An example of Showalter's bias can be seen in a reference to Dr. David Bell's book, *Doctor's Guide to Chronic Fatigue Syndrome.*[23] While re-telling Wessely's fiction about the similarity between contemporary CFS, in this instance the Lake Tahoe outbreak, and the nineteenth century diagnosis of neurasthenia, Showalter cited Bell's list of 43 symptoms found with varying consistency in CFS patients. This single-sentence quote was followed by the statement that 'Like CFS, neurasthenia is most commonly seen among the upper social classes . . . it came from the stresses and pace of urban American life . . .' Bell's book, however, told the story of an outbreak in upper New York State among rural residents of both genders, all age groups and, if anything, slightly below average median incomes.

Stephen Barrett's North American Quackwatch organisation also takes every opportunity to make the point that ME and CFS are psychiatric conditions. Like Caroline Richmond in England, and other British 'health fraud' activists, Barrett sees the arguments around ME and CFS as part and parcel of the arguments around Multiple Chemical Sensitivity, in that sufferers are all, in fact, suffering from psychiatric conditions. Patients have arrived at their beliefs, Barrett argues, being led on by both clinical ecologists and the media.

Psychiatric treatments for psychiatric illnesses

A number of things are implicit in the idea that Chronic Fatigue Syndrome is more imagined than real; not only that the cause of the illness does not have to be explored but that treatment, whether or not it leads to 'a cure', could be simple and inexpensive. The psyc-

---

23 David Bell, *The Doctor's Guide to Chronic Fatigue Syndrome: Understanding, Treating and Living with CFIDS.* Addison-Wesley (USA), 1994; also as a paperback, Perseus (USA) 1995.

hiatrically based treatments for people presenting with ME and other illnesses diagnosed as CFS are Cognitive Behaviour Therapy (CBT), Graded Exercise Therapy (GET) and the prescription of antidepressant pharmaceuticals.

Cognitive Behaviour Therapy is a form of brainwashing. The idea is to get the subject to think differently and 'correctly' about themselves, so, for instance, if they *think* that they are hopelessly ugly and this stops comfortable social interaction, CBT will help them to perceive their looks differently and hopefully produce the confidence needed for social interaction.

> Evidence for the superiority of new ways of thinking about and managing such patients is growing. These new treatments, often referred to as cognitive behavioural therapies, take a new approach [which] is in keeping with the evidence that the perpetuation of unexplained somatic symptoms is best understood in terms of psychological factors [such as] misinterpretation of bodily sensations and unhelpful coping behaviour.

Such therapies can be effective with illnesses like anorexia and bulimia, based as they are on patients' distorted subjective perceptions of their own body shape. How though does CBT work with someone who has Chronic Fatigue Syndrome? Using CBT, the psychiatrist hopes to get patients to correct their 'mistaken illness belief' and think of themselves as healthy. There is a strange meeting point here between new age ideas and the pseudo-science of psychiatry. Some psychiatric professionals evidently believe that it is possible to change the nature of reality purely with thought. Professor Wessely and members of his school believe that the rational mind can both regenerate the body and reinstate the biological balance needed for fitness and good health. So confident are they of these new age powers that they do not even believe in carrying out diagnostic tests for a structural or organic origin of the illness.

Myalgic Encephalomyelitis: A Disposable Illness

The idea of being able to cure CFS by changing the patients perception of their body led one commentator to say that 'In the hands of these psychiatrists, CBT seems to be more a tool to prove the psychological aetiology of the disease.'

There are, however, many problems with the 'successful' trials carried out using CBT on CFS patients. One of the most obvious is that the Wessely school conducts nearly all these trials and report them using colleagues as co-authors. For this reason reports of these trials rarely get proper peer scrutiny.

One other quite fundamental problem is that the Wessely school neither seeks nor advocates any other form of treatment than CBT and GET; it is therefore difficult to put together a control group or do research into any other treatments. After the publication of one CBT trial, Catherine Rye, a subject in the control group, wrote the following:

> I participated in the Oxford trial . . . the article implies that a new successful treatment has been found for ME but that sufferers do not want to accept it. There are facts about the trial that throw into doubt how successful it is. It is stated that patients in the control group received standard medical care. I was in that group but I received nothing. Also, patients receiving treatment had to attend weekly hospital visits, thus excluding the most severely affected sufferers. Patients who 'improved significantly' only increased their score from 70 to 80 on a scale of general functional ability.

While patients are tutored in how to change their attitude and escape their illness, they are also put through a programme of GET. The problem with GET is that a sizeable minority, perhaps a quarter of people who have ME or some forms of Chronic Fatigue, are often unable to get out of bed or walk more than a few steps. The multinational commercially based PRISMA health programme, structured by Professor Wessely, recognises this and proposes to send therapists to work at home with patients. Leaving aside the question of psychiatric aetiology, some patients who have both experienced Chronic Fatigue Syndrome and also immersed themselves in the literature would not want to have GET, because some reports argue that it is totally unsuitable for such patients, leading to exhaustion and sometimes permanent damage.

The final aspect of the psychiatric treatment model is the prescription of antidepressant drugs, this is despite the fact that large numbers of ME and CFS sufferers have been found to be chemically sensitive. While Dr. Michael Sharpe has said that 'There are many anecdotal reports [of the efficacy of antidepressant drugs] in CFS,' and while Professor Wessely has advocated them for PRISMA patients, the majority of trials and the majority of reviews, including the York review which Wessely advised upon, suggest that antidepressant drugs are of very little, if any, use in cases of ME or CFS.

The psychiatric school suggests that a large number of people who present with CFS actually have atypical depressive disorders which can be treated completely with antidepressants. Those who consider ME or other forms of CFS to be physical illnesses point out that secondary depression is almost inevitable in people who have a seriously debilitating illness, especially if the cause of the illness is unknown.

Antidepressant drugs are the boom industry of psychiatry. In Britain, sales of the SSRI antidepressants rose from 510 prescriptions annually in 1991 to 10,442 in 1995, a twenty-fold increase, whilst sales of tricyclic antidepressants rose from 9,000 prescriptions in 1991 to 22,000 in 1995. The Institute of Psychiatry is supported by research grants from a number of the pharmaceutical companies which produce antidepressants, including Eli Lilly, the manufacturers of Prozac.

Myalgic Encephalomyelitis: A Disposable Illness

Ted Shaw, writing about diagnostic testing for depression and the psychiatric aetiology school in Australia, suggests that the marketing of psychiatric drugs is an important factor. Dr. Ian Hickie, the prominent Australian psychiatrist and colleague of Wessely, has developed a CFS psychiatric checklist for general practitioners.♦ Called the SPHERE (Somatic and Psychological Health Report), it has 36 questions to ask patients. A positive answer to any one of the questions can result in a diagnosis of mental disorder. The questions include: 'Over the past few weeks, have you been troubled by: feeling irritable or cranky? A poor memory? Pains in your arms and legs? Feeling nervous or tense? Muscle pain after activity? Waking up tired?'

Hickie, who wrote the programme for the SPHERE, estimates that '1 in 3 people who walk into doctors' surgeries are psychologically ill and 1 in 6 might require a drug treatment.' Bristol Myers Squibb, the manufacturer of the antidepressant Serzone, sponsors the SPHERE and the educational seminars held to introduce it.

While psychiatrists advocate CBT, GET and antidepressants for ME and any form of chronic fatigue, 'health fraud' activists wouldn't be who they are if they didn't also warn against the dangers of any non-orthodox treatments. In an interview in *Top Santé*, Dr. Charles Shepherd, Medical Advisor to the ME Association and HealthWatch

---

♦ Pfizer have also developed a test which can give Gulf War veterans a diagnosis of mental illness. Pfizer's test diagnoses Major Depression on the basis of a few checkmarks, ignoring the extensive medical testing required under the American Psychiatric Association's diagnostic guidelines (DSM-IV specifically states that a diagnosis of Major Depression cannot be assigned until the clinician has performed diagnostic testing to rule out over forty medical conditions which can cause the same nine symptoms.) The new tests diagnose Gulf War vets with 'Chronic Multi-Symptom Illness' (CMI). CMI is defined as a cluster of two or more symptoms such as pain, fatigue, or cognitive dysfunction, the hallmark symptoms of Gulf War Syndrome (GWS), Chronic Fatigue Syndrome (CFS), Fibromyalgia (FM), (cont.)

member, advises low doses of antidepressants and lifestyle changes. Asked about alternative therapies, Shepherd had a perfect opportunity to comment on quacks '. . . beware of quacks who charge a lot of money for strange treatments. Although some people find them helpful, there's no evidence that special diets, large amounts of food supplements or anti-candida treatments will help cure this disorder.'

The consequences of psychiatric treatment

When assessed simply by treatments such as CBT, GET and antidepressant drug therapy, the psychiatric solution to ME and chronic fatigue conditions looks much like the rest of Western orthodox medicine, a combination of guesswork and chemicals which occasionally help and sometimes produce adverse reactions and exacerbate the speed of long term decline. However, the social consequences of a psychiatric diagnosis for patients and sometimes parents of patients can be far more certainly damaging than this.

There can be a developing cycle of adverse responses to patients who refuse to accept that their illness has a psychiatric origin. Psychiatrists, some physicians and a number of judges have agreed over the last decade that in cases where children supported by their parents claim that they have ME or CFS, the parents are guilty of

---

♦ (cont.) and Multiple Chemical Sensitivity (MCS). Clinicians are instructed by new Clinical Practice Guidelines in America to give veterans with CMI's one of two questionnaires which are trademarked and copyrighted by Pfizer, Inc. Both the questionnaires contain a nine-item question which will earmark 'CMI' Gulf War vets as mentally ill and suffering from major depression. Pfizer, Inc. funded the development of both tests to provide primary care clinicians with tools to diagnose depression in eight minutes or less, an average of one minute for the brief form. Pfizer is distributing the tests free. [Taken from a longer, excellent critique of diagnosis and treatments for Chronic Multi-Symptom Illness. 'Nightingale Hunter via Co-Cure Moderators'. Nightingale Hunter: http://www.co-cure.org/digest.htm].

forcing upon the child *irrational illness perceptions*. A number of cases have ocurred, with children being taken into care for enforced psychiatric-based therapy.

The refusal by patients or parents of affected children to accept psychiatric evaluation of their illness, even when that refusal is based upon the most cogent scientific arguments, is reduced to 'resistance', which psychiatrists and social workers claim is yet a further aspect of the patient's psychiatric disorder. In this scenario, psychiatrists will suggest that one of the most significant signs of psychiatric disorder in these patients is their continuing argument that they are physically ill together with their denial that they have a psychiatric condition.

The refusal to submit to psychiatric diagnosis has itself been named a syndrome by some psychiatrists dealing with ME patients. Termed Pervasive Refusal Syndrome (PRS), this condition gives psychiatrists dealing with ME and CFS cases a complete *carte blanche* to determine as mentally ill any parent or child who refuses the psychiatric aetiology and treatments for these conditions. Jane Colby, adviser to the Tymes Trust, a charity dedicated to young ME sufferers, cites one case in which the parents had sought medical help for their child's illness and found their child diagnosed with PRS when both the parents and the child refused to accept the psychiatrist's recommendations.

According to psychiatrists, PRS is 'a potentially life-threatening condition manifested by a profound and pervasive refusal on behalf of the patient to eat, drink, walk, talk or care for themselves in any way over a period of several months.' Contributing to this condition can be sexual abuse and domestic violence. It is possible to see that some children might suffer from such a condition resulting in, for instance, anorexia, where a psychiatric diagnosis is resisted or questioned. To use this diagnosis in the case of a disputed physical illness, however, could be classed as a denial of human rights.

SKEWED

A diagnosis of PRS gives doctors and psychiatrists the right to forcibly feed children by tube and use physical or chemical constraints on them where deemed necessary by doctors. Psychiatric advice on this syndrome suggests that, as in cases of ME, physicians should not try to find the cause of any illness, but should adopt a 'tough love' policy,[24] together with GET, to force the child back into social relations as quickly as possible. Teams of doctors, nurses, social workers and others who deal with cases of PRS are advised by psychiatrists to form close ties with each other in order to stop parents persuading any of them that the child has a physical illness.

The Countess of Mar, a tireless campaigner on behalf of those affected by chemically induced illness, ME and CFS, likens the inter-agency team meetings which take action on behalf of children suffering from ME under the Children Act 1989 to 'Kangaroo Courts':

> In these cases, social workers use the Children Act powers (section 47) to conduct one sided investigations into families; hold secret meetings, and then convene benign sounding 'conferences' to decide whether to place the child on the child protection register as a first step towards care proceedings. To parents who have been gulled into believing that social workers are there to help them and their children, these proceedings seem like 'Kangaroo Courts.'

> Government guidance expects the case conference chairperson to be independent and objective. However, it is not unknown for the chairperson and the person who initiated the case to have discussed the intended outcome beforehand. Biased opinion and hearsay are presented as evidence. Accused parents are denied a real opportunity to present their case. Medical evidence that counters the 'need for protection' is disregarded. Parents' right to a second medical opinion is not on the agenda . . . conference members both give evidence and vote.

---

24 This approach was covered by the BBC *Panorama* Programme called 'Sick and Tired,' transmitted on 8th November 1999.

Myalgic Encephalomyelitis: A Disposable Illness

The literature on PRS suggests that parents' attempts to take children out of therapy is in itself a specific kind of familial behaviour problem, growing from a refusal of the parents and the child to accept the psychiatric diagnosis. Children are only to be returned home to their parents when the parents are willing to agree that the child is suffering from a psychological condition. Dr. Michael Sharpe goes as far as to say that 'A conviction of a solely physical cause for symptoms is the single most consistent predictor of poor outcome.' Jane Colby calls this 'damned if you do, damned if you don't' situation for parents, the 'Witchhunt Syndrome.'

Perhaps the most serious and most fraudulent consequential diagnosis of refusal to accept the psychiatric aetiology of ME and CFS is that of Munchausen's Syndrome by Proxy (MSBP). Here, when a child presented at a surgery or a hospital is found on examination to have nothing apparently wrong, the physician's or psychiatrist's suspicion, is turned upon the mother. After covert psychiatric evaluation, the mother is pronounced to have MSBP, a condition in which the mother inflicts injury on a child (in this case, false illness beliefs) partly in order to elicit attention for herself from a doctor or other professional.

The diagnosis of MSBP♦ is ideal for psychiatric evaluation of childhood ME and CFS, because it gives the psychiatrist or doctor who initially claims that there is nothing medically wrong with the child a label to pin on the parent. Before they thought to use MSBP in this situation, they had to accuse parents of being overbearing or overprotective, and so conditioning the child's perception of its illness. MSBP avoids this area of murky thinking, despite the fact that

---

♦ Professor Sir Roy Meadow is the 'expert' who defined Munchausen's Syndrome by Proxy (MSBP) in 1977 with a paper in *The Lancet* entitled "Munchausen's Syndrome By Proxy: The Hinterlands of Child Abuse." Best known for his involvement in unexplained cot deaths, Meadow has asserted that children do not have ME, only parents who suffer from MSBP. Meadow's evidence was recently disputed (cont.)

it is usually relevant only in cases where parents physically harm children. In ME and CFS cases, an accusation of MSBP clearly does not explain how the parent could *enforce* the illness perception on the child.

In a 1998 judicial review case, the British courts tackled the thorny question of whether or not physicians, psychiatrists and social work agencies had the right to enforce psychiatric treatment for ME and CFS on children. Behind this question was the bigger question of whether or not care orders were a suitable way of enforcing medical treatment on children. The case was argued on the basis that the court was restricted to ordering compliance with medical treatment *agreed by a competent body of opinion*. It was argued that in cases of ME and CFS, the psychiatric treatment following diagnosis did nor represent 'generally agreed' treatment. The judicial review was granted, the judge declaring that 'B's parents have a right to give or withhold consent to elective forms of medical treatment in respect of B.'

Children who present with ME or CFS are also adversely affected, as are their parents, by the programme which psychiatrists employ in order to change their *false perceptions* of illness; this entails the child being given into the custody of the local authority by the courts and separated from their parents, subjected to 'tough love' regimes which have entailed being dropped in swimming pools or forced along pavements alongside heavy traffic and carrying out taxing exercise regimes.

♦(cont.) in the Court of Appeal in the Sally Clark case. He had told the initial trial that the odds of there being two unexplained infant deaths in one family were one in 73 million. This evidence was crucial in sending Clark to jail. It was, however, a claim hotly disputed by the Royal Statistical Society, who wrote to the Lord Chancellor. The Crown continued to use Meadow to give expert evidence until at a second appeal it was shown that the true odds were in the region of one in 100.

Myalgic Encephalomyelitis: A Disposable Illness

There is mounting evidence that psychiatric treatments for CFS harm adult patients or at their best, they are simply ineffective, as has been shown by four major surveys.

Both Action for ME (AfME) in their survey of 2,338 respondents and Dr. Lesley Cooper in a separate survey jointly sponsored by the ME Association and AfME found Graded Exercise Therapy made more people's condition worse more often than any other treatment.[25] A detailed survey and analysis by independent ME researcher D. M. Jones confirmed the same results[26] and a survey carried out by The 25% ME Group for the Severely Affected found that CBT/GET could cause conditions to become both chronic and severe.[27]

The Medical Director of the UK ME Association has published the fact that he continues to receive more adverse reports about Graded Exercise Therapy than any other form of treatment, confirming that many people with ME/CFS are suffering relapses through such programmes.

Other kinds of harm that follow from psychiatric intervention in ME and CFS cases include the refusal or withdrawal of state benefits; difficulties in obtaining insurance payments, with policy holders being refused benefits; the withdrawal of cover by private health companies for those with ME/CFS; an almost total lack of suitable provision or care by the NHS, with no facilities for specialist referral other than to a psychiatrist; as well as an overtly hostile and unfavourable attitude being shown by doctors and other

---

25 *Severely neglected: ME in the UK*. Action for ME, Wells, UK. March 2001. *Report on Survey of Members of Local ME Groups*, Dr. Lesley Cooper. November 2000.

26 *Follow-up Survey of ME/CFS/MCS Patients*. D. M. Jones. 5th April 2001.

27 *ME Questionnaire*; The 25% ME Group. Simon Lawrence (Co-ordinator) – 4, Douglas Court, Beach Road, Troon, Ayrshire KA10 6SQ, Scotland, July 2000.

health professionals. Perhaps a unique form of harm to sufferers generally, is to be found as a consequence of the persistent recommendation from the leading group of psychiatrists that no investigations, or only limited investigations, are necessary or appropriate.

CASE HISTORY FOUR

A case of Pirimiphos-Methyl poisoning[28]

Michael Bright[29] farms 400 acres and grows some 250 acres of grain, which he sells to merchants as milling wheat and malting barley as well as feed wheat and barley, keeping back what he needs for his own cattle. Grain is brought in off the field and during the drying process is of a humidity that allows mites and insects to breed in it; this is prevented by pirimiphos-methyl treatment. Michael has applied Actellic 2% dust[30] since it was introduced in 1976/77. He scoops it out of the bag with a measuring tin and works it into the grain with a shovel. After the grain has been treated, it is checked frequently for moisture content and weevils during

---

28 The whole of this case history is extracted in unchanged segments from Helen Fullerton's 1999 brilliant but unpublished 27-page paper of the same title, written on behalf of Farming and Livestock Concern UK. The paper can be obtained from the author at: 5 Bryngelli, Carmel, Llanelli, SA14 7TL, Wales.

29 This man's name and some other details have been changed to protect his identity.

30 Pirimiphos-methyl, an organophosphate, marketed as 'Actellic', is used to treat grain in store against mite and insect infestation. Its current formulations are 'Actellic 2% Dust' in powder form, 'Actellic D' containing solvents and diluted for spraying and 'Actellic' smoke bomb generator for treating surfaces. Actellic 2% Dust was introduced in the mid-seventies by ICI and is now marketed by Zeneca, formed after an ICI demerger in 1993. The Product Safety Data 1994 (para 15) stated it was 'Not classified as hazardous to users' and 'Do not breath dust. If necessary for personal comfort wear a mask.' The Product Use Manual 1998/99 states that 'under normal conditions of handling and use . . . it is of low toxicity, inhalation is unlikely to cause harmful effects, and in long term exposure, no long term risks to man are associated with it.' Zeneca maintains that Actellic's low toxicity makes it safe for the consumer and safe also for the operator treating the grain. This claim is supported by MAFF's Advisory Committee on Pesticides (ACP). The effects of low level exposure have never been examined.

storage, moved if it overheats and transferred to lorries by front-end loader once it is dry enough to send away. But this is not the end. For years Michael handled it on a daily basis, rolling it for his cattle and mixing it with other ingredients in their feed.

In 1999, John was 56. Since leaving school at 16 he had worked hard at building up the family farm. The dozen cows he was milking in 1958 became 90 cows at one stage and the arable acreage was increased. He was never ill. A neighbour recalls: 'In 1958 you were so fit you could jump over a five-barred gate . . . you were without doubt the fittest man in the area.'

In the early nineties Michael began to suffer muscle spasms, then deteriorated rapidly, overcome by physical weakness, headaches, exhaustion, irritability and anxiety. It was worse at harvest time: he was agitated and worried about everything. There is no reason why he, an experienced farmer, should have become agitated at harvest, but as the grain came off the combine into store he would be treating it with Actellic. He could not understand what was happening to him. In the Summer/Autumn of 1995 he was 'so ill [I] could not stand up.' He had 'fits of shaking . . . horrendous headaches . . .' He was 'too weak to open the gate to let the cows in.' A business colleague later told him: 'When I saw you, you did not know who I was . . . you were very rough with no inclination to move from the sofa . . . we could not conduct business that day.'

Michael kept a diary in which he recorded his activities, and he began to note down every detail of his symptoms. There was endless sweating, but cold feet. He could not hold his water and at other times could not pass it. He had diarrhoea, and a rash on his legs ('the grain gets into your shoes'.) He was disorientated. Short-term memory was impaired. He had hallucinations, anxiety over trivia, bouts of irritability and depression. His near sight began to go. No one knew the cause of his illness. He was in despair.

Under pressure, Michael agreed to attend a behavioural clinic (one run by psychiatrists and psychologists): they found nothing wrong and dismissed his suggestions of OP poisoning. Doctors were unhelpful. One of them told him: 'There is nothing the matter with you, OPs are an imaginary thing.' He had pain in his right leg and was told it was gout. He developed a cough and was told it was farmer's lung.

In 1995 he could no longer manage milking and in November of that year he sold his dairy cows and changed to sucklers. It meant growing about 50 acres more grain, but he felt better after stopping milking: 'I was not having the daily top-up from rolling corn.'

Michael's breathing difficulty suggested a heart problem, but at his local hospital, they found that his ECG was normal. In 1996, his GP referred him to a neurologist about the muscle spasms in his arms and legs, the pain in his feet and the loss of use of his right foot. He took in an empty bag of Actellic and asked for a medical opinion as to whether he should continue using it. He was sent home, together with the empty bag, without advice or treatment. There was no one to turn to. He felt isolated. Medical practitioners suggested it was all in the mind. Family and neighbours thought he was a crank 'putting my life through hell in ignorance.'

His first collapse was in July 1998. He had treated his grain wearing full safety gear at 10.00 am the day before. Next morning he had nausea and a tight painful chest. He rang for emergency help. When the ambulance came Michael was found lying on the lawn, conscious but immobile except for his eyelids twitching and his teeth faintly chattering. He was revived in the ambulance with oxygen. Walking down the hospital passage he was disorientated, going in the opposite direction to the way he was told. He asked if anyone was experienced in potential OP poisoning. No notice was taken: to the hospital his tight chest and difficult breathing suggested heart disease. The ECG was normal. His pulse, normally low at about 50 beats/min was racing at 100. He was prescribed the Beta blocker 'atenolol' for high blood pressure.

Michael was consistently denied red cell and plasma cholinesterase tests and when eventually these were done, the results were not analysed by his hospital or his GP with any degree of concern, nor were further more sophisticated tests done.

As a lay victim of pesticides, Michael always made a point of stating his case to professionals who he felt did not understand the condition. In October 1998, Michael met Dr. David Ray, who had written 'How safe are organophosphorous pesticides?' for *Pesticide Outlook*. In this article he argued that 'there was no convincing evidence for low level exposure effects.'[31] Having read the article, Michael phoned Dr. Ray to challenge his interpretation. It was a long call and Dr. Ray, who was sympathetic, event-

---

31 At the time, Dr. Ray was head of the Medical Research Council (MRC) Toxicology Unit situated at the University of Leicester. *Pesticide Outlook* is a journal of the Royal Society of Chemistry, which attempts to give a balanced view on pesticides. In 2003, what had become the MRC Applied Neuroscience Group moved to the School of Pharmaceutical Sciences in the University of Nottingham. Although it is not a reflection on the independence of either Dr. Ray or the MRC Group, Nottingham is a University heavily reliant upon pharmaceutical company funding. When Lord Sainsbury visited the University Pharmacy Department in 2003, he began his tour with the Glaxo-SmithKline Laboratories, took in the Boots Building and then visited the almost finished new Institute of Drug Discovery.

ually conceded that Michael probably had OP poisoning: 'Although he wouldn't have thought it long term low level. He'd have thought it was acute exposure.'

In June 1999, Michael was fortunate enough to be examined by Dr. Robert Davies who had over the previous decade laid down the criteria for assessing OP poisoning, both low level, accumulative and acute, for the Health and Safety Executive. Dr. Davies diagnosed Michael as suffering from chronic OP poisoning.

At last Michael had a diagnosis. Hundreds of others are not so fortunate. He has neighbours misdiagnosed for years and suffering OP symptoms; Michael does his best to help them. He has victims ringing him up: Actellic users, sheep dippers, crop farmers, local authority workers – all with the same symptoms as himself and facing the same brick wall of denial when they attempt to get a diagnosis. Most are on Prozac. There are broken relationships, broken lives and suicides. Two of his neighbours, sheep farmers, committed suicide. Michael believes: 'I have a duty to hundreds of thousands of farmers. We all have a duty to help each other.'

CHAPTER FIVE

Same Old Same Old

When cited enough, inaccurate studies and other reports may establish a false orientation in the general literature on the discussed issue. [32]

Worry as I may, search as I may, I can find only one cause so all-embracing that it can explain why all of us, rich or poor, are fogged with fatigue, why two people out of three have an illness every month, why work has dropped by one third: we have too little food; wrong food; bad food; poisoned food. [33]

The ramifications of the drive to present MCS, GWS, ME and CFS as psychiatric illnesses echo in the world far beyond the intimate relationship of the patient and physician. Now that the psychiatric aetiology of these illnesses has gained ascendancy in Britain, these ideas determine and dominate policy throughout the social structure, from the Department of Health and the Armed Forces to various courts of law.

In order to maintain psychiatric hegemony, the psychiatric lobby has both to initiate and control any major reassessment of these illnesses in whatever form. The initiation and influence of the Chief Medical Officer's Report into ME/CFS (1998-2002) by the psychiatric lobby is a good illustration of how to practise hegemonic strategy in the area of health.

---

32 Lennart Hardell, Mikael Eriksson and Olav Axelson, On the misinterpretation of epidemiological evidence. *New Solutions* 1994;4;49-56.

33 Franklin Bicknell, *The English Complaint*. Heinemann, London 1952.

SKEWED

In July 1998, at the Royal College of Physicians in London, the Linbury Trust, one of a centrally controlled clutch of private trusts set up by the Sainsbury family, publicly launched a book. Published by the Royal Society of Medicine Press, it was entitled *A Research Portfolio on Chronic Fatigue*. Its contents clearly exemplified the prevailing view of one section of the British medical establishment, that ME no longer existed and Chronic Fatigue Syndrome is a psychiatric condition.

In a review of *A Research Portfolio*, Dr. E. G. Dowsett, honorary consultant microbiologist for South Essex Health Trust, criticised the psychiatric bias of both the book and research which the Linbury Trust had funded, casting doubt particularly on the methodology of Professor Simon Wessely. Referring to the dismissal of ME by Wessely, Dowsett wrote, he 'ignores all seminal papers which have charted the course of the illness over 60 years.'

Dowsett was scathing about the present psychiatric treatment programme for CFS involving CBT and GET, together with the prescription of antidepressants. Dowsett said of antidepressants: 'The expense of antidepressant therapy has reached £239m per annum for the 4 million UK patients already treated, while the use of Prozac and other SSRIs (selective serotonin re-uptake inhibitors) has rocketed by over 700%.'

The book launch was an important event for the Linbury Trust, as it had spent over £4m on CFS research since 1991. It meant that the views of the principal Linbury researchers were now presented in an authoritative and easily accessible form and that those researchers were much closer to having their views adopted as government policy.

The launch at the Royal College of Physicians was celebrated with a lecture by Professor Stephen E. Straus, the US expert on CFS, whose visit to England cost the Linbury Trust over £13,000. Straus was the Director of Virology at the National Institute of Allergy and Infectious Diseases, where over the last fifteen years he had been the principal North American scientist proposing that CFS was primarily a psychiatric or 'psycho-neurotic' illness.♦

In his presentation, Straus wasted no time in setting out the Linbury party line. Giving his audience a 'pop-historical' summary of CFS, he named a jumble of conditions which ruled out any consideration of ME or even forms of CFS as serious neuro-immunological illnesses:

> In the 19th century it was known as 'the vapours.' By 1869, the term neurasthenia was used and, after the First World War, the terms 'effort fatigue' and 'battle fatigue' were coined to describe exhausted soldiers. By the Fifties, country people suffering chronic fatigue syndrome were thought to have 'chronic brucellosis.' Then the term fibromyalgia became used as well as a diagnosis of a very minor heart defect, mitral valve prolapse. More recently it was called candida and then total allergy syndrome.

Not surprisingly, Straus's views on CFS fitted snugly with those of his audience; his belief that Chronic Fatigue Syndrome is a condition adopted mainly by neurotic women echoed almost word for word the

---

♦ According to Donald W. Scott (see footnotes Chapter One), Straus has been arguing against the physical nature of immune damaging illnesses since the 1970's. In October 1999, Straus was surprisingly shifted sideways from his position as the Chief for the Laboratory of Clinical Investigation at the National Institute of Allergy and Infectious Diseases (NIAID) to become the first Director of the National Center for Complementary and Alternative Medicine (NCCAM) at the National Institutes of Health (NIH) with a first year budget of $50 million. The centre was set up to 'conduct basic and applied research (intramural and extra-mural), research training, and disseminate health information and other programs with respect to identifying, investigating, and validating Complementary and Alternative treatments, diagnostic and prevention modalities, disciplines, and systems.' Straus was an odd choice for the position; when he took the job the publicity suggested that he had broad basic and clinical research experience related to many diseases for which there are alternative remedies, including chronic fatigue syndrome.

views of Professor Simon Wessely. According to both Straus and Wessely, Chronic Fatigue Syndrome was nothing more than one end of a spectrum of 'tiredness', common in most psychiatric illness.

Also at the Linbury launch was Professor Alan McGregor, a colleague of Professor Wessely at King's College Hospital, chairman of the Linbury Trust's four-man scientific advisory panel. McGregor took the opportunity of the book launch to put the Linbury's research into a 'health fraud' context. He had become interested in studying 'CFS', he said, after he came across the case of an 18-year-old girl suffering from the disorder; her parents had mortgaged their home and had got into financial difficulties in order to pay for her to be treated by charlatans.

Anyone who noticed that the Linbury Trust had launched what appeared to be a state-of-the-art guide to treating CFS might have been intrigued when the then Chief Medical Officer, Sir Kenneth Calman, a Fellow of the Royal College of Physicians and patron of the 'Kenneth Calman' psychiatric bursary, took the opportunity of the launch to announce a new inquiry into CFS.

Accepting the new Linbury book as if it were a government report, Calman told the press that he was to convene a special Working Group to begin looking, in the next few months, at the best clinical practice and management of Chronic Fatigue Syndrome, 'also known as myalgic encephalomyelitis,' and to produce guidelines for UK clinicians. Sir Kenneth, who was two months away from retirement, said that the Working Group 'would bring together a wide range of orthodox and complementary disciplines and include input from various patient groups.' Giving his support to the book authored by Linbury-funded researchers, he said that the Linbury Trust would also be helping fund the new Working Group.

Whilst perhaps being slightly surprised that the Chief Medical Officer appeared to be organising a government committee in conjunction with a private Trust, anyone who knew anything about the politics of ME and CFS would not have been so surprised to hear what Professor Alan McGregor had to say about the conflicts around CFS. Welcoming the Chief Medical Officer's new committee, he supported Dr. Straus by telling a story. Conveniently erasing a history of officially reported ME, he recalled how he could remember 'the same symptoms now described as CFS being labelled by older doctors as "neurasthenia" a neurotic state.' He went on to explain that 'much of the controversy about CFS' stemmed from 'a refusal from many of those who suffer from it, or who care for those who have it, to accept that physical symptoms could be part of a psychological disease.'

In November 1998, the Department of Health and a new Chief Medical Officer, Professor Liam Donaldson, announced the membership of what had become the CMO's Working Group on ME/CFS.♦ The Group would, the statement suggested, produce guidelines and information, based on the most up-to-date research on aspects of clinical management of the illness:

> This initiative will provide us with a real opportunity to review the practical care and support for patients, carers and healthcare professionals alike. We have sought to ensure that the Working Group reflects a broad range of patient and professional opinion.

Many ME and CFS sufferers who followed the birth pangs of the new Chief Medical Officer's Working Group could have been forgiven for taking reassurances about 'broad ranges of opinion' with a pinch of salt. Many had a strong sense of *déjà vu*, being reminded of dashed hopes following the publication of the Joint Royal Colleges' Report only two years before.

♦ Working Group is the name allotted to what is essentially a three-part committee of inquiry (a Key Group, a Children and Young People's Group and a Reference or Advisory group.) Throughout this work the words Working Group, Committee and Group, are used interchangeably.

SKEWED

In October 1996, the three Royal Medical Colleges published a Report on CFS. This Report had been engineered to challenge the conclusions of the 'National Task Force Report' on ME and CFS, produced by the private charity Westcare and jointly funded by the Department of Health. This major Report had gone some way towards convincing the public that CFS was a 'real illness' with considerable physical consequences. However, buried in the conclusions of the National Task Force Report were the words: '. . . it appears that many CFS patients would additionally meet the criteria for psychiatric disorder, most commonly depression.'

Psychiatrists and adherents of the Wessely school were unhappy with the Task Force Report, because the emphasis placed on psychiatric disorder was, for them, not substantial enough. The Task Force Report for its part, acknowledged that 'People (listing Wessely and some of his school) who gave us their much valued help are not necessarily in agreement with the opinions expressed.' Wessely school members no doubt felt that the Report's discussion of possible organic causes of the illness could lead people to think that continued clinical investigations of the illness was appropriate.

Within two years of the Task Force Report, the Wessely school had responded by producing the Joint Royal Colleges' Report. Despite masquerading as an academic review, prepared at the request of the UK Chief Medical Officer, the Report was in reality a tightly controlled exercise in propaganda. Out of the fifteen members of the Working Group who produced the report, eight were psychiatrists well known for their published views denying the reality of ME; six of them were signatories to the 1991 Oxford CFS case definition, which tried to delete ME from the medical lexicon and which asserted that there are no physical signs in CFS.

The Joint Royal Colleges' Report ignored virtually all the available literature which clearly documented physical anomalies associated with the illness. It cited 256 references, of which half were by the same or associated group of Wessely school authors, with Wessely himself being responsible for 10%; nine of them to unpublished or unreviewed work.

The Royal Colleges' Report dismissed ME as a separate disease entity and recommended protocols for the treatment of CFS which included the prescription of antidepressant drugs, even to patients who were not depressed. Predictably, GET and CBT were both recommended to help sufferers 'modulate maladaptive perception of their suffering.' The Report also advised the need to remove children forcibly from their parents and home if this was 'in the best interests of the child,' and it specifically stipulated that 'no investigations should be performed to confirm the diagnosis.'

In some sections of the medical press, the Joint Report was robustly criticised. *The Lancet*, Britain's most prestigious medical journal, noted that the Royal Colleges' Working Group was heavily weighed with psychiatric experts and appeared to make no effort to collect other viewpoints. An editorial observed that the Royal Colleges' report was 'haphazardly set-up, was biased and inconclusive and of little help to patients or their physicians.'

One American critic of the Report, Dr. Terry Hedrick, a PhD in social psychology with a twenty-year career in teaching and in congressional level research evaluation, described the Report as 'insidiously biased and potentially harmful.' She accused the Report's authors not only of bias but also of basing the work on an incomplete literature review and in at least one important instance of mis-stating the results of others' research.

The lack of scientific rigour in the Report, said Hedrick, suggests that large parts of it were no better than speculative hypothesizing. Hedrick's most serious criticisms, however, stemmed from what she considered to be the double standards used by the Report's authors: when reviewing studies on the organic aetiology, they demanded standards of evidence which they did not require in support of a psychological aetiology of CFS. Disparaging the method of reviewing psychological research, she said: 'Much of the psychological research on CFS takes the following form: a researcher collects information on numerous psychological factors, finds one or more that significantly correlate with some aspects of CFS and then speculates as to how this factor may influence illness behaviour or recovery.' Such exploratory studies, Hedrick said, 'do not constitute evidence of causation or the dynamics of illness behaviour.'

It is difficult to imagine more fundamental criticisms of a serious piece of academic work, yet despite this and other stinging reviews, the authors of the Joint Royal Colleges' Report seemed to have evade any real critique from their peers. The Report did, however, have friends in high places: in support of Wessely, Dr. Stephen Straus wrote of the Report in the *BMJ* that it was 'possibly the finest contemporary position statement in the field.'

Media discussions of the Joint Report were populist and devoid of analysis. It appeared that the best medical minds in the country were baffled by ME and CFS, yet no one inquired why the authors had ruled out well-documented possible neurological, endocrinological or immunological causes.

Dr. Wessely a good natured and affable interviewee, brought his own brand of obfuscation to the published Report when interviewed by Fergus Walsh for the BBC:

> I don't think that there is much doubt that Chronic Fatigue
> Syndrome is a condition that lies between both medicine and
> psychiatry. Now, of course, the problem is that when I mention
> the word 'psychiatry', some people think I am saying it is non-
> existent, it is all in the mind, it is all made up – which is an
> absurd suggestion but nevertheless is a very common one and I
> know brings great difficulties in suffering to CFS patients.

Same Old Same Old

It was not only in England that reports like the British Joint Colleges' Report were being heavily criticised; in fact the same principal figures were involved and the same arguments being used to provoke the same critical responses. In Australia, a Government report took five years to be published after the finishing of the last draft.

A small group of Australian psychiatrists, international colleages of Professor Wessely, also had a controlling interest in work on ME and CFS, and in the Report. During the time that the British CMO's Working Group was being formulated, this group was trying to establish psychiatric treatment protocols for ME and CFS sufferers. In 1996, Dr. Michael Wooldridge, the Minister for Health and Family Services, approved an application to Medicare to provide funding of $130,000 to the Royal Australasian College of Physicians (RACP) to produce Guidelines on the most clinically relevant and cost effective methods of diagnosing and treating CFS.

The first Draft Report of the College's deliberations was released in December 1997 and met with heavy criticism. A second draft was released in June 2001, at the same time that the British Chief Medical Officer's Working Group were formulating their guidelines. Despite the inexplicable four-year delay, however, there were no substantial changes in the new Report. The Report's guidelines for treatment, focused on the psychiatric management of symptoms, ignoring the substantial evidence of organic disease. No research was presented into the cause of the illness.

Criticisms of the Report addressed all the same issues voiced over the Joint Report of the British Royal Colleges. Dr. Abhijit Chaudhuri, a Clinical Senior Lecturer in Neurology at the University of Glasgow and a Consultant Neurologist at the Institute of Neurological Sciences in Glasgow, said of cognitive behaviour and graded exercise therapies:

The RACP seems to suggest that cognitive behaviour therapy (CBT) provides a clear understanding of CFS. This claim is unfounded and lacks evidence . . . CBT is not a specific strategy for CFS where its claimed benefit is still questionable. . . . no long-term study has established that graded exercise programmes can significantly improve aerobic capacity in CFS. The UK experience of graded exercise in CFS has shown that as a single intervention graded exercise was associated with the highest negative grading for its effect on fatigue by the patients.

Chaudhuri alights on the fraudulent history of ME given by psychiatrists and used in the Report to obscure the nature of both ME and CFS:

It is incorrect to propose that neurasthenia is the same as CFS . . . the suggestion that neurasthenia was an alternative term for CFS is to be found largely in the psychiatric literature. Most neurological texts of the 19th century make it clear that neurasthenia was an inaccurate and confusing term and should not be used in clinical practice.

A psychiatrist, Dr. Nicole Phillips, echoes this criticism of fraudulent history:

The term neurasthenia is an outdated English psychiatric term which some CFS researchers are trying to revive. The DSM psychiatric classification system used in America and Australia has not used this term for many years on the basis of its lack of validity. It has no place in a section on 'other terms for CFS' other than to be mentioned and dismissed.

In his overview of the Report, Chaudhuri says:

Sadly, this document contains many flawed statements and observations. In some areas, as already pointed out, the accounts appear biased and inaccurate. In addition, I have deep concerns about the selectivity of the literature review . . . as an example, while great effort has been taken to discuss the psychiatric co-morbidity in CFS, the guidelines do not bring home the point

192

that the rate of psychiatric co-morbidity in CFS is comparable to many other medical and neurological conditions . . .

The document has over-emphasised the psychologically-driven cognitive behaviour model of CFS and has failed to review the appropriate literature on the neurology, neuroendocrinology and neuropsychiatric changes in CFS . . . The paper has devoted much of its clinical discussion on the comparison of psychiatric disorders with CFS . . . The quality of references and review on the neurobiological aspect of CFS is very poor, with several important omissions of research carried out by the international groups in the past three or four years . . . The cited references show a skewed representation of a group of psychiatrists. These features clearly undermine not only the quality of science but also the quality of advice presented in the guidelines.

Dr. Peter del Fante, a highly qualified practitioner, member of the RACP and the Medical Director of the Adelaide Western Division of General Practice, noted, amongst other things, the political manipulation which has taken place with the Report.

These guidelines have been sitting around for years awaiting a revision because they were considered biased and incomplete. A revised version is suddenly thrust upon us . . . and then we are given a short time frame to respond . . . Is this how the RACP (of which I am a Fellow) undertakes rigorous peer review of guidelines? . . . The content has hardly advanced from the biases and incompleteness of the initial draft guidelines . . . This only confirms the perceived lack of professionalism and integrity in creating a balanced and unbiased set of guidelines for CFS.

Del Fante is scathing about the recommendation of CBT in the Report:

All the CBT studies to date ignore the above fact and some even modify the CDC criteria (Judith Prins et al, *Lancet* 2001:357:841-847.) Clearly, all the studies are methodologically flawed and their conclusions biased. Some of the studies even admit this fact . . . CBT does not treat the underlying (as yet unidentified) disease process in CFS.

SKEWED

A number of critiques of the Australasian Report, including that of Laurence Budd a consultant paediatrician, raise the Report's lack of information on multiple chemical sensitivity.

> Multiple chemical sensitivity is barely mentioned, and when mentioned is dismissed as irrelevant. This is an unfortunate position for the committee preparing the Draft Guidelines, suggesting adoption of consensus opinion rather than due consideration of all possible aetiologic factors. The omission of MCS raises serious questions as to the scientific credentials of the document. Perhaps MCS is a politically uncomfortable concept . . . but political sensitivity is not a valid scientific reason to ignore the obvious crossover of symptoms with CFS. I believe it is unfortunate that MCS is ignored in this document. I don't believe that any Guidelines document will have validity if MCS is not given due consideration and recognition.

Speaking as a psychiatrist, Dr. Nicole Phillips makes it clear that following 'a sound psychiatric and physical history' many somatised disorders can be clearly distinguished from CFS. Phillips goes on to criticise a study by Wilson, quoted in the Report 'in which 19% of patients followed up developed "other psychological disorders" ' but which fails to point out that in any chronic illness, co-existent depression is common and most studies provide figures of psychological disorders in other illnesses greater than 19%. Phillips summarises her criticism of the Report bluntly: 'The document shows bias from certain psychiatric researchers.'

The Australian patients' groups, after initial enthusiasm for the Report, withdrew their co-operation from it when it became clear that it did not represent the interests of their members. Judy Lovett, President of the national body, ME/CFS Association of Australia, speaking for the board, expressed the need to dissociate the Association from the Report:

> In conclusion, I must state that our organisation no longer supports the guidelines. We originally co-operated in every way possible. It should be written after extensive, current literature

searches have been evaluated. The content should stand up to rigorous debate and peer review. To accept anything less is totally unjust to the CFS patients. In the light of the vast array of information put before you, please do not continue with the publication of these guidelines.

And Frances B. Sandbach, writing on behalf of the Committee of ACT ME/CFS Society Inc. (Australia) also cites the oddly biased literature review as one of her organisation's reasons for dissociating from the report:

The literature review presented in the guidelines is incomplete and biased. Information reporting the organic view of CFS is under-represented or substantially absent, whereas that involving psychiatric opinion and psychological aspects is over-represented.

One might imagine that similar criticism of reports in Britain and Australia, might provoke a serious discourse that could influence governments and put research into ME and CFS back on track? After all, is this not what happens in democracies, in matters of science as well as politics: ideas are debated, guidance is given by experts, views are changed, people convinced and public policy flows with what becomes broad consensus?

A North American fix

The question of whether academics and research workers, so prone to conflicting interests and so close to industry, rather than clinicians, should formulate policy on ME and CFS became an issue in North America.

In the years that the British CMO's Working Group was sitting, Professor Wessely and his colleagues were also involved in high-level US policy debates. In 1999, the Centers for Disease Control and Prevention were forced to apologise publicly after it was found that they had diverted nearly nine million dollars of ring-fenced funding for CFS research into other health-related programmes and unaccountably mislaid another four million dollars meant for this research from a \$22.7 million Congress budget.

Angry patients made the point at a meeting with CDC senior officials that the misuse of funds was about something more than money and that what the CDC had done 'reinforced a perception amongst some doctors that their illness is a mental problem, an excuse for laziness or even a joke.'

In January 2000, the CFIDS Association of America had to work hard against time limits to persuade the Department of Health and Human Services (DHHS) that the National Institutes of Health (NIH) should not down-grade one of its prestigious State of the Science conferences on CFS to a less important meeting.

The campaign by CFIDS had become necessary after normal protocols were ignored while organising the prestigious 'CFS: State of the Science' conference, which determined research allocation and ultimately patterns of clinical practice. World-renowned experts in ME/CFS, such as Professor Nancy Klimas, were not only not invited to take part but were actively excluded and the names of those who were to speak were not announced until days before the meeting. The two main named speakers were Professor Simon Wessely and Dr. Michael Sharpe.

The outcry was such that activists succeeded in getting the February 2000 meeting re-classified, and the State of the Science meeting on CFS postponed until the following October, when a more balanced panel of speakers was able to attend. During negotiations to stop the biased meeting, trying to explain their position, NIH officials told representatives of the CFIDS Association of America that CFS was considered by many in the broader scientific community to be a 'political disease.' This idea would be strengthened, they said, if the government were seen to bow to political pressure and withdraw the 'State of the Science' category from the February meeting. In the end, however, the blatant nature of the fix proved too embarrassing for the Department.

A political awakening

In Britain, the Joint Report of the Royal Colleges, so obviously lacking in science, precipitated a profound change in mood amongst ME/CFS sufferers, patient groups and activists. The issue was suddenly understood as a political one and grievances were addressed to parliament and professional bodies.

Because the many informed critical responses to the Joint Royal Colleges' Report were ignored or dismissed by the Presidents of the three Royal Colleges, the ME community in Britain organised a petition asking that the Report be withdrawn. Called 'Fighting for Truth' (ForT), the petition was signed by 12,500 people. In November 1997, in the House of Lords, it was presented by the Countess of Mar to the Minister of State for Health. The petitioners hoped 'that the House of Lords will take note of the Petition organised by Fighting for Truth which calls for the rejection and withdrawal of the Royal Colleges' Report on Chronic Fatigue Syndrome . . . and further that the House of Lords will call upon Her Majesty's Government to review the scientific evidence upon which diagnosis and treatment of ME are based.' The Government acted immediately in rejecting the petition. When, a year later, sufferers heard the announcement of the new Chief Medical Officer's Working Group, they were understandably sceptical about the intentions behind it.

Behind the scenes, activists began to assemble information about the Linbury Trust and to scrutinise the names of Working Group members. Questions were asked in the House of Lords about the Linbury Trust's involvement with the Department of Health.

Both the Department and the offices of the Chief Medical Officer, however, withstood this political squall and pursued the setting up of the Working Group and its attendant mechanisms within the Leeds headquarters of the NHS Executive.

In March 1998 the Countess of Mar and a small group of others were granted a private meeting with the Chief Medical Officer. The hope was that some kind of inquiry would be initiated into the causes of ME and CFS. Between March and the announcement of the CMO's Working Group in July 1998, however, those who believed in a psychiatric aetiology had moved quickly to ensure that any inquiry was restricted to looking at treatment.

A last chance for sufferers

The Report of the Joint Royal Colleges was unequivocal that ME did not exist except in the mind of sufferers, and that CFS had a psychiatric aetiology; the Australasian Report said the same thing. Consequently, those who knew about the complex politics under-lying these illnesses had serious doubts about whether the CMO's Working Group would have anything new to say. They knew that unless the Working Group took on board facts established in clinical research in other countries, that there were many biomarkers indicating an organic aetiology for the illnesses, the CMO's report was bound to fail to generate any new ideas about treatment.

Importantly, whoever drew up the remit of the CMO's Working Group had most expediently restricted it to looking *only* at what was described as 'best practice' treatment or management of the con-dition. From the outset, the Working Group was precluded from considering the difficult areas of causation, prevalence and ap-propriate lines of investigation, upon which treatment should inevit-ably be based.

Same Old Same Old

Following the announcement of Working Group members, concerns about the predominance of the psychiatric view within the Group began to develop. Established critics of psychiatric involvement and government policy in this area pointed out that clinicians and scientists who had many years' experience in the field of ME were expressly excluded from participating. Professor Malcolm Hooper and Sally Montague, the writers of a paper critical of the way in which the CMO's Working Group set about their task, explained the attempts that had been made by concerned parties to ensure that the CMO's report was not a replay of the Royal Colleges' Joint Report.

(Long) before the setting up of the CMO's Working Group on ME/CFS and during its deliberations, numerous patients, carers, politicians, peers of the realm and others have made informed and concerned representations to various Government bodies. These representations raised specific and exact issues about ME/CFS, yet for over a decade the response has consistently been no more than a standardised letter which failed even to acknowledge the specific issues raised . . . Many attempts have been made to put right this unacceptable situation, including personal visits to the Chief Medical Officer himself.

. . . many written representations have been made to various members of the Working Group and to members of the NHS Executive at Leeds during the lifetime of the present Working Group, all to no avail. Correspondence has gone unacknowledged, including correspondence sent personally to the Chairman, Professor Allen Hutchinson. Letters sent directly to the CMO have been forwarded to Leeds to be dealt with by the NHS Executive. Written submissions provided for the Key Group by interested parties appear to have been studiously ignored.

Moreover, by letter dated 14 March 2000, Mrs. Helen Wiggins of the NHS Executive Headquarters stated: 'Regarding contacting members of the CFS/ME Working Group . . . as a result of numerous requests . . . and correspondence to members of the CFS/ME Working Group, a decision was made to stop facilitating these requests so that Working Group members would not be inundated with unsolicited correspondence.'

Channels of communication with members of the Working Group were further restricted when the Official Secrets Act was introduced into the situation. On 16 June 2000, Mrs. Helen Wiggins wrote to members of the Working Group enclosing a document entitled *Chief Medical Officer's Working Group on CFS/ME Procedures and Papers*. The letter stated: 'The attached procedures and papers guide is . . . intended to inform you about the working practices that the CFS/ME Working Group we will be adhering to ensure that this is the case' (sic).

The attached document stated: 'Advice to the Chief Medical Officer is given in the strictest confidence. It is most unlikely that official information provided to the CFS/ME Working Group will be covered by the Official Secrets Act. Should it be necessary to provide such information, a full explanation of members' obligations under the Act would be given . . . RESTRICTED classification will be used for. . . papers on sensitive issues.'

Even the mention of the Official Secrets Act seemed in stark contrast to the information given in the CMO's Working Group on CFS/ME Key Group Briefing No 1, of March 1999, which stated: 'Key working principles: The Group must have maximum 'transparency' i.e. as much information about its activities to be distributed as possible to all potential interested parties.'

The Montague/Hooper paper describes how, at a later date during the sitting of the CMO's Working Group, it again became apparent that the Group was unwilling to consider professional or lay concerns put before it:

There were a number of official attempts to involve lay participants in the work of the CMO's Report on CFS/ME, none of which gave any real chance for people to present serious scientific concerns to those involved. In particular we mention that at the *Adult Sounding Board Event* held on 7 June 2000, supposedly as a forum for the Working Group to note invited people's concerns about ME/CFS, the opportunity to put forward those concerns was tightly proscribed by the officials present; the agenda was narrowly defined and had been pre-arranged by the officials in advance. Attendees were permitted to discuss only certain 'acceptable' issues, which gave rise to considerable resentment.

This lack of willingness by the government to allow an open debate and consider all the evidence from lay sufferers and experts, as well as carefully chosen Working Group members, contrasted starkly with the unilateral manner in which they had taken associates of a psychiatrically leaning Linbury Trust onto the Working Group in exchange for a payment of £15,000.

The Linbury Trust

Thirty years ago, the great majority of scientific research was funded by government through the various Research Councils, or government departments; today the Wellcome Trust funds as much research as the Medical Research Council, while other private Trusts, commercial organisations and companies fund great swathes of scientific research both inside and outside the universities. While there are clear commercial advantages in this situation, there are also clear disadvantages and it is generally agreed that the privatisation of research in the field of medicine throws up singular problems in relation to ethics, methodological standards and the distribution of results.

The Chief Medical Officer is the highest ranking health official in the country; he is not only senior officer in the Department of Health, he is an advisor to all the Departments of Government and their ministers on any matters to do with health. Those policies to which the Chief Medical Officer puts his name are government policies. If the CMO's position were not so serious, the manner in which the CMO's Group on ME/CFS was organised would be amusing. How could a committee be assembled seemingly without the slightest regard for matters of bias, track record or vested commercial interests? How could a government advisory committee be convened without requiring members to declare any potential conflicts of interest?

Mainly an arts and humanities Trust, the Linbury Trust has, since 1991, invested over £5 million in Chronic Fatigue Syndrome research. The Trust has only three Trustees: Lord Sainsbury of Preston Candover, his wife Lady Sainsbury, and the solicitor Judith Portrait. Judith Portrait is solicitor for all the family Trusts, each of which is directed by family members.

At the end of the 1990s, the Linbury Trust had a total income of around £150m with an annual income of around £9m. In 1998 it paid £620,000 in grants to Chronic Fatigue Syndrome Research, by far the largest amount granted, apart from one capital grant of £4.5m to the Royal Opera House. The majority of each year's Linbury funding to Chronic Fatigue has gone to individuals and organisations which support the psychiatric aetiology of ME/CSF. From the beginning, the Trust appears to have been locked into what is now Guy's, King's and St. Thomas' Medical School. In supporting the Wessely school, the Trust has been partially responsible for the idea that ME/CFS has a psychiatric aetiology becoming the most dominant medical view of the disorder in the UK.

Lord Sainsbury of Preston Candover

Lord Sainsbury of Preston Candover educated at Stowe School and at Worcester College, Oxford. He entered the family business in 1950, becoming a Director in 1958. He took the Sainsbury's company through flotation in 1973 and retired in 1992 when he was made Life President. He was Chairman of the Board for twenty years from 1969 to 1989.

His interests are mainly in opera, ballet and the visual arts, leading to a number of appointments in these areas. He has served as a trustee of the National Gallery, the Westminster Abbey Trust and the Dulwich Picture Gallery, and since 1995 has been Chairman of the Governors of the Royal Ballet. He was knighted in 1979 and created a Life Peer in 1989.

Lord Sainsbury of Turville

It is difficult to understand to what extent each of the Sainsbury Trusts are separate entities, or whether another Sainsbury family member who is not a trustee, might advise on grant giving. All the Trusts are housed in one building, a number of them have common trustees and they all have the same solicitor. As a Trust directed by Lord Sainsbury of Candover, lover of the arts, seems an odd choice to support the highly contentious medical area of ME and CFS, including issues related to pharmaceuticals and chemicals, it is worth taking note of the interests of Lord David Sainsbury, Trustee of other Sainsbury's Trusts.

In July 1998, Lord David Sainsbury resigned as Chairman of the Sainsbury's supermarket chain to become the New Labour Government Minister for Science. This post made him Parliamentary Under-Secretary of State for Science and Innovation, responsible for the Office of Science and Technology and the chemical and biotechnology industries, as well as all the Research Councils, including the Medical Research Council. The Office of Science and Technology monitors all government funding of research and controls official science policy.

The Department is now based at the Department of Trade and Industry (Dti), after its precursors spent years in the wilderness while various government ministers pondered the problem of science and its linkage to industry. In 1992, the Conservative Government set up the last of the 'pure science' departments, the Office of Public Service and Science, under William Waldegrave.

SKEWED

One of its designated functions, implicit in the overlap between science and medicine and science and food, was the role of scientific assessment for consumers; in this guise the Department found itself fleetingly involved in the assessment of alternative and complementary medicine. Since then, the pharmaceutical and other industries have worked determinedly to get science policy inside the Dti.

Between 1996 and 2001, David Sainsbury donated £7 million to the Labour Party. He became Lord Sainsbury of Turville in 1997. He owns two genetic research companies, Diatech and Innotech Investments, the shares for which, together with his £1.3 billion worth of shares in Sainsbury's, have been put into a blind trust. The Gatsby Charitable Foundation, one of the Sainsbury Trust's, worth £22.5 million in 2000, has granted millions of pounds to the study and development of GM food. Since being appointed Science Minister and up until 2001, David Sainsbury's Department granted the Biotechnology and Biological Research Council (BBSRC) an extra £50 million in funding. The Chairman of the BBSRC in 2000 was Peter Doyle, former executive Director of the pharmaceutical and biotech company Zeneca.

A year into his job, in 1999, it was revealed that Lord David Sainsbury had been having meetings with Monsanto. It was reported that he held confidential discussions with three Monsanto executives in his private office at the Department of Trade and Industry only three weeks after he had attended the first meeting of the Cabinet's Ministerial Group on Biotechnology and Genetic Modification.

In January 2001, David Sainsbury personally brokered a deal with the North American finance house Stevens Inc., when the Royal Bank of Scotland announced that it would not extend an overdraft facility of £22.5 million to Huntingdon Life Sciences (HLS) in Cambridgeshire. The Home Office condemned the laboratory in 1997 for cruelty to dogs. Despite this and its pre-election pledge to improve animal welfare, the Labour Party holds 75,000 shares in what is considered to be Europe's largest vivisection research laboratory. Current drug company customers of HLS include Eli Lilly and Company, Zeneca Group plc, Glaxo Research & Development Ltd. and Novartis UK Ltd.

David Sainsbury has also personally attempted to push through a planning application by the University of Cambridge to build the biggest primate research centre in Europe, after the original application was unanimously rejected by the City Council in February 2001.

Incestuous relations

Whether or not Lord Sainsbury of Preston, or his brother Lord David Sainsbury, the Minister for Science, were influential via the Linbury Trust, in the setting up and staffing of the CMO's inquiry, we shall never know. The Linbury Trust, presumably led by its advisors, had in the past given money to research organised by a group attached to the pharmaceutical industry; in November 1999, it funded and participated in a Novartis Foundation symposium on CFS. The Novartis Foundation, which used to be the Ciba Foundation, is the academic arm of the Novartis pharmaceutical company.

In 2001, the four-man scientific group advising the Linbury Trustees was made up of Professor Richard Frackowiak, Professor Les Borysiewicz, Professor Alan McGregor and Dr. Tom Craig. Both McGregor and Craig are members of the same London University as Professor Wessely; one of them is from the Department of Psychiatry.

Professor Alan McGregor is the Head of the Department of Diabetes, Endocrinology and Internal Medicine at Guy's, King's and St. Thomas' School of Medicine. This School of Medicine, created in 1998 by the merger of three famous London Medical Schools, is now the largest medical school in Britain with an annual budget in 2000 of £80m, of which £36m was received in research grants and contracts from government and the independent sector. It includes the Institute of Psychiatry and the Department of Psychological Medicine, in both of which Professor Wessely holds senior positions.

Dr. Tom Craig is also at GKT School of Medicine, where he is Professor of Community Psychiatry. He is also a member of the steering committee of the primary care research group, along with Simon Wessely, of the Department of Psychological Medicine at the Maudsley Hospital.

After the CMO's Working Group members were chosen, the entire group was divided into subgroups, one group being called the Key Group, another group the Children and Young People's Group and the remaining members constituted as a broader Reference Group. All three groups consisted of professional experts and some representatives of CFS and ME organisations.

Excluding the Chair, Professor Allen Hutchinson, Director of Public Health, School of Health and Related Research, University of Sheffield, the Key Group originally comprised thirteen members. Of these, Dr. Trudie Chalder, Dr. Anthony Cleare, Dr. Peter White, Dr. Alison Round and later Professor Anthony Pinching, who was moved from the Reference Group to the Key Group and appointed Deputy Chair, have all in the past strongly promoted the view that CFS has a psychiatric aetiology. Dr. Charles Shepherd is colleague of Professor Wessely from the Campaign Against Health Fraud.

Dr. Trudie Chalder, originally a Registered Mental Health Nurse, became a behavioural psychotherapist and has built her career on researching Professor Wessely's beliefs on Cognitive Behavioural Therapy. She is now a researcher at the Institute of Psychiatry and Reader of Psychology and Nursing at GKT. She is a frequent co-author with Wessely on psychiatric research into CFS.

206

Same Old Same Old

In the years 1999 to 2001, Trudie Chalder received a grant of £43,578 from Linbury to research CFS. Dr. Cleare and Professor Simon Wessely co-authored the study. Chalder and Wessely have also received large grants from the Department of Health to research CBT, £337,713 from 1998 to 2001, in illnesses such as irritable bowel syndrome, which Wessely believes should, together with CFS, be classified as a psychiatric disorder. The majority of Chalder's published papers have been co-authored with Professor Wessely.

Dr. Anthony Cleare, as well as holding a position with Professor Wessely at the Institute of Psychiatry, is a Linbury Trust Fellow. In the Linbury Trust Annual Report for 1999 the Trustees describe Dr. Anthony Cleare's promotion to the Working Group in the following words: 'The Trust is contributing to the deliberations of the Working Group through the membership of the Working Group of the Linbury Senior Research Fellow.'

Dr. Charles Shepherd was, with Professor Wessely, an early member of HealthWatch and was also an adviser to the Ciba Foundation Media Resources Centre, the academic front organisation for what used to be Ciba Geigy. Dr. Peter White, a consultant psychiatrist at St. Bartholomew's Hospital, is considered to be a member of the Wessely school and has co-authored papers with other members.

Wessely himself was nominally a member of the Reference Group as opposed to the decision-making Key Group. It is thought by observers that he was made a member of the Reference Group only because there would have been too much of an outcry if he were seen to be a member of the influential Key Group. Whichever group to which they nominally belonged, the role played by both Wessely and Pinching in the work of the CMO's Group cannot be overestimated.

SKEWED

Although the CMO's Working Group had originally made the decision that it would commission no original research to support its work, in 1999 the Department of Health commissioned the Centre for Reviews and Dissemination (CRD) at the University of York to carry out a systematic review of the literature on the most effective management strategies for CFS. The Cochrane-style review was deemed to be wholly impartial and perhaps the most important evidence which the Working Group would consider. In effect, this review did almost all the work of the Chief Medical Officer's Working Group.

Established in January 1994, the NHS Centre for Reviews and Dissemination is a sibling of the Cochrane Collaboration and was set up to provide the NHS with guiding information on the effectiveness of treatments, the delivery and organisation of health care. The Centre is part of a network of 'evidence based' medicine review organisations that is headed by the Cochrane Collaboration.

The literature review was to be carried out by a team of five. As none of these individuals had any experience of ME or CFS, they were advised by a panel of experts. Those experts included Professor Wessely, Professor Pinching and Dr. Harvey Marcovitch, a strong supporter of Wessely in the past.

Professor Wessely provided his own database of CFS literature for use by the review team. As the only person on the CRD advisory panel familiar with Cochrane-style reviews, Wessely inevitably played a considerable part in determining the outcome of the review.

Although Cochrane-style systematic reviews♦ are considered state-of-the-art, there are many problems with them, not least that

---

♦ The Cochrane Collaboration, originally based in Oxford, is a group of people who are producing an internationally available meta-analysis of what its members consider to be the most effective treatment and management regimes for all medical and psychiatric conditions; its recommendations are intended to become the definitive database of 'evidence-based' treatment approaches.

they depend entirely upon the chosen database which usually tends to consist of double blind trials. Cochrane-style systematic reviews are intended to inform NHS policy and general practice.

The review carried out by the CRD for the CMO's Working Group was published in 2001 as *Effectiveness of Interventions used in the Treatment and Management of Chronic Fatigue Syndrome/ Myalgic Encephalomyelitis (ME) in Adults and Children*. It was authored by four staff from the NHS centre at York: Anne-Marie Bagnall, Penny Whiting, Kath Wright, and Amanda Sowden. The review, while conceding that there is no effective *treatment*, not surprisingly found that the most promising management results were achieved with CBT and GET.

It was not made clear how many of the studies reviewed under these headings had been carried out by Professor Wessely or his colleagues. Most other therapeutic approaches came under the heading of 'insufficient evidence' to warrant inclusion in the systematic review. The review did, however, came to negative conclusions about the use of antidepressant pharmaceuticals in cases of CFS. The considerable literature arguing against Professor Wessely's advocacy of this treatment left the reviewers with no other credible conclusion.

The systematic review that discusses CFS, its aetiology and symptoms, and the method, research and findings of the work, has eighty six references, one third of which refer to the work of Professor Wessely or like-minded colleagues, 'followers' or researchers. The review was commissioned to look only at the treatments and management of CFS, thus the remit yet again blocked any understanding of the illness or its physical causes.

It might be said that the York Review was the most significant piece of work to come out of the CMO's Working Group. It argued absolutely for psychiatric aetiology and psychiatric treatment. It was published a year before the official Report and funded by the Department of Health, and, or the Linbury Trust.

Opposition to the CMO's Report

After the first flurry of protest at the involvement of the Linbury Trust in the CMO's Working Group, concerned observers outside the Group quietly tried to tender their own evidence and made what they could of the 'Sounding Board Event.' As the Working Group continued its deliberations, and information inevitably leaked, many observers began to suspect that the final Report was not going to address the most important issues, namely, the need to investigate what was *causing* an increase in the disorder, recognition of the biomarkers which indicated organic multi-system disease and the investigative and diagnostic methods to be used for such complex abnormalities.

Of enormous concern was the advice which it was known was being integrated into the CMO's Report, that in cases of CFS/ME only *basic and limited* investigations were appropriate; specifically, that there was no need to perform immunological or neuro-imaging investigations.♦ It is these areas of research that are presently delivering hard evidence of the serious nature of the disorder. To advise that nothing more than basic testing should be done was reminiscent of the cover-up of the 1996 Joint Royal Colleges' Report.

Early in 2001, a group of severely affected sufferers, many of them with a clinical and medical research background, wrote a paper addressing the question of diagnostic testing. They felt strongly that UK clinicians should not be deliberately denied information about the tests necessary to reveal evidence of the illness.

♦ Research using neural imaging has found 'punctuate lesions' in numbers of ME patients.

Same Old Same Old

They obtained the support of Professor Malcolm Hooper, Emeritus Professor of Medicinal Chemistry at the University of Sunderland. Hooper, a critic of the psychiatric aetiology of Gulf War Syndrome who had already crossed swords with Professor Wessely, assisted the paper's authors with the biochemistry section of the paper.

In a foreword to the paper, Hooper wrote that he was happy to be associated with a 'challenging document written out of the "white heat" of the suffering and neglect that is so often the lot of people with ME, 25% of whom are severely affected and wheel-chair, house or bed bound.' Hooper pointed out that the need for science was 'emphasised throughout the document; this provides a sound basis for the diagnosis of ME, a multi-faceted condition. These studies need to be kept in the forefront of the minds of decision makers who are responsible for advice that will affect the care and management of ME sufferers.'

Hooper also put the case briefly for what he called *functional medicine*, which would help determine the biochemical dysfunction found in those affected by ME/CFS, suggesting that 'such measurements must be allied to understanding how the whole system is integrated into the functioning of the whole person.' Finally, he suggested that diagnostic and clinical testing was the only way forward: without it no one would be able to identify the various subsets of the illness. He ended with a call for a holistic understanding of the illness to encompass 'support structures including the environment, nutrition and nutritional supplements, particularly as drug therapy in these patients is often precluded by serious adverse reactions.'

Despite the clear and relatively orthodox thinking in Professor Hooper's introduction and the considered approach set out by the authors of the paper, it was immediately clear from the response of members of the CMO's Working Group that the views expressed in the paper were totally opposed by some members of the Group.

The Montague/Hooper paper

The paper, by Professor Malcolm Hooper and Sally Montague, published in May 2001 and entitled *Concerns about the forthcoming UK Chief Medical Officer's Report on Myalgic Encephalomyelitis (ME) and Chronic Fatigue Syndrome (CFS), notably the intention to advise clinicians that only limited investigations are necessary*, was the only serious public criticism of the CMO's Working Group. It was circulated to other clinicians, sufferers and campaigners.

The contents of the paper fall under two headings. The authors tried to make the case for CMO's inquiry being biased in favour of a psychiatric view of CFS. To show the bias, they drew attention to the membership of two Working Group members, and the association of another, with the 'health fraud' campaign Health-Watch. The authors then sketched in the link between HealthWatch, its approach to pharmaceutical medicine, its previous dismissal of ME, and contemporary 'official' views on CFS.

The Montague/Hooper paper is sixteen pages long and contains eighty nine references; it gives a thorough overview of all the available clinically cited diagnostic tests for ME and CFS. The first two pages of the paper make criticism of the CMO's Working Group and in particular its one time HealthWatch members, Dr. Charles Shepherd and Professor Simon Wessely, whom it takes to task for arguing against any review of diagnostic testing or aetiology. This quasi-sociological analysis, which hints at motive and vested interests, is not something that is normally done in what is primarily a medical and scientific paper. However, there are precedents for analysing vested interests along with science in medicine and in this particular case it is difficult to avoid.

Following circulation of the paper, those associated with it were subjected to a barrage of criticism contained in letters from Dr.

Shepherd. Dr. Shepherd carried on correspondence with the Vice Chancellor of Professor Hooper's University as well as the University's Public Relations Officer, in an attempt to get Professor Hooper disciplined. Dr. Shepherd wrote to Professor Allen Hutchinson, Chairman of the CMO's Working Group and to the Chief Medical Officer himself. He wrote to members of the Scottish Parliament in an attempt to question a long-standing speaking engagement of Professor Hooper's at a parliamentary meeting on Gulf War Syndrome. Finally, Malcolm Brahams, HealthWatch Chairman and solicitor, sent a legal letter from Messrs. David Wineman of Kingsway, London, to Professor Hooper.

Professor Hooper found himself embroiled in a situation experienced by others who have criticised HealthWatch and its members. This deliberate policy creates a threatening and quasi-legal 'paperfall', which attempts to stifle critics while confusing and obfuscating the real issues at the centre of the conflict. The strategy is to turn the argument into a personal one and further create a threatening situation, which in turn creates a critical moratorium. As Hooper and Montague state in their reply to the HealthWatch solicitor's letter:

> Overall, it is noted that Dr. Shepherd has not addressed the fundamental issues in the Montague / Hooper document. He has concentrated only on what he considers to be his personal position and fails to address the wider concerns set out in the original paper.

Hooper and Montague meticulously addressed and answered every point which Dr. Shepherd raised in his grapeshot correspondence with a precise and combative critique of vested interests, which they and others considered present in the CMO's Working Group.

In his correspondence, Dr. Shepherd tries to obscure statements and positions previously taken by himself and his HealthWatch colleague Professor Wessely. For example, he flatly denied that, as suggested by Hooper and Montague, Professor Wessely was in favour of pharmaceutical intervention in cases of CFS. Hooper and Montague were able to quote Professor Wessely's express recommendations for the use of antidepressants in ME/CFS patients in no less than twelve published instances.

The veil of confusion which frequently falls over the arguments of HealthWatch and its members, together with threats of litigation, argues more eloquently than could any patient campaigner that HealthWatch and its members have objectives other than those stated in the organisations literature. The correspondence which followed the Montague/Hooper paper shows that those who campaign for a more scientific appraisal of ME and CFS could find themselves handicapped by threats of legal action, academic discipline and unspecified but worrying social retributions.

Multiple Chemical Sensitivity
and Munchausen's Syndrome by Proxy

Despite frequent warnings from his parents, Ruth and David, eight-year-old Joe took a can of organophosphorous (OP) insecticide into the garden on a summer's day in 1993 and sprayed it on an ants' nest. His mother found him in a cloud of vapour. Three weeks after the exposure, Joe was admitted to the family's local north of England hospital suffering from *mesenteric adenitis*. While he was in hospital it was noted that he had been suffering from breathing difficulties for the previous three weeks, however, neither Ruth nor David connected these symptoms or his vague tummy pains with his chemical exposure.

Joe became more ill; the first evident symptom was a loss of balance. From being a well co-ordinated eight-year-old, he began to inexplicably fall over, or off chairs. By Christmas, Joe was too ill to play with his presents, and stayed in bed.

His parents took Joe to the local paediatrician, ignorant of the fact that the family GP had previously recorded in Joe's notes that his mother was 'over anxious.' In actual fact, Ruth was a teacher of many years' experience who had specialised in the counselling of parents with sick children. The first lesson she had learned in counselling was to listen to the parents. Joe now had had the following symptoms: lack of balance, rotting smell in the nose, low grade temperature, sweats, nightmares from which he could not be woken, a change in taste so that food tasted 'bad', anxiety, pains in joints, difficulty sleeping, a strange green colour and a wet, greasy looking swollen face, a 'bitter' body odour, mouth ulcers and red painful spots on and around his genitals and under his armpits. Despite this, Ruth was unable to convince the paediatrician that there was anything physically wrong with him.

In January of the following year, after making contact with a new doctor, the family were sent to see a Harley Street consultant, who diagnosed ME. He suggested that Joe should stay off school for the rest of the year and be tutored at home. A series of conventional tests were embarked upon, these were sent for analysis to a microbiologist, Dr. Sykes, and they all proved negative. Ruth asked her GP about the possibility of OP poisoning but neither he nor Dr. Sykes, who failed to reply to Ruth's letter, gave her a satisfactory answer.

Looking back, Ruth now thinks that it was a serious mistake not to pursue the question of OP's. She continued annually to expose Joe to the same insecticide for six years after his initial exposure. For instance, she sprayed Joe's bedroom to rid it of ants.

Joe's headmaster was happy for him to take time off school and be tutored at home, however, reaching the age of eleven, three weeks before the end of the summer term, his parents were summarily told that he could not go on to his local public school as children with ME did badly in their GCSE's. Instead, Joe attended the local middle school, at first on a part-time basis, then more regularly. He did exceptionally well transferring to the senior school at fourteen.

In 1999, he took part in the local Young Musician of the Year competition and despite his persistent illness, Joe worked hard to obtain one of the best GCSE results in his year. His parents thought their son was on the mend. However, just before he took his GCSE's Joe's health went into rapid decline.

Same Old Same Old

Having discovered a scientist in North America who was researching Gulf War Syndrome and ME, Joe's parents went back to their doctor and from there to Dr. Sykes, who had carried out previous tests. It was at this time that Joe's mother began to meet a determined resistance to test Joe for any physical causes of his illness. Dr. Sykes prevaricated, in the end after pressure, at some expense to Joe's parents, samples for both Joe and Ruth were sent to North America. Joe's samples came back positive for the micoplasma M. Hominis.

At the next interview with Dr. Sykes, Ruth learned why he had been prevaricating. Apparently, he did not believe the Gulf War veterans were physically ill and, when she asked him about Organophosphates, he shrugged it off, saying that it was not possible. After confusingly telling Ruth that he could have got the tests done in England, Dr. Sykes accepted the recommendation of the US researcher that Joe should be prescribed antibiotics while suggesting to Joe's doctor that he might take up Graded Exercise Therapy and meditation.

In June 2001, Joe's parents sought advice at a private hospital which had been treating ME patients. Here they were told that their son was very ill and, in the opinion of the doctor they saw, the antibiotics which Joe had been prescribed had placed further strain on his gut. Unfortunately, many of the symptoms recognised by the private hospital were not ones recognised by orthodox medicine. Over the next year, Joe was treated with vitamins while being desensitised to various foods and chemicals. Despite missing another year of school, Joe's health slowly began to improve.

Inevitably, treatment at the private hospital cost money and because the NHS did not provide any treatment for either

ME or chemical sensitivity, Joe's parents began a search for funding; they got nowhere. In fact, the doctor Chairman of their local NHS Trust ended up shouting down the phone to Ruth that he did not believe in OP poisoning.

Almost six months after the family first asked for help from the NHS, they were granted an appointment with the local consultant neurologist. At first they saw him privately and had a long consultation about Joe which they considered satisfactory. Ruth asked the consultant if it would be possible for Joe to see a neurologist in London who specialised in OP's, she was told that this would be possible. The next appointment which they attended, however, was to be a bizarre affair, termed now by Ruth as 'sinister'.

When the family arrived they found themselves to be the only people waiting for a consultation in what was usually a teeming waiting area. They were finally invited into a small room and confronted by three people: an unidentified man squashed into one corner, the consultant seated at his desk and an enormous 'male nurse' who seemed to fill the rest of the room. After the family sat, the 'bouncer nurse' stood with his arms folded behind David's with his knees against the back of the chair, his body language radiating menace. When Ruth shifted to get more comfortable, he leant over her. The neurologist was no longer affable, and after examining Joe, he returned to the room saying that as he thought, he had found nothing. While he examined Joe, Ruth ascertained that the man in the corner was the hospital Registrar, responsible for administering any vitamin treatment if the neurologist agreed it. Joe would not, they said, have to visit a private hospital in the future.

After he had pronounced that there was nothing wrong with Joe, the neurologist suddenly began to investigate David and Ruth. What did they know about OP pesticides? Leaning across the table, his nose almost touching David's, he wondered whether he had attended all Joe's consultations. During a break in this posturing, Ruth asked about the appointment with the neurologist specialising in OP's. It could be arranged at a few weeks notice, she was told. More than one year later, the family still awaits this appointment.

Ruth complained to Joe's doctor about the consultation and suggested that something was going on. Her suspicions soon proved to be grounded. David and Ruth had applied to the NHS for Joe's medical notes when considering a legal action against the OP spray's manufacturer. The notes arrived a few days after the second consultation with the neurologist. Going through them Ruth found a note from Dr. Sykes to Joe's doctor. In this he stated that Joe's US test for micoplasmas was positive but he added:

> I am sure the Mum/Joe interaction is contributing to Joe's symptoms but do not dare broach this until some improvement allows for natural progression.

The next letter from Sykes, sent late in 2001, made the most serious accusation that could be made of any mother.

> I feel compelled to say that I feel uneasy about how Joe's situation is being managed by his mother. It seems to me there is a possibility that Joe himself may not be unwell but has been rendered so by his mother – some form of Munchausen's by proxy perhaps. I am not an expert in this field at all but I put this forward as a consideration. I am mindful that a direct confrontation will make matters worse. It may be reasonable to discuss this initially with the child psychiatrist to determine how best to approach the matter if you feel this is a reasonable option. I am happy to write directly to the child psychiatrist to ask for her advice if you feel that this is a possibility worth exploring.

In February 2002, the family had to resort to asking the local vet to spin blood to send to the private hospital as Dr. Sykes refused to do so. Ruth and David complained to the Health Authority and feel now that the following Munchausen accusation was made out of spite. Shortly after Ruth had complained about Sykes' he wrote a more determined letter to Joe's doctor, the neurologist and the Health Authority Chairman.

> I would strongly urge active exploration of Munchausen's by proxy, if we are to help Joe.

Reading the notes and remembering the 'sinister' consultation, Ruth realised that she and her husband had been very close to having Joe removed from their care.

In an attempt to counter the damaging notes in Joe's medical file, David wrote to all the doctors concerned demanding an apology, a retraction and the removal of the three offending letters and any other information from the file. All replies amounted to obfuscation.

In April 2003, Joe had a blood test sent to a world expert on pesticide poisoning in North Carolina. He confirmed that Joe has a 'significant increase in autoantibodies against neuronal and glial proteins in his serum. This is consistent with brain damage from exposure to neurotoxic chemicals such as organo-phosphorous insecticides.' Ruth brought these results to her GP and asked him to notify the Health Authority Chairman and the neurologist only to be told that they would not accept them.

Joe has now been ill for ten years but has coped very well. In August 2003 it will be two years since the NHS was asked for advice and funding for treatment after he relapsed and which he still needs. Nothing has been done for him. He is now back at school studying for his 'A' levels. Ruth says that she has knowledge of far worse measures, obscured by court secrecy laws, being taken against mothers by doctors and family courts, she wants these mothers to tell their stories.

CHAPTER SIX

The Wood and the Trees

'It's just that most psychiatrists tend to read portents into normal behaviour . . .'
'Living with a psychiatrist can be tough . . . My wife's had her fill of me recently.' [34]

In no other medical controversy have physicians used sick people as political footballs for personal, financial, and political advancement. Even the scientific method has been corrupted. Only an article that concludes that MCS is psychiatric is politically correct and acceptable for publication. [35]

A substantially covert battle has been fought over the last decade to enlarge the parameters of mental illness at the expense of previously categorised and verified physical illnesses of unknown cause. The guiding hand behind the broad reconstruction of mental illness, especially in relation to chemical sensitivity and environmental illness, appears to have been industry generally, and in particular the chemical and insurance industries.

If the narrative throughout this book lacks analysis, it is principally because the largest part of analysis, in this case, must be made up of motive. While most of the usual motives can be examined, it is important with respect to the academics and scientists involved, that we retain a balanced perspective. We have to assume

---

34 Jonathan Valin, *Second Chance*, Dell Publishing, New York 1991.
35 Dr. Ruth Gordon McGill, M.D.

that these individuals have sincerely held beliefs, which they act out according to their professional understanding. Given this, conclusions are difficult. In this final chapter I have tried to address a number of the themes that grow out of the previous sections.

At war with the laity

When Dr. Anne Macintyre was working on a revised edition of her book *M.E. PostViral Fatigue Syndrome: how to live with it*, she included more information about Ean Proctor than had been included in the first edition. Although using another name for Professor Wessely, he claimed that he could be identified. Not only Dr. Macintyre but also her publishers, Thorsons, an imprint of Harper Collins, were threatened with demands that the name be removed, despite the fact that the publishers had on successive readings of the manuscript raised no objections to what was a completely factual account. The pressure put upon the publishers was such that they gave in removing any recognisable reference to Professor Wessely in relation to the case of Ean Proctor. Despite the fact that a discussion of this case was in the public interest and was a matter of public record, a more detailed account was left out of the book.

It is clear that HealthWatch members, and those who support like organisations, are unwilling to accept even the most rudimentary public debate, let alone lay or professional criticism. Instead, they appear to want to substitute the less public discipline of law or other quasi-legal tribunals. As soon as something is written about them, even before it is published, members telephone writers and journalists, write to MPs or Peers, asking for meetings at which they produce pre-emptory assertions that do not necessarily bear public scrutiny.

The legal and quasi-legal threat is a strategy used by 'health fraud' activists to make it appear that it is *they* who are being maligned and wronged. Such claims are cleverly orchestrated to make it appear that patients and practitioners who believe in complementary medical approaches are part of a large campaigning and even criminal 'cult', able to call on heavy and powerful resources to wreak vengeance.

Even more worrying is the fact that some professionals inside and outside medicine who support psychiatric aetiology also run campaigns against patients, accusing them of all kinds of calumny. In the cynical climate of the contemporary developed world, you get ill with ME, CFS, MCS or GWS, you are accused of being mentally ill, denied effective treatment, then when you campaign for 'real science', you are accused of terrorising those who do not believe in your illness.

Writing about the lawsuit served by Health Freedom attorney Carlos F. Negrete against Stephen Barrett and his 'health fraud' associates in North America, Tim Bolen says '. . . techniques he (Barrett) and his followers have used over and over against practitioners of alternative health methods are lawsuits, and threats of lawsuits.' Both the British and North American supporters of the psychiatric aetiology of MCS, ME and CFS portray continuous stories of feuds, dirty warfare and hate mail directed at them by sufferers from these illnesses. So concertedly is this done and with such unerring repetition that it could be considered an organised campaign.

While it is obviously the case that people suffering from little-understood but debilitating illnesses will want to reply critically to articles, books and statements which are biased against them, the idea that this amounts to a kind of terrorist campaign comes straight from the textbooks on psychological warfare operations.

After all, if your message is that people who say they are suffering from MCS, ME or CFS are mentally ill, then accusing them of irrational attacks adds strength to your case. Accusations of mental illness and terrorism give sustenance to the professionally and publicly held views on ME and CFS. This relentless 'behind the scenes' attrition projects a public image of sufferers as being difficult, neurotic and non-legitimate.

Richard Sykes was the Director of the ME charity Westcare until it was taken over by the charity Action for ME. Over the past fifteen years Sykes used the good offices of his charity to support a holistic approach to CFS and ME. In 1993, he put the organisational power of Westcare behind a National Task Force to inquire into the illnesses. Westcare also became the UK organisation which distributed the *CFIDS Chronicle*, the journal of the major North American CFS support group.

The issue of the *CFIDS Chronicle* for Spring 1994 contained a hard-hitting article written by two British women about the published academic views of Professor Wessely. Looking at actual quotations from Professor Wessely's published work, the article raised serious questions about the credibility of his views. Before the journal was distributed, pressure was put on Richard Sykes to tear out the offending piece. Being a small charity unwilling to risk litigation, Westcare removed the article from every journal they distributed. UK subscribers were furious when they received defaced copies of a journal for which they had paid in advance and against which there had been no injunction.

In place of the *Chronicle* article a note was inserted which read: 'It is regrettable that an article has had to be removed from this issue since it could possibly be held to be defamatory by the British Courts . . .'

Elaine Showalter's late arrival in the ME fray and her impeccable academic credentials have not deterred her from entering into rude reposte to CFS sufferers who have criticised her work. Following the publication and worldwide distribution of her book which claimed that CFS and GWS patients were hysterics, and their claims to be ill, little different from those who suggested that they had been abducted by aliens, Showalter made much of alleged threats she claimed were made against her life.

The web site for information about Princeton University, where Showalter is a Professor of English, included in 2002, along with adulatory items such as, 'Renowned Feminist Critic,' information about 'Activist Protesters' who have spoken out against Showalter's writing. A feature profile by Nicole Plett made much of the threats against her.

> With her all-American bob haircut, maternal demeanour, and impeccable Ivy League credentials, literary critic Elaine Showalter hardly seems a likely target for terrorists. Yet her latest book, *Hystories: Hysterical Epidemics and Modern Culture*, published in April by Columbia University Press, provoked a serious threat from a chronic fatigue syndrome activist at a Washington bookstore last month.

> Retelling the story in the modest comfort of her Princeton home of 30 years, Showalter seems more generally disturbed than fearful for her life. Beside her she places an inch-thick folder of hate mail, most of it, she is quick to note, from members of a *well-organized chronic fatigue syndrome lobby who have not read the book*, but who have heard about it on radio, television, or via the Internet.

Months before *Hystories* was launched, Showalter claims, a colleague, Joyce Carol Oates, had forewarned her not to go on any book tours because she might be assassinated. Showalter, who is clearly capable of perceiving herself as a character in a post-modern woman's crime fiction, gives a classically hysterical account of the later conspiracy to assassinate her:

> Showalter says her Washington talk was winding down when the young man confronted her. 'He was in army fatigues with long hair and a baseball cap, wearing all kinds of badges,' she recalls. 'He had a bright blue ribbon on his fatigues which is a sign the chronic fatigue syndrome people wear. He turned around and said, 'You should have taken your friend Oates' advice about not

going on this tour.' So I said, 'Do you mean about being assassinated?' And he said, 'Yes, that's just what I mean.' And I said, 'Is this a threat?' And he said, 'Well it's not from me,' – sort of implying that somebody else is going to get you. And at that point my driver, said 'I think you'd better leave.' And we left.

So this is what it means to be a radical intellectual in contemporary America – a Salman Rushdie of Chronic Fatigue Syndrome. After all, Showalter only used her scholarship and status to suggest that thousands of US and British citizens suffering from debilitating physical illnesses are mentally ill. For this, frighteningly, she was approached by a man wearing lots of badges and ribbons.

One of the most serious intellectual critiques of Showalter's book was written by Mary Schweitzer, a CFS sufferer who was at that time on two years' medical leave from her position as Associate Professor in the Department of History at Villanova University. In the Spring 1997 issue of the *CFIDS Chronicle*, Schweitzer wrote *Chronic Fatigue Syndrome and the Cynics*; the review was an objective critique of the CFS chapter in Showalter's book.

Seemingly not content with the disparity of power which exists between a well-published academic and her targeted CFS sufferers, Showalter responded to Schweitzer's review by sending the *Chronicle of Higher Education* a newspaper clipping from a recent issue of a chronic fatigue sufferers periodical depicting Schweitzer, fist raised, leading a demonstration in San Francisco. This depiction of her critic, supposedly as a liar and cheat, was, Showalter appeared to imagine, a proper intellectual response to serious criticisms of her work.

Michael Fumento has a section on his web site entitled 'Hate Mail', in which he mercilessly scorns those who write critically of his support for industry and the chemical companies. Rather than enter into a dialogue with these critics, Fumento pokes fun at their poor grammar and inarticulateness. Interestingly, a patent sincerity shines through the lack of education in many of the letters. All of which, when viewed together with Fumento's power-exuding publicity photographs, leaves a hard aftertaste of arrogance.

Criticism of patients and practitioners, and the maintenance of the fiction that they are the most powerful players structuring the game, run like a vein through the last decade of 'health fraud' material in both Britain and North America. Under the heading 'Demonstrators Disrupt Allergy Workshop,' the NCAHF Newsletter reported on a demonstration at a 1991 meeting of the American College of Allergy and Immunology in San Francisco. The meeting was set to discuss how to work with patients who reported with environmental illnesses but in reality suffered psychiatric problems.

> We arrived at our workshop to find a number of patients
> confined to wheel chairs with oxygen masks in place, or wearing
> filters, who were identifiable as patients with so-called
> environmental illness. Approximately 4-hours into the workshop
> a clinical ecologist (MD) accompanied the demonstrators as they
> forced their way into the workshop. When asked to leave they
> refused and the ecologists demanded to have access to the
> platform. The workshop was recessed and the speakers dispersed
> to reconvene after the demonstrators had been evicted by the
> security personnel and local police. It would appear that any
> programs that might address issues surrounding the effects of
> unproven and controversial methods of diagnosis and treatment
> may be targeted for such demonstrations in the future.

Reporting on the lessons from this disrupted conference, the *NCAHF Newsletter* quotes from a paper by Stewart in the *International Journal of Mental Health*: 'Emotional disorders misdiagnosed as physical illness: environmental hypersensitivity, candidiasis hypersensitivity, and chronic fatigue syndrome,' which noted:

> Support groups not only lobby for legislation in recognition of
> their disabilities, and try to get the media to carry stories about
> people disabled by these disorders, but also threaten legal action

against those who criticize the practice of clinical ecology and attempt to interfere with objective study of these disorders.

The first part of this quote comes close to suggesting that to lobby for the recognition of a disability and to try to get the media to take on an issue is subversive; the second part turns facts on their head. While clinical ecologists and their patients have often been the subject of a variety of legal actions and denigrating newspaper articles, the NCAHF or any other quackbusting group would find it almost impossible to cite cases of legal action *against* themselves or any other critics of clinical ecology.

In Britain in 1990, members of the Campaign Against Health Fraud were involved with two cancer research charities, the Imperial Cancer Research Fund (ICRF) and the Cancer Research Campaign (CRC), in a combined research project. The study, which looked at the work and results of a small alternative health clinic in the South West of England, the Bristol Cancer Help Centre, concluded that women who attended the centre were three times as likely to die as those who sought conventional treatment. Following this internationally publicised study, which brought the centre to its knees, loyal women breast cancer patients organised a campaign to expose the faulty research of the cancer charities.

While the study was being carried out, a reporter, David Henshaw, researched a two-part television programme about the Centre. Unbeknown to the staff, who had assumed that the programmes were supportive of the Centre, the programmes were actually scheduled to be shown in support of the flawed research.

In 1994, three years after both the research and the television programmes, and long after Sir Walter Bodmer had publicly retracted the research, an edition of *Uncensored*, a throw-away supplement produced by the Sunday *Observer* newspaper, carried an article by the journalist and writer Duncan Campbell. In the article, Henshaw was quoted claiming that although he had worked on films about Colombian drugs barons, he had never before received the terrible threats which had followed the programme about Bristol Cancer Help Centre.

In her halcyon days of the early Campaign Against Health Fraud, Caroline Richmond was a past-mistress of the throw-away insult to sufferers and many of her remarks have echoed in the writing of others, suggesting that perhaps they had their origins in some corporate policy. Always one to come up with a quick empirical diagnosis, Richmond wrote about an ME patient in the *Medical Monitor* in 1989:

> One person sent me a magazine article with a photo of a sufferer sitting in a wheelchair and she described how she was getting progressively weaker. And she looked fulfilled, happy, healthy, attractive and well presented.

From the earliest days of the Campaign Against Health Fraud, Caroline Richmond was tireless in her attacks upon those suffering from chemical sensitivity and against those claiming to suffer from ME.♦ In one article, Richmond dwelt on the idea that ME and CFS sufferers are chronically self-obsessed. She used the little trick of turning the initials M. E. into 'me', the aim being to denote self-obsession on the part of sufferers.

♦ Caroline Richmond's published articles involving ME include: Cases involving 20th-century diseases start landing in British courts, *Can Med Assn J* 1992: 146: 4: 585-586; When allergy becomes craze, *Hospital Doctor* 12 March 1992:60-61; Judge condemns clinical ecology, *GP* 17 January 1992:62; Princess Aurora and the wandering womb, *BMJ* 1989:298:1295-6; Yours disgustingly, *Medical Monitor* 16 June 1989:36; Myalgic encephalomyelitis: a new name for old symptoms, *Pulse* 14 October 1989:92; Finding a new approach in practice to the post viral fatigue syndrome, *Pulse* 2 April 1988; Supplying facts that ME sufferers will buy, *Doctor* 27 July 1989; What is ME?, *The Oldie*, November 1992:26-7.

SKEWED

The continuing British 'health fraud' approach to ME over the last decade owes much to Caroline Richmond's prejudice against sufferers. 'Health fraud' supporters have appeared to vie amongst themselves to produce the nastiest ME jibe. In 1995, Dr. Douglas Carnall wrote a Bluffers' Guide in *Doctor* in which he said:

> Yesteryear's neurasthenia . . . modern day bluffers prefer the term chronic fatigue syndrome . . . if [patients] insist on a physical diagnosis, tell them that chronic fatigue syndrome is a complex disorder in which multiple bio psychosocial factors are mediated via the anterior hypothalamus – in other words, it's all in the mind.

A more contemporary issue of *Doctor* magazine published a supposedly humorous 'Question and Answers' quiz in which the question 'What would be your initial response to a patient presenting with a self-diagnosis of ME?' was correctly answered with, 'For God's sake pull yourself together, you piece of pond life.'

A further recent illustration of malign ignorance geared to generating distress in people with ME and CFS was an article by Julie Birchill on 9 August 2001 in the *Guardian* called 'Grin and Bear It' in which she wrote:

> The great thing about the great Victor Lewis-Smith, the TV critic . . . is his tireless baiting, beyond the call of duty, of the ME – or the Me, Me, Me lobby . . . Victor has incidentally discovered that he also has the power of healing these unfortunates, as every time he tosses them a tasty taunt, they spring into action . . . he memorably wrote 'My articles seemed to have great therapeutic value for ME sufferers, provoking them to feats of physical exertion of which they had no idea they were capable (by writing letters to the newspaper in response to his articles) and I therefore considered it my duty to write deprecatingly about ME on a regular basis in a bid to boost their energy levels and get them firmly on the road to recovery.' Of course, what Victor was mocking was the idea put about in recent years by professional bleeding hearts that what might best be called unfortunate habits – lazing around . . . feeling a bit miz – are actually 'illnesses',

their victims deserving as much attention, sympathy and
resources as those people suffering from, say, terminal cancer . .
. Treating self-destructive behaviour as a comedy rather than a
tragedy may actually have a more bracing effect on sufferers
than endless sympathy, therapy and treatment.

While one should not necessarily pay serious attention to a magazine columnist who is unable to differentiate between greatness and
cynicism and who uses the expression 'a bit miz', Birchill's message does has a serious side.

This more serious message was illustrated in a recent article in
GP magazine written by Dr. Bogdanovic, a collaborator of Professor Wessely and an academic registrar in Oxford, who, in a review
of illness management, wrote: 'The provision of disability services
and benefit payments is a controversial issue.' If people with ME or
CFS receive state benefits, he wrote, it could 're-enforce' their idea
that they are sick. This, of course, goes for any kind of medical
advice from doctors; perhaps doctors should only give diagnostic
advise and recommend disability benefits to those who categorically state that they are well.

This suggestion that receipt of services and benefits might well
be seen by those presenting with ME or CFS as 'secondary gain' is
a frequently made comment of those who believe in psychiatric
aetiology. It posits the idea that those who present with ME or CFS
as a physical illness are actually constructing an elaborate plot to
accrue personal gains of varying kinds.

In October 2001, *Pulse*, like *Doctor* and *GP* a pharmaceutically
supported supplement for doctors, carried an article on ME in which
three doctors were invited to give their opinion; one of these doctors
was Dr. Mary Church, a Principal GP in a practice in Blantyre,
Lanarkshire, in Scotland, and a member of the BMA Medical Ethics
Committee. In total seriousness, she gave this unequivocal opinion:

Never let the patients know you think ME doesn't exist and is a disease of malingerers. Frustrating though it is to see these patients return with inconsistent symptomatology, certain members of the profession are true believers . . . Never advise an ME patient to make a review appointment. At the end of the consultation, I say goodbye, not *au revoir*. Always refer ME patients to a local expert. It's a wonderful way of passing the buck.

The flawed methodology of academic psychiatry

Ted Shaw, an Australian CFS activist, began an address to the 1999 ME/CFS Conference in Sydney with the case history of an eleven-year-old girl. Living with her divorced mother and thirteen-year-old brother, the girl had developed an illness similar to glandular fever. Apart from a high temperature, swollen glands and a headache, she suffered debilitating tiredness. She recovered from this bout of illness but two months later was struck down again and experienced vomiting, abdominal pains, sore throat, swollen glands and nausea. The girl's GP diagnosed ME/CFS.

Six months after the girl recovered she was again ill. During this attack she developed severe ear pains, vomiting and diarrhoea and, unsurprisingly, she cried a lot. She collapsed and from that time found it first difficult and then impossible to walk. 'Her body was like jelly and she had trouble co-ordinating her movements.'

In the summer of the following year the girl was twice taken to a large general hospital in her area. The doctors, having failed to find any cause for her illness, placed her under the care of a hospital psychiatrist. In hospital she became the recipient of a 'tough love' regime and put under constant pressure to get better and mix with others. Over the next six months, she spent time at home and in hospital, while at home she made gradual improvements, at the hospital she found the programme of enforced activity stressful.

The Wood and the Trees

When her psychiatrist attempted to push her into attending a full week's school with no lunch break or rest periods, her mother took her away from the hospital.

Finding that the child had left the hospital, the psychiatrist activated the Suspected Child Abuse and Neglect (SCAN) team. The girl's mother was told that her daughter could be forcibly removed from her and taken back into the hospital. In an attempt to help with the girl's deteriorating condition and in the hope that she might find alternative advice, the mother took her to another hospital, only to find treatment there worse than in the first hospital.

> After spending ten days on the medical ward, the young lady was shifted into the psychiatric ward. The psychiatrist at this hospital introduced himself by coming into the room, opening the blinds to let in the bright sunlight, putting her bed straight up and stating that he was going to refer to her as the 'wah wah baby' every time she cried.

> In the new hospital, the psychiatrist reactivated the SCAN team and the child was removed from the custody of her mother and placed into the care of the department of family services. They are now seeking a foster home for the child when she is released from hospital. The report from the hospital psychiatrist is highly inaccurate. He attempts to cast the child in the worst possible light to justify his opinion that her symptoms are psychological.

Shaw concluded a number of things from this case history, especially that in Australia, parents have no voice in care hearings when a judge, psychiatric and family services are involved. Remarkably similar case histories are repeated internationally; they take place in a world where psychiatrists have access to draconian powers and where, despite being causes for extreme concern, the facts rarely seems to filter through to the saner world.

Embodied in this case history, however, and others like it, is the conundrum at the heart of CFS. Here is a conflict between State trained and employed professionals, whose theories, actions and clinical outcomes are shrouded in secrecy, circumscribed by interest conflicts but defended by the State, and ordinary citizens beset by crippling illnesses who turn to these professionals for support and treatment. How have psychiatrists developed such immense power, which extends far beyond the sanctioned evidence of regular physicians?

Psychiatry is not an exact science, it is not even a science; it does not depend on verifiable quantitative material or laboratory results. Psychiatric theory and diagnosis are faddish in the extreme. Any psychiatric diagnosis is an interpretation, and as such is often skewed to fit the view of an individual doctor whose judgement is affected by prevailing commercial, cultural and ideological influences.

At one time or another the cause of virtually every new illness has been claimed to be psychiatric. At its most gross, psychiatric theory has laid claim to theories of racial superiority and homosexuality as an illness. Dorothy Rowe points out in her introduction to *Making Us Crazy*, that 'Benjamin Rush, the father of American psychiatry, coined the mental illness of "anarchia" for people who were unhappy with the American political structure. He found that the people most prone to this disease were negroes and poor whites.'

Psychiatrists once dubbed Multiple Sclerosis the faker's disease. They theorised that Parkinson's disease was a psychiatric condition, its tremors caused by a frustrated wish to masturbate. Early in the twentieth century, it was psychiatrists who asserted that diabetes was the last strand of neurosis caused by sexual repression. They have also prescribed a psychiatric aetiology to asthma and stomach ulcers.

'Evidence based psychiatric medicine' would appear to be an oxymoron. In treatments for ME and CFS, frequent scientific papers suggest that psychological treatments become a *first* port of call when doctors are ignorant of, or unwilling to investigate, the physical evidence of illness.

The Wood and the Trees

The historical comparison of one apparently psychiatric condition with that of others in another century, such as the claim that CFS and ME are the same condition as neurasthenia, is gobble-degook and has no intellectual or rational validity. Ways of record-ing illnesses are culturally specific. Information about states of mind; social, sexual and psychological influences and, for example, the ideas influencing the male physician's view of the female patient, have changed radically over the last century and a half.

The treatments so persistently advocated for ME and CFS, CBT and GET, are used following the adoption of ideological and subjective opinions about the nature and cause of these illnesses. In the case of antidepressants, a mainstay of the psychiatric industry in ME and CFS, the literature is unequivocal: they do not help. To interpret patients' symptoms with a minimum of clinical invest-igations, to conclude that these illnesses originate 'in the mind,' and then to give them psychotropic drugs and therapies which help them see that they are suffering from false illness beliefs, runs counter to any idea of good medical practice.

Psychiatric diagnosis has increasingly come under attack in the last decades in areas other than ME and CFS. The textbook of diagnosis, the *American Psychiatric Association's Diagnostic and Statistical Manual of Mental Disorders* (DSM), was a small spiral notebook of less than 150 pages selling for $3.50 in 1968; today, it is over 900 pages, defining more than 300 psychiatric disorders and costing $55. At least three highly critical books have been written about the contemporary *DSM-IV*. Dr. Thomas Szasz, one of America's most radical psychiatric thinkers, wrote, in support of *The Selling of DSM, The Rhetoric of Science in Psychiatry*, that the book 'exposes the pretence that psychiatric diagnoses are the names of genuine diseases and the authentication of this fraud by an unholy alliance of the media, the government and psychiatry.'

SKEWED

Paula Caplan, author of *They Say You're Crazy*, says of *DSM-IV* that 'by dint of a handful of influential professionals' efforts, the subjective determinants of diagnosis masquerade as solid science and truth.' Carol Tavris, reviewing Caplan's book, said that 'Mental Health professionals need to read this book to cure themselves of Delusional Scientific Diagnosing Disorder and the public needs to read it for self protection.'

Throughout the second half of the twentieth century, there have been serious misgivings about the construct of mental ill health. Foucault suggested that mental illness was almost entirely a justification for medical power; Szasz has suggested that mental illness is a disguise with which we cover moral conflicts and Thomas Scheff suggests that it is a label used when a person's behaviour defies other explanations. R. D. Laing believed that conventional professional psychiatry, with its emphasis on technology and incarceration and its alienating distance between professionals and patients, was unable to help those in mental pain. In fact, all of these explanations, none of which has anything to do with objective science, could explain the use of psychiatry against ME and CFS patients.♦

It has been suggested that there are serious problems relating to the research instruments which are used in determining a variety of psychiatric illnesses. In one of the most intelligent analyses of a psychiatric ascription for CFS, Leonard Jason says that the 'use of the original case definition of CFS and the type and scoring of psychiatric tests appear to have produced erroneous estimates of the extent of CFS co-morbidity with psychiatric disorders.'

Jason says that assertions of psychiatric researchers that depression occurs in about 50% of CFS cases and anxiety and other disorders in about 25% of cases has, despite these studies having introduced bias, affected the conclusions of other academics that CFS is primarily a psychiatric illness. The initial fault, Jason sug-

---

♦ Michel Foucault, 1926-1984. Thomas S. Szasz 1920- . R. D. Laing 1927-1989.

gests, has been amplified by mutual attribution in papers, letters and articles. Mutual attribution, in the words of Irene Welkenfeld, a critic of the USDA Report on Chemical Sensitivity, involves 'researchers sending their papers to hand-picked colleagues who they can count on for a favourable review . . . [which] can result in . . . everyone quoting the same statistics and conclusions.'

Jason points out that studies of sub-groups of ME and CFS patients show that there are higher percentages of depression and psychiatric difficulties in only small numbers of patients, while, overall, psychiatric problems are of the same order, if not lower, than in the general population. Despite this, or perhaps because of it, some psychiatrists consistently select ill-defined patient cohorts, with high levels of psychiatric diagnoses for 'CFS' research.

Many of the minor symptoms for CFS are contained in the *Diagnostic and Statistical Manual of Mental Disorders*, fourth edition (*DSM-IV*). Jason cites Demitrack (1993), Johnson, DeLuca, and Natelson (1996), who all found that giving mental attribution to symptoms, i.e. stress, anxiety, depression, 'nerves', etc., rather than simply physical descriptions, inevitably and dramatically affected the diagnosis of somatization in CFS patients.

Jason also points out that while the Diagnostic Interview Schedule (DIS) has frequently been used to assess psychiatric co-morbidity in CFS cohorts, the instrument was not designed for use with medically ill populations. Physical symptoms reported in answer to the DIS are evaluated psychiatrically, if *one* physician has described them as being of psychiatric origin, no matter how many other physicians have suggested that the complaints are primarily of physical origin. As Jason points out: 'Many physicians still do not accept CFS as a legitimate medical disorder, so it is possible that many patients would have had at least one physician who diagnosed their medical complaints as being a psychiatric disorder, thus increasing the likelihood that people with CFS would receive a psychiatric diagnosis.' He might also have added that cohorts for study will often arrive at the psychiatric researcher's door via their psychiatric workplace whereas cohorts taken from the practice of non-psychiatrists will be evaluated in a quite different manner.

Jason makes clear that, as with much social and psychological research, open-ended qualitative interviews have produced quite different results from the more quantitative behaviourist box-ticking interviews. Some CFS investigators have used the semi-structured clinical interview (SCID) to assess psychiatric illnesses. The use of the SCID is, however, supposed to be restricted to use by highly trained interviewers. When Hickie and others used SCID, they found the pre-morbid prevalence of major depressive disorder to be no higher in CFS patients than in the general community. One study compared the Diagnostic Interview Schedule (DIS) and the SCID for a CFS sample; using the DIS, 50% of the individuals diagnosed with CFS received a psychiatric diagnosis, but using the SCID only 22% received this diagnosis.

Jason points to many other biases in the psychiatric evaluation of diagnosis and treatment of CFS, including under-reporting in epidemiological studies which have not included large numbers of lower income group patients who have less access to the health care system, problems relating to the evaluation and usefulness of Cognitive Behaviour Therapy by psychiatric researchers and considerable problems for research introduced with the new 1988 and 1991 definitions of CFS in America and Britain.

One of the most serious problems relating to the research of CFS is the constant failure of British physicians and psychiatric researchers to properly review the cause, diagnosis and treatment of CFS and ME. Any such review not only needs to be international but independent and it needs to avoid the pitfalls of focusing on the massive number of papers and articles written by the minority of UK psychiatrists who presently control the field. Another linked problem is the inability of British clinicians to review the available data on the organic aetiology of ME and CFS.

While psychiatrists might try to persuade us that people present with an illness entirely for psychological reasons, unfortunately for government coffers and those presenting with the illness, proper diagnosis of any illness can only be established following bio-medical testing. The physical nature of any illness is the nuts and bolts of medical science and cannot be jettisoned either to please insurance companies, because governments choose not to provide funding or because a group of ideologically disposed academics offer allegedly cost-effective but unproven management inter-ventions.

Conflicting interests

'Health fraud' activists and greenwashers advance the idea that their battle against the concept of environmental illness is a reaction to a groundswell of irrational, and sometimes psychotic views, expressed by clinical ecologists, alternative medicine practitioners and misguided patients. It is in the train of this main argument that they are able to argue that theirs is a small voice of reason threatened by an engulfing sea of powerful vested interests; that they are the constantly rebuked stalwarts of liberality. In one of the only papers to analyse the growth of a resisting counter-culture against orthodox professional medicine and psychiatry, *Conflict of interest and special interest groups: the making of a counter culture*, medical doctor Giovanni A. Fava argues that the process is exactly the opposite.

Fava suggests that special interest groups, such as those involved in pharmaceutical company marketing, have over the years convinced people to perceive orthodox medicine as unquestionably in the people's interest. Gradually, as it has become apparent that this perceived general good is actually only the good of specialised interest groups, a public opposition begins to grow.

In order to challenge vested interests, Fava suggests a collective resistance to sponsorship of all kinds and a movement towards a truly independent review of information in the field of medicine. This approach of resistance to established conventional corporate market forces is one that has been taken up in other spheres by the anti-globalisation movement.♦ In the field of medicine and health, it implies a democratically conceived and community-based access to medical information and alternatives to the wall-to-wall prescribing of hospital and general doctors.

The professional critics of psychiatry, once a marginalized philosophical clique, now constitute a school: Peter Breggin wrote *Toxic Psychiatry* in 1993 and Lucy Johnstone's classic book *Users and Abusers of Psychiatry* (Routledge, 1989), was republished in a new edition in 2000. Herb Kutchins and Stuart A. Kirk provide a trenchant critique of the 'psychiatric bible' – the *Diagnostic and Statistical Manual of Mental Disorders* – in *Making Us Crazy*. Kutchins and Kirk lay bare the scientifically bankrupt nature of some psychiatry and its involvement with politics and drug companies. Dorothy Rowe, who has written books about depression and anxiety (*Depression: The way out of your prison*), exposes the inadequacy of psychiatry in dealing with distress. Rowe has also written introductions to *Toxic Psychiatry* and *Making us Crazy*.

In her introduction to the 1999 UK edition of *Making Us Crazy*, Rowe wrote:

♦ See the book *No Logo* by Naomi Klein, January 2000, Vintage; Random House, Canada.

The Wood and the Trees

> The crucial difference between medicine and psychiatry can
> perhaps be best summarised by saying that whereas medical
> scientists study bodily functioning and describe patterns of it,
> psychiatrists behave *as if* they were studying bodily functioning
> and *as if* they had described patterns there, when in fact they are
> studying behaviour and have assumed – but not proved – that
> certain types of pattern *will be* found there.

Much of the contemporary resistance to psychiatry rests upon practitioners easy prescription of mind-altering drugs, many of which have disastrous psychological and physical consequences.

The safety of the new generation of antidepressants pharmaceuticals, SSRIs, was brought into question in Britain in 1997, when Charles Medawar of Social Audit began campaigning with his paper The Antidepressant Web in the *International Journal of Risk and Safety in Medicine*. In his paper, Medawar drew attention to the dependency-creating properties of these drugs. Summing up his finding he said:

> . . . there is now overwhelming evidence that (in particular)
> SSRI antidepressants are as much drugs of dependence as
> benzodiazepines – though they fall outside current definitions of
> 'dependence' in ICD-10 and DSM-IV . . . the present problem
> may be more serious, because of bullish statements, notably
> from the Royal College of Psychiatrists, about the lack of any
> dependence risk with SSRIs, together with advice about the need
> for long-term, if not indefinite treatment. The Medicines Control
> Agency and Committee on Safety of Medicines clearly share this
> view.

Serious scientific information about the side-effects of the SSRI drugs has, since their early production, come to be overshadowed by a constant conflict between sections of the academic and scientific research community, some psychiatrists and doctors, and the drug companies. Like other conflicts in a post-modern society, the one around SSRIs has turned into 'a hundred years war,' one in which enemy positions, the producers on one hand and the resistance on the other, remain more or less static. There are of course casualties and skirmishes on both sides, but little progress is likely to be made until the profit potential of the drugs has been expended or a new fashion is brought to the market. For the duration of the war, the only real victims are consumers and citizens.

Loren Mosher M.D., Clinical Professor of Psychiatry at the University of California, San Diego, and a pioneer in establishing programs of psychosocial community care, resigned very publicly from the American Psychiatric Association in December 1998. In his resignation letter, circulated on the Internet, he said: 'Psychiatry has been almost completely bought out by the drug companies.' He proposed that the organisation consider changing its name to the American Psychopharmacological Association.

In his letter of resignation to Rodrigo Munoz M.D., President of the American Psychiatric Association, Mosher said:

> The major reason (for my resignation) is my belief that I am actually resigning from the American Psychopharmacological Association. Luckily, the organization's true identity requires no change in the acronym.

> At this point in history, in my view, psychiatry has been almost completely bought out by the drug companies. The APA could not continue without the pharmaceutical company support of meetings, symposia, workshops, journal advertising, grand rounds luncheons, unrestricted educational grants, etc. etc. Psychiatrists have become the minions of drug company promotions.

> We condone and promote the widespread overuse and misuse of toxic chemicals that we know have serious long-term effects: tardive dyskinesia, tardive dementia and serious withdrawal syndromes. So, do I want to be a drug company patsy who treats molecules with their formulary? No, thank you very much.

Later in an article in an October 1999 issue of *Psychology Today*, Mosher wrote his own 'not in my name' account of his resignation:

The Wood and the Trees

> The APA supports the National Alliance for the Mentally Ill,
> which believes that mentally ill patients should be coerced to
> take medication. I am appalled by this level of social control.
> Mentally ill people should be given a choice to have their illness
> treated in alternative ways.
>
> Recently, it was dues-paying time for the APA, and I sat there
> looking at the form. I thought about the unholy alliance between
> the association and the drug industry. I thought about how
> consumers are being affected by this alliance, about the overuse
> of medication, about side effects and about alternative
> treatments. I thought about how irresponsibly some of my
> colleagues are acting toward the general public and the mentally
> ill. And I realized, I want no part of it anymore.

In February 1999, in the wake of Mosher's resignation, Gregg
Birnbaum & Douglas Montero of the *New York Post* began breaking
the story of psychiatric drug companies and covert marketing.♦ A
Post investigation found that leading psychiatrists and a high-
ranking official at the state Psychiatric Institute in Manhattan, the
state clearinghouse for drug research, had been taking drug
company money in speakers fees, consulting deals, board member-
ships, and subsidised international trips.

Two members of the Psychiatric Institute in-house panel
responsible for protecting the rights of mentally ill patients had
financial ties to drug firms like Eli Lilly, Glaxo Wellcome and
Bristol-Myers Squibb. These drug makers were also funding research at the Psychiatric Institute, where their products were tested
for the treatment of depression, hyperactivity and schizophrenia.
They found that drug-company-funded studies were often led by the
same researchers who had private money deals with the producing
firms.

♦ The *New York News* and the *Milwaukee Journal Sentinel* also produced similar
stories at this time.

SKEWED

The *Post* investigation found at least 10 key players at the Psychiatric Institute who profited from side deals with a host of drug companies. They include a top Institute official, prominent researchers and psychiatrists serving on a special watchdog panel, charged with safeguarding patients in experiments. The Psychiatric Institute's Deputy Director's outside income was so extensive that he had to attach extra pages to the standard financial disclosure form. Funding companies mentioned in the article included: Eli Lilly and SmithKline Beecham, Wyeth-Ayerst, Solvay, Janssen Alza Corporation, Bristol-Myers Squibb, Richwood and Glaxo.

In January 2000, Ashley Wazana published a review paper in *JAMA* which concluded that the provision of gifts, free meals and travel subsidies to psychiatrists by pharmaceutical companies led them to prescribe those companies' products. He found that influential psychiatrists were paid up to $10,000 by pharmaceutical companies to give a single talk; repeat performances were dependent on the psychiatrist saying the right thing about the company's product. Wazana also found that some phase 3 trials of antidepressant medications had been compromised by professionals who reported incorrect information in order to make more money.

In February 2002, the *Guardian* reported on a US study which showed that psychiatrists in England were being paid large amounts of money to ghost-author papers on drug trials, which endorsed new drugs. Often the stated author of the paper had not even seen the trial data, and some had simply put their name to a paper written by a pharmaceutical company employee.

Fuller Torrey, executive director of the Stanley Foundation Research Programmes in Bethesda, Maryland, found in a survey that British psychiatrists were being paid around $2,000 (£1,400) a time for symposium talks, plus airfares and hotel accommodation, while Americans got about $3,000. Some payments ran as high as $5,000 or $10,000.

246

The Wood and the Trees

Marcia Angell, editor of the *New England Journal of Medicine* told the *Guardian* that after commissioning an editorial about psychiatrists and vested interests, 'we found very few who did not have financial ties to drug companies that make antidepressants.'

According to David Healy, a North Wales-based psychopharmacologist who has given evidence for families of psychiatric drug victims against pharmaceutical company insurers, drug producers rely on articles apparently authored by scientists who have never seen the raw data. Dr. Healy has said: 'It may well be that 50% of the articles on drugs in the major journals across all areas of medicine are not written in a way that the average person in the street expects them to be authored.'

Dr. Healey, a critic of Prozac, has paid the price for going up against the psychiatric drug manufacturers. In 2001, he was awarded a post at the University of Toronto, only to see it rescinded after Eli Lilly, the manufacturers of Prozac, put pressure on the University's Center for Addiction and Mental Health. In recent years, the Center had received more than $1.5 million from the drug company. Healy also suggests that a well-connected U.S. psychiatrist who has had close research ties to Lilly may have pressured University officials not to hire him.

Healy has been outspoken on Prozac, saying for instance that the drug has driven between 40,000 and 200,000 people to commit suicide worldwide during its 13 years on the market. He came to this estimate by extrapolating from a British drug study on suicides and federal reports on suicides among Prozac users.

In Britain, conflicting financial interests in science have until very recently gone completely unquestioned, so much so that it is almost taken for granted that science remains unaffected by sources of funding or government administrations. The British respond to the question of funding and conflicting interests with hurt pride, as if raising the issue were a rude affront. Those who are challenged usually begin their reply with the statement, 'I hope that you are not suggesting . . .'

The level of the debate around vested conflicts of interest is so low in Britain that hardly any mention is made of anything other than overt financial vested interests. One exception to this was a letter from David Horrobin in the *BMJ*.♦ Horrobin pointed out that some non-financial interest conflicts could be more serious than financial ones. He cited four types of non-financial conflict: single issue fanaticism, political commitment, philosophical bias and a pre-determined commitment to a particular theoretical framework. 'Health fraud' activists and members of the psychiatric profession involved in constructing a psychiatric aetiology for ME and CFS might be accused of being mired in at least the last two of these interest conflicts.

In June 2003, Professor Wessely wrote to the 'quick response' site of the *BMJ*, with his view about conflict of interests. While some of the best professional minds in both North America and Europe have made this issue a priority, Professor Wessely suggested, with typically English understatement, that it was a non-issue.

> And what about the blandishments from industry? Have they
> perverted my clinical practice over the years? A meticulous
> search of the wreck that is my desk reveals nine pens, including,

---

♦ Dr. David Horrobin, a brilliant and hard working English 'alternative' nutritional scientist, died on April 1st 2003. The editor of the *BMJ* gave his obituary to Caroline Richmond, a friend and colleague of Professor Wessely and a long-standing detractor of alternative medicine, its researchers and practitioners. The obituary in the 19th April 2003 *BMJ* sparked off a considerable debate on conflict of interests, after Richmond did an awful hatchet job, stating for example, that Horrobin might prove to be 'the greatest snake oil salesman of his age.' It is ironic that Horrobin should have written such an evidently honest letter to the *BMJ* about conflict of interest and his life should have been summed up in the same journal by a women who set up the Campaign Against Health Fraud, an organisation which is only transparent in one thing, the obfuscation of its motives and arguments.

miraculously, a Parker pen long thought lost, two of which have clear company logos on them. As an academic I travel a lot – I attend academic meetings, usually overseas, at least once a month (personal communication from my wife, made between gritted teeth.) I think that means over 200. I am certain that on at least four occasions I have been sponsored by industry – Pfizer, Lilly and two others that I can't remember, since you ask – possibly slightly more. I am not sure. I can remember the cities (Copenhagen twice, Vienna once and somewhere else), but not always the company. Has that made me into a drug company lackey, slavishly promoting their products? Who can say, but I doubt it.

It is time we all grew up. Everyone has conflicts. Everyone has agendas. Everything affects patient care. Our own personal prejudices, likes and dislikes, the time pressure we are under, the number of patients left to see, family and cultural backgrounds, the influence of our teachers for good or ill, how tired or jaded we are, the volume of paperwork we still have to complete, fear of litigation, the list is endless – there is very little in our lives that does not affect how we manage patients. A few pens, a sponsored sandwich lunch for our weekly research meeting, and even a trip to another forgettable conference, probably are rather low in the list of things that affect our decision making.

Why should Professor Wessely have pitched the level of intellectual debate about conflict of interest so embarrassingly low? Why should he have made a jokey personal narrative out of a growing structural problem in scientific research? By equating conflict interests with free pens and making a direct correlation between funding source and trips to conferences, he is evidently minimising the nature of the problem.

What about the relationship between government funding and policy towards defence department personnel with Gulf War Syndrome? What about British and US government research grants and bio-markers for Gulf War Syndrome? What about the relationship between ME and CFS researchers and the insurance industry? What about the reluctance of the major chemical companies and their insurance experts to agree upon the existence of Multiple Chemical Sensitivity? What about the power which medical research workers have to determine the treatment of thousands of powerless patients? Professor Wessely's letter presents a bizarre picture of a society which works by accident, where things happen as they might on the Magic Roundabout, without reason or personal motive, absent of any ultimate adverse effect upon the powerless. In this world, a personal joke about his wife's gritted teeth and lost Parker pens appears to have more meaning to him than a real analysis of the power of corporations in the modern world. Grown up, I should coco!

British health care and medical research, especially in its upper reaches, has been honeycombed with conflicting vested interests for decades. Whether it is research into migraine or research into pesticides, some pecuniary or commercial interest is invariably pulling strings, deciding levels of patient care and determining scientific outcomes.

The areas of medicine, health care, environmental and occupational health research have changed immeasurably over the last forty years. Until the late seventies, there was hegemony of state-funding in most areas of academic and professional work. Research funding was centralised and filtered through the not perfect but reasonably objective Research Councils. In the last twenty years, private, and often publicly undeclared funding has seeped into research at every level and bias of different kinds has followed. The idea of a peer review system authoritatively based in a few well-established journals has disintegrated, enabling pharmaceutical companies to fund research into their own drugs, which is then published in journals or through papers which they themselves influence, own or control.

One of the problems is that a complex modern world presents no venue for open public and genuine debates about the integrity of science. In a global society, however, a single unverifiable article or paper arguing the position of the chemical companies can be spun round the world in seconds by those whose vested interests it protects, later to seep authoritatively into books, journals, papers and policies. In the great majority of cases, the argument that scientific method is unaffected by funding is specious and those who use it are either blind to their own prejudices or insincere.

With the oceans of money lapping over research in America, the final resolution of conflict interests is that scientific research will dissolve into industry and government, becoming utterly self-serving, asking and answering only those questions which profit the economic and political establishments. The only way that this process might be halted is by a proper implementation of the precautionary principle, down to the lowest level of research and an international declaration that financial support from vested interests will not only be declared but will also increase the burden upon authors to authenticate research results through independent and vigilant peer review.

There should be very clear rules of disclosure for anyone who is either publicly employed or a member of a certified profession and receives payments or acts as an adviser from insurance companies. Declarations should be made in grant applications to patients and in relation to any work likely to relate to public policy.

In difficult investigations into illness, insurance and treatment, we have to look not only at conflict of interests which move the agencies and the actors 'on the ground,' but also at the corporate interests which manipulate these actors and agencies. It seems clear that in relation to ME, CFS, GWS and MCS, there are definite corporate interests which stand to gain by the denial of these illnesses and stand to lose by the public disclosure that they have organic causes.

Quite clearly the chemical and pharmaceutical companies stand to gain simply on the level that any real disclosure of the relationship between chemicals and illness would cost them dearly. Insurance companies, especially those who specialise in disability, stand to lose millions of pounds were it to become generally accepted that these illnesses have a diagnosable organic aetiology. The pharmaceutical companies which produce antidepressants have a great deal to gain in escalating profits from psychiatric drugs. On a lower tier, psychiatrists who extend the diagnosed boundaries of mental illness which can apparently be alleviated by antidepressants, have something to gain, through career advancement, insurance company consultancy fees and research grants, by pursuing a continuous denial of any organic diagnosis to these illnesses. Last but not least, in a great many areas, especially involving the military, in North America and Britain, the State stands to gain by the continued refutation of an organic origin of these illnesses, especially Gulf War Syndrome.

The Chief Medical Officer's Working Group

With the continuing diminution of public spending and the increased use of private funding in a whole series of areas, any question of vested interests becomes increasingly important. The formation of Government Committees and Working Groups of all kinds should be controlled by strict protocols to avoid either accidental or contrived bias.

Ideally, the personnel of any Inquiry should be quite separate from the evidence givers. To have a system such as the one which begat the CMO's Working Group, in which evidence givers with undeclared interests carried out the Inquiry itself, is a stupid system, which might lend itself to chicanery and corruption. There are good arguments for 'hearings' conducted in almost judicial public form, in which evidence givers are called and questioned by impartial inquirers.

While it is not unusual for the government to have a supportive or 'watching brief' in a committee set up by an organisation outside government, it is very unusual that a government committee under the auspices of the Department of Health and the Chief Medical Officer allows a private interest to 'buy' a place on an Inquiry. After all, the final report of the Chief Medical Officer, if accepted, would most likely determine NHS policy on, and provision for, ME and CFS for the foreseeable future.

Even if the ad hoc nature of the Chief Medical Officer's Working Group allowed the Department of Health to slip up rather than to conspire, there can be no excuse for accepting funding from the Linbury Trust. This financial handshake, though relatively small, put the seal upon what appears to have been an orchestrated strategy by a group of medical academics to control government policy on ME and Chronic Fatigue Syndrome.

As important as getting into bed with the Linbury Trust, is that a government Department chose as members of the Inquiry two individuals, Dr. Charles Shepherd and Professor Wessely, who were or had been members of HealthWatch. While the Department of Health might think it appropriate to take an inclusive view of this charity, the experience of a number of other individuals is of an illiberal and highly litigious organisation of 'would be' regulators, whose members have many axes to grind, quite aside from the fact that some of the organisation's members have in the past vehemently denied the existence of ME.

In the event, the placing on the Working Group of people with a pre-determined view of the aetiology of ME and CFS actually went some way towards wrecking the Working Group and threw the final report into disrepute. In November 2001, the Working Group collapsed in disarray. Having finished two final drafts, during November, four members of the Key Group and one member of the Children's Group, known collectively as 'the psychiatrists', withdrew from the Working Group.

Those members were, from the Key Group, Dr. Peter White, a psychiatrist and strong Wessely school adherent, who had previously made it known that he wanted *all* mention of any physical signs of ME/CFS removed from the report; Dr. Anthony Cleare, psychiatrist and Wessely school member at King's College, also the Linbury Research Fellow drafted onto the Working Group; Dr. Trudie Chalder, Wessely's closest working associate at the Institute of Psychiatry; Dr. Alison Round, a Public Health official in Devon, who is an adherent of the Wessely school; Professor Elena Garralda, a paediatric psychiatrist well-published on the view that CFS is brought about in children by their inability to adapt psychologically to changing schools, a very strong adherent of the Wessely school.

The walk-out of psychiatrists from the CMO's Working Group in the last days of the Report's formulation, seems to indicate a latent fear amongst them that their arguments were losing ground. As often appears to be the case with this group of academics and physicians, this fear seems to be manifest in an exaggerated manner for propaganda purposes.

Despite calls for the unfinished Report to be published as a majority Report in the absence of the psychiatrists, at least one of the represented patient groups, The 25% ME Group for the Severely Affected, refused to support it. Simon Lawrence, the group's representative, said that this was mainly because the Report deliberately failed to inform people that ME is formally classified as a neurological disorder and had been so classified in the ICD since 1969; it was pervasively psychiatric in tone; it stipulated that the only feasible management of the illness was by CBT and GET; it stressed that no immunological or neuro-imaging investigations were to be done and finally, it failed to give consideration to the known bio-markers of organic pathology.

Is this inability to debate essential scientific issues, this unmediated conflict mired in undeclared vested interests what voters and health care consumers want and expect from government?

The publication of the CMO's Working Group Report on January 11th 2002 was met in the press with enthusiastic applause for the medical establishment's acceptance of ME as a 'real' illness. The media, as always light on analysis and heavy on soundbites, made little of the fact that the psychiatrists had walked out of the Working Group before the Report was agreed.

Those who dominated the CMO's Working Group, however, seemed to get what they wanted from its Report, despite their ostentatious protestations. Described at its most simple, firstly they got the Cochrane style literature review on treatment, which concluded that CBT and GET were the best management strategies; secondly, they stalled yet again any serious discussion about the possible organic causes of ME/CFS.

The fact that most previous reports on ME and CFS had said that the illnesses were 'real', and that few people had ever said, in such terms, that they were 'not real', escaped most of the media, who seemed to think that the central conflict was between patients who maintained they were ill and a few ill-informed doctors who turned them away. Little was said about the actual conflict between a small group of physicians who insisted that these illnesses were the product of mental aberration and other scientists and physicians who maintained that their origins, though not yet identified, were physical and organic.

A proper analysis of the conflict going on between psychiatrists and others in this area is fundamental to an understanding firstly of research goals and secondly of treatment regimes. The psychiatric lobby wants nothing to do with further research into the aetiology of these illnesses, mainly because individuals have staked their professional reputation on the advocacy of three treatments: anti-depressants, CBT and GET. Those who believe that the illnesses have an organic aetiology are determined to see more research which will give a better understanding of the mechanism of the illnesses and their potential treatments.

The Report's bias towards the psychiatric interpretation of the illnesses can be seen clearly in one instance, in its recommendation that, in relation to young people, consultant psychiatrists as well as paediatric consultants are the people to deal with the problem.

The reactions of those sympathetic to the psychiatric arguments which followed the Report's publication, were voiced in extreme terms. It is hard to believe, however, that those physicians who wrung their hands in abject fear of losing their professional grip on these illnesses surely did not hold the belief that government reports determine the direction and focus of medical diagnosis or treatment. As the last twenty years in the treatment of ME and CFS has shown, it is the 'experts' and consultants on the ground who treat patients, carry out the research, speak at conferences and publish papers who inevitably determine policy.

Some physicians reacted to the Report as if it had suggested that psychiatrists should be banned from dealing with ME and CFS patients – not a wholly unreasonable idea. In the *Guardian*, Mike Fitzpatrick, an east London GP, wrote a plaintive, almost whining piece of rhetorical propaganda meant to make you weep for doctors bullied into diagnoses with which they did not agree by ignorant, if not mentally disturbed, patients. Disagreeing with this article, how-ever fundamentally, is not to question Dr. Fitzpatrick's profession-alism but simply to take up the right of reply to his opinions on this issue.

The Wood and the Trees

The *Guardian,* which is frequently poor in its analysis of medical issues involving pharmaceutical or professional medical interests, published Fitzpatrick's article under a sub-heading which proclaimed that the 'medical profession's latest ruling on ME (or chronic fatigue syndrome) is nothing short of disastrous.' The problem is, of course, that the Report was not the 'medical profession's' latest view, it was the medical profession's old view which appeared to have been compromised a tad by the introduction of patients and patients groups. It was this fact which apparently infuriated Dr. Fitzpatrick, and he quoted the Chief Executive of Action for ME, who had suggested that patients might now use the Report in arguing with GPs who insisted that their patients were imagining their illnesses. That patients might bring this kind of evidence to bear on GPs and even in the final recourse report GPs who fail to acknowledge the illnesses, Fitzpatrick found disturbing. In the usual manner of the psychiatric lobby, he turned the world on its head: to act in this way would be, he said, to use a 'dogmatic and authoritarian approach.'

In a following soliloquy about the labels ME and CFS, Fitzpatrick places himself clearly in the psychiatric camp and makes some alarming statements. In his surgery, he says, ME *is always* a self-diagnosis:

> Somebody comes in, sits down and says: 'I think I've got ME, doc.' This is what we in general practice call a 'heartsink' encounter. Once a patient has accepted the ME label, it seems to become a self-fulfilling prophecy, and it is very difficult to deflect them from a course of prolonged incapacity, with all its adverse consequences.'

Hopefully Dr. Fitzpatrick will not take up fiction because his dialogue is poor. His assertion that everyone who comes to his surgery and ponders whether they might have ME is actually seeking acquiescence in a course of prolonged, and presumably undeserved, 'incapacity', is simply a re-run of the ME patient as malingerer story. Fitzpatrick then goes on to repeat another old chestnut which flies in the face of all the research, describing nearly all patients who suggest that they might have ME as 'young, female and middle class; teachers, nurses, social workers.' He follows this statement with a less comprehensible one: 'In more recent years, ME has appeared in the children of the above, and, unlike wealth, it has shown a tendency to trickle down into less affluent sections of society.' Does this mean while working class adults do not get ME, their children have begun to claim to have it? One wonders what Fitzpatrick means by this and what he tells these children when they attend his surgery.

Dr. Fitzpatrick is clearly not going to be easily influenced by one recommendation in the CMO's Report that research should be carried out into the aetiology of ME and CFS, in order to uncover the biomedical or organic origins of these illnesses. Like a small number of other doctors and psychiatrists, Dr. Fitzpatrick has made up his mind, there in his practice in London's East End he has seen all the cases he wants to see and made his own empirical judgements – who needs research!

Dr. Fitzpatrick accuses the Report, and by implication patients who insist that they have organic illnesses, of setting medicine back 300 years. This is the time, he says, that it has taken medicine to piece together the philosophy that illnesses are a delicate conjunction of mind and body. In other words, people who believe that ME is an organic biomedical illness and demand further research, are forcing medicine back into the dark ages. Others might argue that to refuse research into an illness and to describe it, without material evidence or even a theoretical model, as a psychiatric condition, is the incantation of a profession trying hard to disguise its ignorance.

Unfortunately, Dr. Fitzpatrick doesn't stop with his accusation of medievalism; he berates those who believe in an organic aetiology of ME and CFS with 'endorsing the stigmatisation of mental illness.' With perverse logic, he suggests that if you argue ME and CFS have an organic or biomedical aetiology, you are in fact arguing that the illness has no psychological dimension and denying mental illness its proper place in medicine. You could only be doing this because you believe that admitting to a psychological dimension to any illness stigmatises the sufferer. Clearly, it is much better for everyone concerned if patients just admit to mental incapacity, take their antidepressants and go along to be re-educated at a Cognitive Behaviour Therapy Centre.

As if all this wasn't enough, Dr. Fitzpatrick throws together all the usual suspects in presenting his picture of contemporary mental illness:

> Others complaining of symptoms for which no cause can be found are offered labels such as 'irritable bowel syndrome,' 'repetitive strain injury,' 'fibromyalgia', 'food allergy' or even 'multiple chemical sensitivity.' The new diagnostic labels are descriptive rather than explanatory. Far from opening up the prospect of treatment, they merely confirm the hopelessness of the sufferer. ♦

How many doctors share Dr. Fitzpatrick opinion, it is impossible to know, but having read his opinions it is hard to be optimistic about even the most minor recommendations in the Report.

Dr. Fitzpatrick's view must be seen, at the best, as ideological and at the worst as irrational when compared with the views of more knowledgeable commentators. The Countess of Mar has consistent-

---

♦ *Allergy, the Unmet Need*, the 2003 report of the Royal College of Physicians, states: 'Food allergy is a major cause of fatal reactions and the most common cause of childhood anaphylaxis in the UK.' (pp. 53) 'Anaphylactic deaths due to food allergy usually occur in patients who know they have a food allergy, but have been unable to obtain medical advice, either because GPs lack knowledge of allergy, or because there was no allergy service available locally.' (pp. 54)

ly championed the cause of those affected by chemicals, those who have ME and CFS. Being herself a victim of OP poisoning, she is well aware of both the reality of the illness and the impossibility of getting doctors to take the condition seriously.

Following the publication of the CMO's Report, the Countess of Mar put forward a balanced but critical view of the Report in the House of Lords in April 2002. To show that the populist attack mounted on ME/CFS by the Wessely School was still going strong, she quoted from a copy of the *BMJ* for that month, which apparently in order to mitigate the perceived damage done by the Report, had launched a 'non-disease' survey, in which ME/CFS was included. According to another speaker in the same debate, the media listed the results of this 'survey' according to equal percentages: ME on a par with Obesity at 13%, and Gulf War Syndrome lumped with Transvestiteism and pre-menstrual syndrome, followed by Diabetes with Osteoporosis.

Margaret Mar was definite in her criticism of Professor Wessely who, she suggested, had 'been relentless in his proposition that ME does not exist.' She quoted him saying in the *Journal of Psychological Medicine* in 1990 that ME only existed because well-meaning doctors had not learned to deal effectively with what he called 'suggestible patients.'

Being the most realistic of parliamentarians, Mar explained to the Lords that the question posed by the Wessely School of ME was far from an academic question.

> Their influence pervades every aspect of ME sufferers' lives,
> including their ability to obtain social security and private
> medical insurance benefits, social services assistance and home
> tuition for children. Tragically, children with ME have suffered
> disproportionately. As I have already explained, the prevailing
> perception of the illness is that it is bio-psychosocial, whatever
> that means. Children presenting ill-defined symptoms that do not

improve quickly are regarded as having been harmed by their carer. Proceedings under the Children Act 1989 are instigated. Children are removed from loving families and made wards of court and severe gagging orders are placed on parents.

Mar lambasted the Report for what were its ultimate offerings, the recommendation of two treatment regimes, CBT and GET. Pointing out that neither CBT nor GET were proven therapies, she asked the Government Minister of Health how the therapies could possibly be recommended to British NHS doctors.

> Thus, by virtue of the conflicting opinions on risks and benefits set out in the report, the NHS exposes itself to the risk of treating patients unlawfully. Will the Minister please explain how that can be 'good clinical practice' and why such flawed advice got through the scrutiny net?

She asked whether 'the Minister [was] happy to rely on such manipulation of the scientific evidence as appears in the Report? To show how the Report had furthered the cause of the psychiatric approach to 'treatment', the Countess quoted from the introductory literature for a conference on 'Chronic Fatigue Syndrome: Research and Practice,' to take place at the John Radcliffe Hospital in Oxford: 'The recent government guidelines have endorsed the value of CBT and graded exercise as the most useful patient management approach so far.' She wondered how the facts could get so outrageously distorted through a Government-sponsored Report.

The Countess of Mar's last question about the CMO's Report was about its suggestion that the Medical Research Council (MRC) be trusted with the task of further research into ME and CFS.

> May we know who has been appointed to the independent scientific advisory group? May I also have an assurance from the Minister that psychiatrists will not dominate the group, as they have done hitherto, and that there will be a reasonable balance of funding for biological research?

The Countess could clearly see no reason why the same charade of bias towards the 'psychiatric school' would not occur again.

Baroness Noakes also made a reference to the MRC in the Lords Debate. It was supposed to have agreed an independent scientific advisory group, terms of reference and a timetable for research by the end of February 2002. Baroness Noakes was surprised at the results of her recent April inquiries:

> Since [the Report], there appears to have been a deafening silence. I could find no trace of an advisory group, terms of reference or a timetable. Certainly the MRC's website is completely silent on those aspects.

The real effect of the CMO's Report can be gauged by the fact that when the new research into ME and CFS did break silence, it was announced that the MRC was to give £2.6 million to a previously unsuccessful but re-submitted bid for yet more psycho-social research into CFS.[36] The money was to research into the combined use of CBT and GET, the use of CBT alone, and research into the use of 'pacing' as an effective management strategy. The money was to be split between several centres, including Simon Wessely's department at King's, the grant naming Trudie Chalder, Dr. Michael Sharpe in Edinburgh and Dr. Peter White at Barts. There was to be no biomedical research into the causes of ME or CFS.

On 14th January 2003, there was a meeting at The Royal Society of Medicine entitled 'Chronic fatigue syndrome and factitious♦ illness: interface between child psychiatric and paediatric services.' Speakers included Professor Elena Garralda, a psychiatrist and one

---

36 After 1998, professor Wessely was a member of three MRC Boards: Health Services and Public Health Research Board, Neurosciences and Mental Health Group and Monitoring, and Evaluating Steering Group (MESG).

♦ Contrived or insincere rather than genuine; not real or natural but artificial or invented.

of the authors of the 1996 Joint Royal Colleges' report on CFS; Dr. Harvey Marcovitch, editor-in-chief of *The Archives of Disease in Childhood*, a Wessely supporter; and Dr. Peter White, who led the walk-out of psychiatrists from the CMO's Working Group, with Professor Sir Roy Meadow, Emeritus Professor of Paediatrics and Child Health, known for his view that there are no children with ME, only parents who suffer from Munchausen's Syndrome by Proxy.♦

* * *

It is difficult to understand why a particular group of academic psychiatrists would argue with patients that they can not have an organic illness which has been well recorded for over half a century. It is even harder to understand why those psychiatrists would argue that those presenting with the symptoms and signs of the illness are actually part of a substantial and growing pool of psychiatrically ill people. Finally, it is almost impossible to readily understand why, if these physicians are sure of their case, they are consistently unable to report the exact psychiatric mechanisms, which provoke the psychiatric condition from which they suggest these patients are suffering.

Most philosophical ideas about 'the academy' insist upon the public deposition of theories, usually in the form of writing with unquestionably independent peer examination but also, in France for example, the public dissertation. The British psychiatrists, who are adamant that ME does not exist and CFS is a somatization disorder, appear to have junked the most important safeguards of academic and scientific rigour. They have sectioned themselves off into a closed self-serving group, which consistently fails to put its theories and ideas discursively to the broader academy or, more importantly, the public.

♦ Munchausen's Syndrome is now known as 'FII', which stands for 'Fabricated and Induced Illness.' (See footnote in pp. 173-174.)

SKEWED

Considering the millions of pounds that have been spent upon human genome research, there is an untenable lack of logic in refusing to carry out diagnostic testing on patients who present with ME and CFS, Gulf War Syndrome or similar illnesses. It is clear that as far as it is possible, we need to understand the epidemiology and the biochemistry of these disorders before we turn to examine their psychiatric profile or their treatment. This examination of the phenomena has to be subject to open debate and independent peer review. To approach the question of illness in the obverse way, making statements about psychiatric illness and giving experimental treatments based only upon a hotchpotch of populist historical guesses, is to swim determinedly against the tide of scientific rationalism and to give way to an oppressive form of medical ideology. Anyone who argues that we don't need to search for the exact aetiology of complex modern illnesses is, *for some reason*, arguing against rational intellectual systems and against scientific method.

* * *

In this last chapter of the book, I have tried to draw together all the disparate strands of a situation which has adversely affected a large number of sufferers of chronic illness in Britain. There is absolutely no doubt in my mind, that there are matters here which have to be corrected, wrongs which have to be righted. Yet it must be one of the most overstated factors of contemporary British life that commerce and profit has long overtaken either the curiosity of science or any desire that those in government have to properly administer to the vulnerabilities of the disadvantaged (in this case the chronically ill.)

Medical science in the UK seems to suffer from a terminal malaise, the cause of which, unlike that of CFS, is not at all obscure. Medical and scientific opinion in Britain is shaped almost entirely by industry and its search for profit. It might always have been this way: it is just that previously the glittering prizes in industry's sights were never as huge as they are now. Something else is different: while it might have appeared in the past that scientists left their political lives behind when they donned their white coats, now scientists take home and into the radio and television studios the political views which they develop at work.

As medical science and industry are increasingly involved in battles with the general public, citizens and consumers, over issues ranging from vaccination to the use of pesticides, the views of some scientists are increasingly shown to be entrenched, authoritarian and undemocratic. The compulsory use of CBT, GET and antidepressant drugs for individuals who have presented with the symptoms of ME and CFS might rationally be construed as experimenting on patients. The consequences of doctors and medical scientists turning away from the committed scientific investigation of illness, and practising treatments which are unproven, do not bear thinking about. In the case of ME and CFS, GWS and pesticide poisoning, however, we are bound to consider these issues.

In a complex society, explanations of all manner of things might be obscured for different reasons. In a post-modern world, collating the information that explains illness is a painstaking, difficult but extremely valuable scientific task. Epidemiology involves bringing a measure of global consensus into a world that appears hopelessly disintegrative. For as long as commercial interests take precedence over human suffering, there will be financial gain in finding the wrong cause of some illnesses, while failing to find any cause for others, and epidemiology will be used, avoided and abused by different parties in order that the public do not see the truth.

Unfortunately, the control of, and investigations into ME and CFS have operated without the insights of classic epidemiology, and manifestly in favour of the insurance companies, the pharmaceutical companies and the orthodox professional medical establishment, rather than in defence of science or patients. It is clearly time that proper safeguards were erected for patients, ensuring that they are able to protect their rights and defend themselves against both physicians and psychiatrists who insist on putting arbitrary psychiatric diagnoses before physical investigation.

The battle which has taken place around ME and CFS over the last twenty years, is as complicated as the battles which have gone on over secondary smoking and cancer, as obscure as the debate over exhaust particulants and cancer, as shimmerous as the investigation into the aetiology of HIV and AIDS-related illnesses. Such battles have been shaped and precipitated by corporate vested interests and the development of public health care in a privatised economy.

We can all hope for change, we can campaign for it but there is a cynicism abroad which informs us that we would be unwise to hold our breath in anticipation of a serious, well funded, scientific, medical or even judicial examination of the cause of ME and other fatigue illnesses. Until someone holds an authoritative inquiry into the condition of patients and the motives of researchers, the British public will be left to the mercy of corporate interests and those who act consciously or unconsciously as their agents.

Index

Index

Index

Index

Index

Organisations, Web Sites and Literature

U.K. support organisations for ME/CFS

MERGE, The Gateway, North Methven Street, Perth PH1 5PP Scotland. Tel: 01738 451234.

The 25% ME Group (for the Severely Affected), Co-ordinator Simon Lawrence, 4, Douglas Court, Beach Road, Troon, Ayrshire, KA10 6SQ Scotland. Tel: 01292 318611.

RiME (Research into ME), Paul Davis, 10 Carter's Hill Close, Mottingham Lane, London SE9 4RS.

RiME is a campaigning organisation focusing on the need for research into the organic aetiology and pathogenesis of ME and is particularly concerned about the plight of the severely affected.

UK Gulf War organisations

National Gulf Veterans & Families Association, 53/54, The Pavillion, 536 Hall Road, Hull HU6 9BS England. www.ngvfa.com

The Gulf Veterans Association, 4th Floor, MEA House, Ellison Place, Newcastle upon Tyne NE1 8XS England. www.gulfveteransassociation.co.uk

US CFIDS support organisations

The CFIDS Association of America, PO BOX 220398, Charlotte, N.C. 28222-0398 USA. www.cfids.org

Our Toxic Times, Chemical Injuries Information Network, PO BOX 301, White Sulphur Springs, MT 59645 USA. www.ciin.org

Some of the best web sites for CFS/ME

Association of Youth with M.E. (AYME): www.ayme.org.uk

MERGE: www.meresearch.org.uk – This website has a comprehensive data base of published papers on CFS / ME.

The 25% ME Group (for the Severely Affected): www.25megroup.org

The ME Action UK site has an extensive Research Study Database almost exclusively concerned with organic aetiology of ME and CFS, at: www.meactionuk.org.uk

A good list of **UK support groups** can be found on UK ME web site at: dspace.dial.pipex.com/comcare/ME

Mary Schweitzer's web pages have an excellent list of varied organisations, including a list of commercial labs that test around CFS, at: www.cfids-me.org/marys

Canberra Fibromyalgia and CFS pages which have a very good listing for web sites are at: www.masmith.inspired.net.au

Co-Cure. CFS and FM Information Exchange Forum, has various discussion sites where people can talk to each other about their illnesses and post new research information. e-mail: Co-Cure-Mod@listserve.nodak.edu

The CFIDS Report; Cutting Edge News and Commentary for the CFIDS Community, organised by Craig Maupin, at: www.cfidsreport.com
Carries a very good article about research into CFS, by him, *Shaky Foundations; Sloppy Research Standards or Innovative Science.*

Some of the best web sites critical of psychiatry

The **Anti Psychiatry Coalition** web site at:
www.antipsychiatry.org/index.htm – Contains, amongst other things a comprehesive, 12 part critique of psychiatry by Lawrence Stevens.

A number of professional and campaigning psychiatrists have web sites, including: **Dr. Peter Breggin** and **Dr. Thomas S. Szasz**.

The **Critical Psychiatry** web site at:
www.critpsynet.freeuk.com/antipsychiatry.htm – Seem to have everything on their web site, including an incomparable list of articles and book reviews.

Some of the best web sites for Multiple Chemical Sensitivity

The **MCS survivers** web site is one of the most comprehensive at: www.mcsurvivors.com – This has substantial book and articles lists on allergy, MCS, Environmental Illness, CFS and GWS amongst other subjects.

The book lists can be found at: www-rohan.sdsu.edu/staff/lhamilto/mcs

Albert Donnay's **MCS Referral and Resources** can be found at: www.mcsrr.org – As described on the site, MCS Referral & Resources, Inc., is a non-profit organization engaged in professional outreach, patient support and public advocacy devoted to the diagnosis, treatment, accommodation and prevention of Multiple Chemical Sensitivity disorders. It was founded by Grace Ziem, MD, DrPH, and Albert Donnay, MHS, in 1994 and incorporated in Maryland in June 1995. Our mission is to further the diagnosis, treatment, accommodation and prevention of multiple chemical sensitivity disorders.

I have always liked **Gordon and Jacki's Place**, particularly because of its canary decorated background to its pages and because it is slightly quirky in a very American way. This is one of the only sites which goes into detail about the danger of chemical perfumes. You can reach extensive lists of other organisations, accounts of personal experience, safe products, as well as a copious and descriptive list of books at: ourlittleplace.com/index.html

Environmental Health Center, Dallas: www.ehcd.com/resources.html

Buying books on these subjects

With the above sites, as well as considering buying books from them, you might research the titles and authors of books on the **www.abebooks.com** web site, where you might find new or near to new copies at very low prices.

Sociological, investigative and humanities papers and articles

How the law is being abused to force treatment on children: *Parents of ME sufferers are being victimised by the Children Act*, The Countess of Mar, *Daily Telegraph* 11th July 2001.

Organisations, Web Sites and Literature

Ill defined notions, Ziauddin Sardar, *New Statesman* 5th February 1999.

"Must try harder" is sometimes more relevant to education professionals than the children in their care, Jane Colby, *Special Children* magazine Oct 2001 pp. 34-35.

When 'no' means mental illness, Jane Colby. On the confusion between the psychiatric diagnosis Pervasive Refusal Syndrome and ME. *What Doctors Don't Tell You* magazine Oct 2001 vol. 12 no. 7 p. 12.

Chronic Fatigue Syndrome / ME, Jane Colby. Impact of the Chief Medical Officer's Working Group Report on the education of pupils with CFS/ME. *Special Children* magazine Feb. 2002 p. 9.

Politics, Science, and the Emergence of a New Disease: The Case of Chronic Fatigue Syndrome, Leonard A. Jason, DePaul University; Judith A. Richman, University of Illinois at Chicago; Fred Friedberg, State University of New York at Stony Brook; Lynne Wagner, Renee Taylor, Karen M. Jordan, DePaul University. September 1997, *American Psychologist* vol. 52, no. 9, 973-983.

What is ME? What is CFS? Information for clinicians and lawyers, December 2001, by E. P. Marshall, M. Williams and M. Hooper. Available from Malcolm Hooper, Emeritus Professor of Medicinal Chemistry, Department of Life Sciences, University of Sunderland, SR2 7EE, UK.

A 56 year old woman with CFS, A. L. Komaroff. *JAMA* 1997. 278.14:1179 1184.

Myalgic encephalomyelitis or what?, A. M. Ramsay, *Lancet* 1988:100.

Severely Neglected: ME in the UK. Report from Action for ME. March 2001.

Epidemiological study of an epidemic diagnosed as poliomyelitis occurring among the personnel of Los Angeles County General Hospital during the summer of 1934, Gilliam A. G. *Public Health Bulletin*, US Treasury Department No. 240, 1938.

An investigation into an unusual disease in epidemic and sporadic form in general practice in Cumberland in 1955 and subsequent years, Wallis A. L., University of Edinburgh Doctoral Thesis 1957.

The Clinical Syndrome Variously Called Benign Myalgic Encephalomyelitis, Iceland Disease and Epidemic Neuromyasthenia, E. D. Acheson, *Am J Med* 1959:569 595.

SKEWED

Icelandic Disease (Benign Myalgic Encephalomyelitis or Royal Free Disease), A. M. Ramsay, E. G. Dowsett et al., *BMJ* May 1977:1350.

Outbreak at The Royal Free, E. D. Acheson, *Lancet* 20 Aug. 1955: 304-305.

Myalgic Encephalomyelitis: A Baffling Syndrome with a Tragic Aftermath. A. Melvin Ramsay, pub.: The ME Association, November 1981.

Quality of Life in Chronic Fatigue Syndrome, R. Schweitzer et al., *Soc Sci Med* 1995:41:10: 1367 1372.

Estimating rates of Chronic Fatigue Syndrome from a community based sample, Jason L. A. et al., *American Journal of Community Psychology* 1995:21557 568.

Prevalence of Chronic Fatigue Syndrome in an Australian Population, Lloyd A. R. et al., *Medical Journal of Australia* 1990:153:522 528.

The Organic Basis of ME / CFS, E. G. Dowsett, D. M. Jones. Information and Statistics presented to the Chief Medical Officer in person at a meeting on 11th March 1998.

Reporting the high suicide risk, Ian Franklin, *Perspectives* Summer 2001:12. Pub. by The ME Association, Stanford le Hope, Essex, UK.

The Epidemiology of Myalgic Encephalomyelitis (ME) in the UK, E.G. Dowsett, J. Richardson. Evidence submitted to the All Party Parliamentary Group of Members of Parliament, 23 Nov 1999.

Long Term Sickness Absence due to ME/CFS in UK schools; An epidemiological study with medical and educational implications, Dowsett E. G., Colby J. The largest epidemiological study of ME available to date, studying a sample of 333,000 schoolchildren and 27,000 staff over a 5 year period. Much new evidence for the seriousness of the problem in schools and further evidence for the theory that ME is of infective origin.

The Royal Colleges' Report on CFS: Insidiously Biased and Potentially Harmful, T. Hedrick, *CFIDS Chronicle* 1997:10:1:8-13.

Publication bias and the integrity of psychiatric research, S. M. Gilbody, F. Song, *Psychological Medicine* 2000:30:253-258.

Scientific papers

Engaging with Myalgic Encephalomyelitis, Professor Malcolm Hooper. Available from: Malcolm Hooper, Emeritus Professor of Medicinal Chemistry, School of Sciences, University of Sunderland. Sunderland SR2 3SD, UK.

Organisations, Web Sites and Literature

Multiple Chemical Sensitivity in CFS, J. N. Baraniuk et al., *AACFS Seattle*, Jan. 2001 # 124.

Demonstration of delayed recovery from fatiguing exercise in Chronic Fatigue Syndrome, Paul L. A. et al. *European Journal of Neurology* 1999:6:63-69.

Chronic fatigue syndrome following a toxic exposure, D. Racciatti et al., *Sci Total Environ* 2001:1-3:27-31.

Chronic Fatigue Syndrome as a Delayed Reaction to Chronic Low Dose Organophosphate Exposure, P. O. Behan, *J Nutr & Environ Med* 1996:6:341-350.

The Clinical and Scientific Basis of Myalgic Encephalomyelitis Chronic Fatigue Syndrome, pp. 42, 62, 70, 73, 87, 89, 91, 268, 376, 427 430. Ed: B. M. Hyde, J. Goldstein, P. Levine. Pub: The Nightingale Research Foundation, Ottawa 1992.

Neurological dysfunction in chronic fatigue syndrome, Chaudhuri, A. and Behan P. O., *JCFS* 2000:6: (3-4):51-68.

Presentation by Dr. Paul Cheney. Chronic Fatigue Syndrome National Consensus Conference, Sydney, Australia, 1995.

Chronic Fatigue Syndrome is an Acquired Neurological Channelopathy, A. Chaudhuri, P. Behan. *Hum Psychopharmacol Clin Exp* 1999:14:7-17.

Chronic Fatigue Syndrome findings now point to Central Nervous System involvement, D. S. Bell, *Postgrad Med* 1994:96:6:73 81.

Brainstem perfusion is impaired in patients with chronic fatigue syndrome, Costa D. C., Tannock C. and Brostoff J., *Quarterly Journal of Medicine* 1995:88:767 773.

Diseases of the Nervous System, Lord Brain. Sixth Edition. *Oxford University Press* 1962.

Cardiac and Cardiovascular Aspects of Myalgic Encephalomyelitis, B. M. Hyde, A. Jain. In: The Clinical and Scientific Basis of Myalgic Encephalomyelitis and Chronic Fatigue Syndrome. Ed: B. M. Hyde, J. Goldstein, P. Levine. Pub: The Nightingale Research Foundation, Ottawa, Canada 1992.

A chronic illness characterized by fatigue, neurologic and immunologic disorders, D. Buchwald, P. R. Cheney, D. A. Ablashi, R. C. Gallo, A. L. Komaroff et al., *Ann Intern Med* 1992.116:103 113.

Reports

Allergy: The Unmet Need, Royal College of Physicians Working Party. Chairman Professor Stephen Holgate. 2003. £17 from the RCP Publications Department.

Chemicals in Products: Safeguarding the Environment and Human Health, Royal Commission on Environmental Pollution. Chairman Sir Tom. Blundell FRS. 2003. ISBN: 01 01 582 722 CM5827 – £27.20 from the Stationery Office.

Chronic Fatigue Syndrome, Report of a Joint Working Group of the Royal Colleges of Physicians, Psychiatrists and General Practitioners (CR54) pub: RCP October 1996.

Report from The National Task Force on Chronic Fatigue Syndrome, Post Viral Fatigue Syndrome, Myalgic Encephalomyelitis. Westcare, Bristol, 1994.

Books

Alternative Treatments For Fibromyalgia & Chronic Fatigue Syndrome: Insights From Practitioners & Patients, Mari Skelly Alameda, CA, U.S.A., Hunter House, Incorporated, 1999.

Boundless Energy: The Complete Mind/Body Program For Overcoming Chronic Fatigue, Deepak Chopra. Vintage/Ebury (A Division of Random House Group), London, UK, 1995.

Chemical exposures; Low levels and high stakes. Second Edition. Nicholas A. Ashford and Claudia S. Miller. New York: Van Nostrand Reinhold, 1998.) ISBN 0-442-02524-6.

Chemical sensitivity, William Rea. Four volumes, published by CRC Press and Lewis Publishers. Information about these books can be found on the American Environmental Health Foundation web site.

Chronic Fatigue Syndrome: The Hidden Epidemic, Stoff, Jesse A., M.D.; and Charles R. Pellegrino, Ph.D. Harper Perennial New York, NY. 1992. Jesse Stoff. Quality Paperback.

Defining Multiple Chemical Sensitivity, Bonnye Mathew. McFarland & Company Jefferson, North Carolina 1998.

Organisations, Web Sites and Literature

Denigration by Design? A Review, with References, of the Role of Dr. Simon Wessely in the Perception of Myalgic Encephalomyelitis (1987–1996) by Eileen Marshall and Margaret Williams, Volume I, August 1996. £15 including postage, with reductions for numbers of copies. Available from D. M. Jones, 176 Perth Road, ILFORD, Essex, IG2 6DZ, UK.

Denigration by Design? A Review, with Reference, of the Role of Dr. (now Professor) Simon Wessely in the Perception of Myalgic Encephalomyelitis UPDATE: 1996–1999, Volume II, Autumn 1999 by Margaret Williams. ME Research (UK). £15 including postage, with reductions for numbers of copies. Available from D. M. Jones, 176 Perth Road, ILFORD, Essex, IG2 6DZ, UK.

Dirty Medicine; Science, big business and the assault on natural health care, Martin J. Walker, Slingshot Publications, BM Box 8314, London 1993.

Doctor's Guide To Chronic Fatigue Syndrome: Understanding, Treating, and Living With CFIDS, David S. Bell. Boston, MA, U.S.A. Addison-Wesley Longman, Incorporated, 1993.

50 Things You Should Know About the Chronic Fatigue Syndrome Epidemic, Neeyah Ostrom. New York, NY, U.S.A. St. Martins, 1993.

From Fatigued To Fantastic: A Manual For Moving Beyond Chronic Fatigue and Fibromyalgia, Jacob Teitelbaum. New York, NY, U.S.A. The Putnam Publishing Group, 1996.

Knowing ME: Women Speak out about Myalgic Encephalomyelitis and Chronic Fatigue Syndrome, Caeia March (ed), The Women's Press. London 1998.

Living With Chronic Fatigue Syndrome: A Personal Story Of the Struggle for Recovery, Timothy Kenny. New York, Thunder's Mouth Press, 1994.

Making Us Crazy – DSM: The Psychiatric Bible And The Creation Of Mental Disorders, Herb Kutchins and Stuart A. Kirk. ISBN 0-684-82280-6.

ME – Chronic Fatigue Syndrome: A Practical Guide, Dr. Anne Macintyre. Thorsons, 1998.

ME – The New Plague, Jane Colby. ISBN 1860832156. Available online via: www.youngactiononline.com

Osler's Web. Inside the Labyrinth of the Chronic Fatigue Syndrome Epidemic, Hillary Johnson, Crown Publishers Inc (Random House), New York 1996.

SKEWED

Recovering From Chronic Fatigue Syndrome: A Guide to Self-Empowerment, William Collinge. New York, Berkley Publishing Group. 1993.

Running On Empty: The Complete Guide To Chronic Fatigue Syndrome (CFIDS), Katrina Berne. Bloomsbury, 1992, and Alameda, CA, U.S.A., Hunter House, Inc., 1992.

Shattered: Life with M.E., Dr. Lynn Michell. Thorsons (Harper Collins) 2003.

Stricken: Voices from the Hidden Epidemic of Chronic Fatigue Syndrome, Peggy Munson (ed), The Haworth Press. London and New York 2000.

The Downhill Syndrome: If Nothing's Wrong, Why Do I Feel So Bad? Yutsis, Pavel; Walker, Morton. New York, NY, U.S.A. The Putnam Publishing Group, 1996.

The Night Side: Chronic Fatigue Syndrome and Seven Years In the Kingdom Of the Sick, Floyd Skloot. Brownsville, Story Line, 1996.

The Rebellious Body: Reclaim Your Life From Environmental Illness Or Chronic Fatigue Syndrome, Janice Wittenberg. New York & London, Plenum, 1996.

They Say You're Crazy: How The World's Most Powerful Psychiatrists Decide Who's Normal, Paula J. Caplan, M.D. ISBN 0201407582.

Martin J. Walker was born in 1947 and trained as a graphic designer. He has written books and articles while being an activist, political poster artist, investigator and a research worker.

SKEWED is his seventh book. His last book, *Dirty Medicine: Science, big business and the assault on natural health care*, was about the 'health fraud' movement in Britain and North America. His other books include, *With Extreme Prejudice: A study of police vigilantism in Manchester*; with Geoff Coggan, *Frightened for my Life: An account of deaths in British prisons*; with Jim Coulter and Susan Miller, *State of Siege: politics and policing in the coalfields, the miners strike 1984*.

His next book, *The Gate Keepers*, due to be published early in 2004, is about the lives and work of alternative cancer therapists in Britain over the last century.

~

Martin Walker is presently seeking information on the life and career of Dr. Franklin Bicknell and the Food Education Society.

~

Slingshot Publications
BM BOX 8314, London WC1N 3XX, England

Slingshot Publications

Dirty Medicine: Science, big business and the assault on natural health care. Martin J. Walker.

Loic Le Ribault's Resistance: The creation of a treatment for arthritis and the persecution of its author, France's foremost forensic scientist. Martin J. Walker.

A Cat in Hell's Chance: The Campaign to close Hillgrove cat farm. Written by the campaigners.

Slaughter of the Innocent: The use of animals in medical research. Hans Ruesch.

SKEWED: Psychiatric hegemony and the manufacture of mental illness in Multiple Chemical Sensitivity, Gulf War Syndrome, Myalgic Encephalomyelitis and Chronic Fatigue Syndrome. Martin J. Walker.

BM BOX 8314, London WC1N 3XX, England